PRESCRIPTION |
Life skills to live

Published by **Good Day University Publishing**
Copyright 2022 by Harris Jensen, MD.
harrisjensenmd.com

DISCLAIMER:
All stories in this book are fictional. This is to protect the privacy of those people who contributed to the story. Any similarities to actual people and events are a coincidence. The stories are representative of what can happen in our shared human experience. This book's purpose is to show how a positive attitude can change people's lives. However, this book is not in any way giving advice on what people should do in their life. The publisher of this book is not providing medical, psychological or other services to the reader. The publisher of this book is not replacing or otherwise interfering with medical or psychological or other professional services a person may be receiving. If a person feels they need professional support, then they should seek consultation with a qualified physician or psychotherapist.

First **Good Day University Publishing** Edition, 2022
Bulk purchases are available.
Address all inquiries to:
hjmedicalpractice@outlook.com

Good Day University Publishing, LLC
3500 John F. Kennedy Parkway, Suite 210
Fort Collins, Colorado 80526

Library of Congress Cataloging-in-Publication Data
Jensen, Harris (Prescription For Positivity. English)
Includes bibliographical references (p.) and index.

ISBN (cloth) 978-0-9913942-0-3
ISBN (pbk) 978-0-9913942-1-0
ISBN (ebook) 978-0-9913942-2-7
ISBN (audiobook) 978-0-9913942-3-4

1. Prescription For Positivity. 2. Self Help. 3. Health and Fitness.
4. Neuropsychology. I. Title

PRESCRIPTION FOR POSITIVITY

Life skills to live your best life!

by Harris Jensen, MD

OPTI MISM!

PREFACE
MY STORY xxi

FORWARD
BOOK
ORGANIZATION xliv

01

WHY YOU NEED POSITIVITY

1

02

HOW I LEARNED POSITIVITY 35

03

POSITIVITY HAS MANY BENEFITS

63

04

LEARN MEDITATION EASILY WITH POSITIVITY! 121

05

HOW TO BECOME "HIGH VALUE" FOR YOURSELF 133

06

HOW POSITIVITY PRINCIPLES WORK TOGETHER 161

07

HOW "INITIATIVE" SKILLS SOLVE BIG PROBLEMS!   199

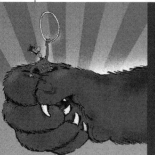

08

HOW "SETBACKS" CAN MAKE YOUR LIFE MORE MEANINGFUL 221

09

HOW "HOPEFULNESS" LIGHTS UP YOUR LIFE! 273

10

HOW "ACCOMPLISHMENTS" OCCUR WHEN YOU "LET GO" 293

11

THE FOCUS ON "LEARNING": YOUR GENIE IN A BOTTLE — 315

FIGURE 1.0.0
"Positivity creates hope." Get in your positive attitude, then let go of what weighs you down. By Toso Borkovic.

The
Prescription

FIGURE 1.0.1
The choice: positivity versus negativity.
By Esther Phingmoo.

Preface: my story

PRESCRIPTION FOR POSITIVITY

Pessimism messed up my life

I was crying and couldn't stop, and I was in bumper-to-bumper traffic on Interstate 5, one of the busiest highways in Southern California. I realized that my life was a wreck. I'd become a reporter to help people but really I could do very little to help others. I just wrote stories about people's problems. Others in the media wrote about solutions for problems but I couldn't find those jobs.

I was stuck. My career was killing me. But worse than that, I'd lost my positive attitude about my future and had stopped making progress in my personal life. I was lost. I felt hopeless and empty inside. I was giving up on my future. Tears stung my eyes. Tears blurred my vision. The pain was a deep, gut wrenching spasm of emotion from a soul at the moment it felt its imminent destruction.

That hopeless feeling was what hurt so badly. Had I worked so hard for five years in college to find a good career only to fail?

But the "hopeless" feeling was also a clue, I discovered. It highlighted the fact that I'd become pessimistic.

The Oxford English Dictionary[1] (OED) defines pessimism as, "A tendency to see the worst aspect of things or believe that the worst will happen; a lack of **hope** or confidence in the future."

That was me.

In previous years, I had an attitude of optimism or positivity, which is the opposite of pessimism—in fact it gets rid of the hopelessness of pessimism. Positivity questions and destroys the assumptions of pessimism (like your future is hopeless) and inoculates you against letting pessimism infect your mind again.

Positivity is the cure for pessimism.

Positivity, however, may sound cheesy, juvenile, or even petty to you. But look at the definition. According to the OED[2] positivity is an optimistic attitude, and optimism is "hopefulness and confidence about the future or the successful outcome of something."

There is nothing wrong with looking forward to something working out. Or looking forward to the "future." However, optimism is ignored or even questioned on college campuses, in social media and in mainstream media. The people who put down optimism and the idea of progress are the same people who use the benefits of progress—smart phones, computers, modern systems of business and science. That makes them guilty of a double standard: progress is bad or elitist except for how I live my life. Do as I say, not as I do.

In truth it is hard to live without the benefits of progress from modern science and technology and democracy. It's everywhere you look.

From vaccines that have saved billions of people's lives, to the internet and smart phones that connect billions of people and raise their standard of living, we are surrounded by the benefits of science and the optimistic people who do that science. Optimism contributed to these benefits, which have raised the standard of living for every country, every race, sex, religion and culture—for practically every decade since 1950.

But at the time of my crisis of hopelessness I had no clue about these facts. I had no clue what was wrong with me or how to fix it. I just knew I felt pessimistic and hopeless. I was lost.

I let pessimism take over my mind

My optimism died in college. There, unknown to me at the time, I was taught to be skeptical about everything regarding science and progress: modern society was corrupt. This was the attitude in environmental science and literature classes. I was taught there is no big "narrative" about progress happening all over the world or what can better people's lives. Everything is just a mindless power struggle. Everything I'd been taught in high school about the importance of honesty, hard work and self-improvement—was just "kid's stuff." In fact everything was really going down the drain with environmental destruction and poor people getting poorer. The flakey thing was that these classes showed only the facts to back up their claims, no facts that questioned it.

These textbooks never considered that there was an alternative view that progress could be happening, and it was helping everybody. This one-sided view should have been a tip off I was a sucker and was being taught pseudoscience.

A pseudoscience claims that certain things are scientific facts but avoids key elements of the scientific method:

VIEW FROM PESSIMISM

PERSPECTIVE   REAL LIFE

FIGURE 1.0.2
Perspective of pessimism versus real life.
By Esther Phingmoo.

VIEW FROM OPTIMISM

PERSPECTIVE   REAL LIFE

FIGURE 1.0.3
View from optimism (positivity) versus real life.
By Esther Phingmoo.

- Empirical studies that get verifiable results, results that are repeated by others.
- Alternative points of view and evidence for them.

In reality, the world was continuing to see a steady, measurable growth in peace and prosperity in every decade since World War II (more on this later). These facts, however, were kept from me.

As I looked at myself a few years after college, I saw I had pessimism because I had all the symptoms:

- Failure to focus on goals and accomplishments (there's no such thing as progress, remember?)
- Taking setbacks personally
- Failure to learn from experiences

How did I know these were the symptoms of pessimism? I didn't learn it from a book. I looked at my experience. I looked at the basic elements of positivity (show initiative on goals, take accomplishments personally, learn from temporary setbacks) and saw I was doing just the opposite! And the opposite of positivity is pessimism, so that must be what I was doing—the actions of pessimism. That explained how hurt and lost I felt. Because pessimism leads to a feeling of nihilism, that everything is pointless and worthless. Pessimism is like a virus in our attitude. It interferes with how our attitude works by getting us to look at the worst in ourselves instead of the best. This insight that pessimism trapped me was a massive breakthrough for me.

Looking at our brain like it's a smart phone

A modern way of looking at my experience of pessimism is to say I didn't have a good user experience. Smart phones and their apps are designed so you can have a good experience using them. Engineers design how apps look and work by adding buttons and drop-down lists to increase functionality. It should be the same way with our brain. Our brain should work for us. Our attitude in our brain should work for us. **Your** attitude should work for **you**.

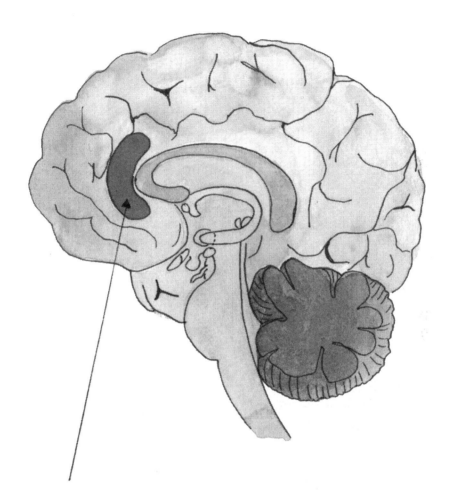

ROSTAL ANTERIOR CINGULATE CORTEX

FIGURE 1.0.4
The brain's positive attitude area: rostral anterior cingulate
cortex (RACC). By Esther Phingmoo.

Your attitude is an application in the most amazing piece of technology you will ever own: your brain. The positive attitude functions deep in your brain in an area roughly between your eyes and between your ears in an area called the rostral anterior cingulate cortex (RACC). It teams up with another area, the amygdala (used for processing fear and social meaning) to get the job done. It should work for you smoothly and efficiently so you can be happy pursuing your goals and living your best life. It often doesn't. It should have features that let you quickly do and get what you want so you can have the best user experience. Like apps in a phone, our attitude always seems to need little changes to adapt to new needs, new situations.

Your attitude is actually an "app" (application) in your brain so you should treat it like that: a piece of technology. This book is an upgrade for your attitude app, a massive upgrade so you can get the most out of that app and your brain and your life. Pessimism often disrupts positivity, which is exactly what happened in my career crisis. And almost no one is talking about the fight between pessimism and a positive attitude, so pessimism is now running free, in the media and elsewhere, causing stress, ruining lives and causing mental illness. When something is causing illness, I see that as something I should deal with. I'm a doctor after all. Fighting illness is my calling. This book is me acting on my calling.

But I digress. Years before my career crisis, I'd been optimistic in high school where optimism was taught, and that was such a guiding light for me. If you went to a high school like I attended, positivity was taught there. Teachers were excited to teach you things they thought improved the lives of others and would improve your life. I mean, that's the whole point of education. Improve your life. Improve everyone's life. So you can get a job you are interested in that benefits society.

In science we were taught about amazing discoveries that improved our lives, like inoculations and the use of electricity. Human lives were improved. Science and technology are solving problems like famines and plagues that had killed millions of people for eons. There is more peace and prosperity than ever before. Education works. Science and technology work.

Democracy works. This positivity helped me succeed in high school and college. I later learned that the essential elements of positivity are:

- Set goals and take your accomplishments personally (like a good grade on a test)
- Don't take setbacks personally (like a bad grade, just learn to study differently)
- Learn from everything (so you are ready for final exams)

There is a fight between positivity and pessimism in the world and in our souls. The outcome of this fight can be disastrous. That's what led to my crisis of hopelessness. However few schools and few books talk about the impact of pessimism or the necessity of positivity.

Pessimism ruins a feeling of hope

When pessimism takes over your attitude, you can lose your sense of hope, meaning and purpose. This makes pessimism toxic. Pessimism creates an inner conflict. You may feel that what you value won't be valued by others or yourself in the future. Pessimism causes people to doubt positive future outcomes. You sacrifice to get ahead at work, and pessimism causes you to doubt your efforts will amount to anything. In this way pessimism creates mental illness—depression, anxiety and possibly addiction.

Gradually I found a way to defeat pessimism and put positivity back in charge in my life. I even found a way to use a "heads up attitude" to empower my positive attitude and guard against pessimism. A heads up attitude is anticipating problems so you are ready for them with a plan. These techniques helped me become the doctor I am today. These techniques also helped me to help hundreds of my pessimistic patients pick up the pieces of their lives and build better lives based on a positive outlook.

In other words, I taught them to think like a doctor. They went on to chart success in work and family life. I'm passing on these strategies in this book.

Pessimism: the dead zone of the mind

The real-world consequences of letting pessimism take over your mind are frightening. Pessimists have higher rates of illness, depression and failure in their business and personal life, according to a review of scientific research on the topic by scientists at the University of Sienna in Italy[3]. It is not good to lose focus on taking care of yourself and your future.

There is a pandemic of pessimism

Unfortunately, there is a pandemic of pessimism, and it is getting worse.[4] In an article entitled "Most People Around the World Are Overly Pessimistic," the World Economic Forum reports that a global survey by the polling company Ipsos MORI found people in every country feel negative about their future[5]. Ipsos MORI has conducted more than 200,000 interviews in 40 countries in its global "Perils" study.[6] It turns out most of us are pessimistic and routinely overestimate rates of murder, violence, terrorism, income inequality and other social justice issues in the world around us.

Pessimism gives us a distorted, scary view of the world and a distorted, weak view of our own potential because we perceive the world as being messed up.

The international experts that follow show that there is no factual basis for pessimism since about 1950. It is a viewpoint hopelessly out of date.

Physician and international health professor Dr. Hans Rosling concludes in his New York Times Bestseller *Factfulness*[7] that the world is better off than we think in terms of health, safety and opportunities to prosper, but we have 10 mental roadblocks that prevent us from recognizing it. No wonder we have been duped by global marketing in this pandemic of pessimism. Mentally, we are our own worst enemy.

To make it easier to upgrade your view of the world with the facts, Dr. Rosling and others created the *Worldview Upgrader*. It is a free quiz that follows the basic goals of the United Nations to combat problems facing humanity, such as poverty, income inequality, disease and famines. Upgrade your perspective by taking the *Worldview Upgrader* quiz.[8]

You can also upgrade your attitude. Three pessimistic ideas are setting up students for failure in life, according to a human rights attorney Greg Lukianoff, and New York University Ethics Professor Jonathan Haidt, who wrote the runaway New York Times Bestseller, *The Coddling of the American Mind: How Good Intentions And Bad Ideas Are Setting Up A Generation For Failure*[9]. The pessimistic ideas are that it is ok to:

- be emotionally fragile
- believe your emotions no matter what
- believe that people are in a conflict between those who are either good or hopelessly bad

What should be done about these bad ideas? Reject them! Work on becoming emotionally strong. Work on "weeding out" emotions that are irrational, like that Western Civilization is hopelessly bad. Don't "write off" people as hopelessly bad, but see the good and the bad in their ideas.

Another (incorrect) pessimistic idea taught in some schools is that Western Civilization hasn't done anyone any good—it's just propping up corporations to make more profit. This idea is detailed in the Wall Street Journal Bestseller *Cynical Theories*[10] and its authors, Helen Pluckrose and James Lindsay. This kind of "cancel culture" ignores facts such as Western Civilization's vaccines alone have saved at least 5 billion lives. (See Steven Pinker, "Enlightenment Now," page 64.).

When you let pessimism take over your mind, you get emotionally weak, emotionally gullible, and afraid of conflict or even a conversation with someone with a different point of view. That was me in the grips of fear caused by pessimism. "Problems are bigger than me and I'm fragile and I'm a victim." All this begs the question: how pessimistic are you?

FIGURE 1.0.5
Cleaning the window of your attitude.
By Esther Phingmoo.

Measure your pessimism

How pessimistic are you about yourself? Take the unhealthy pessimism quiz in the appendix at the back of this book. There is a positivity quiz there, too. And you can take both quizzes at the end of each chapter in this book and see if you are getting more positive just by reading this book.

It is worth it to repair your attitude by getting rid of pessimism? I know about the impact of pessimism. My mental blocks wouldn't let me believe in myself or the world when I was 25. The results lead to a crisis because of irrational beliefs about myself and the world. Questioning my doubts about society and progress got the ball rolling.

How I cleaned up my attitude

First, I began to doubt my pessimism. That is how you start to clean up your attitude. Doubt the doubts. Be a skeptic of the skepticism. One little step at a time. Identify an issue, check the facts, and adjust your attitude to fit the facts. I learned many facts that the world was getting better in terms of prosperity and that made me want to be a part of that progress.

Maybe the world isn't so bad off, I thought. "Maybe I'm not so hopeless. Maybe the world isn't so hopeless." Maybe there are strategies to create more hope and purpose in my life. Maybe the world is making progress. Use sentences with "maybe" in them if you want to liberate yourself from limiting beliefs such as "my life is hopeless" or "the world is hopeless."

Maybe. At least I was open to the idea of me getting more hopeful. There is so much power in the word "maybe."

I saw I got what I deserved

In a flash of insight, I saw I was where I deserved to be. I made the choices that got me to where I was. And therefore, I could make different choices to get myself out of this mess. If my future was going to be better, somehow I had to learn from my accomplishments and setbacks and make myself more **valuable**. Valuable to myself and other people. Then I would be able to build a better future for myself. Then I would be able to join the progress that was happening in the world.

But how? I needed action strategies and a better attitude.

The six principles of positivity

I owned up to the fact that if I created the mess I was in, I could create a way out with a better attitude. But what was that attitude like exactly? It was easier to be positive when everything was structured for you in school. Now I was on my own. But I recalled the basics of positivity. It involved six principles:

- **Take initiative.** Positive attitude people are leaders in their life and show initiative by writing down goals in order to finish projects. I would make finding a new career my project. I would structure my day to make that happen.
- **Make the most of setbacks.** I would view my situation as an opportunity to learn how to find a career with a good fit for my personality. I had a setback, it was frustrating, but it wasn't the end of the world. I would focus that frustration on making some progress every day on my project. In this way I used my setback as a source of energy and inspiration.
- **Hopefulness.** I had given up hope. But I saw hope is an attitude. It is a choice. I decided to make that choice. I would do my best and give the rest up to God. Prayer boosted my feelings of hope.
- **Appreciate accomplishments.** I had taken my accomplishments for granted. I had come a long way from that shy, insecure skinny teenager who was afraid of his own shadow. I spent time appreciating my accomplishments and taking them personally. And I appreciated the accomplishments to come. It would feel so good to find a better career for my personality! I would do the hard work to get that accomplishment.

- **Let go.** I had made mistakes, lots of mistakes. But instead of dwelling on them, and how unfair life is, and how unjust society is, I would let go of the past. My future required my total focus in the present moment. I couldn't afford to waste time thinking about the past.
- **Learn.** Instead of dwelling on my problems, I would focus on finding solutions for them. I would focus on learning and be excited about possibilities. This brought me back to my old positive attitude, looking at life as an adventure in learning.

I organized the key elements of positivity into these six principles. They are key principles because you can remember them simply by recalling the acronym "**I SHALL.**" An acronym is a word or saying in which each letter represents other words that are part of a larger and powerful concept. It is a way to prompt your memory. This acronym is not fool proof. But many times if you feel stuck in a feeling of negativity you can recall this acronym and it will prompt you to start thinking positively again. That can get you out of a mud hole of melancholy. They are also key principles because if you leave one principle out, all the other principles for your freedom to live your best life—are weakened.

The I SHALL acronym is in the rating scale for positivity at the end of the book and is also the way I've organized the chapters in this book. If you leave one out, a positive attitude starts to fall apart. They are key because they can unlock your potential for making progress on your hopes and dreams. They did just that for me.

I charted a new course for my life

I showed initiative and got busy. Every day after work I made up my mind to make a little progress. I often went to the library to help me focus and do research. To find a better career fit I used the technique of lists to take an inventory of my likes and dislikes. I interviewed people about their careers and imagined what it would be like to be in that career. After months of work, I found the best career to fit my interests was a career in medicine.

That was so unexpected because of all the mental blinders I used to have about science, but I had ripped those blinders off.

Then I used another toolbox of skills over the next several years to get into medical school and graduate. I have practiced medicine for 20 years now. The skills that helped me succeed can help you in your success.

How can I make that promise? I was a first-rate pessimist! And you live in the same world I live in. Also, I've taught these skills to hundreds of people who have told me of their success in:

- school
- starting a career
- relationships and starting a family
- dealing with losses or illness

I'll be sharing dozens of these stories in the chapters that follow. To cut to the chase, this book is all about developing powerful new habits. Awareness is everything. Once you are aware of a new habit, it is easier to practice it. Habits are action skills used repeatedly. Here are some of the game changing habits that dramatically empower your positive attitude:

- RAMP method
- Healthy diet
- Healthy sleep routines
- Meditating to interfere with pessimistic thinking
- Meditating to feel self-acceptance
- Focus on preparation
- Making success the only option in your thinking
- Good posture
- Good hygiene
- Physical fitness
- Exercises for mental fitness
- Clean up after yourself policy
- No excuses policy for yourself
- Zero tolerance for pessimism
- Infinite tolerance for defeat when pursuing goals
- Act on what your advisor advised
- If there are strong emotions about something, double check that
- Get a hero if you don't have one
- Let go of what drags you down

FIGURE 1.0.6:
Earth smiling in its orbit. By Esther Phingmoo.

There is no reason to be pessimistic in an unhealthy way, with all these tools that can help you start making progress today.

If you still believe the world is getting worse instead of better, I sympathize with you. I once was there. I know what it's like to be caught up in those self-limiting beliefs. But I have some news for you. Your beliefs are 70 years out of date. Sorry! You're getting left behind like I was!

You are also surrounded by a global wave of positivity

Pessimism about the world doesn't fit the facts! There is a global wave of pessimism, but also one of optimism or positivity. Open your eyes. Where did your cell phone come from? Your computer? Your car or bike? The clothes on your back? The shoes on your feet? Your standard of living?

These all came in part from companies that are part of Western Civilization. Companies made of people that focus on their goals, show initiative, weather through setbacks and you can fill in the rest of the qualities of positivity. They come from companies and individuals committed to making useful things that consumers demand. Companies are succeeding in their goals of providing goods and services for consumers to raise their standard of living.

The companies that made these products use the STEAM fields of study to make these things. STEAM stands for science, technology, engineering, art and math. (See this Wikipedia article: https://en.wikipedia.org/wiki/STEAM_fields). Art helps creative problem solving and to show the excitement for new technological breakthroughs. Look no further than your cell phone for an example. Companies use all these fields to make better products and sell them—and that keeps their employees in jobs and keeps customers satisfied.

One man I know who worked for Hewlett Packard regularly did Zoom calls with people from China, India and countries in Europe—all at the same time! He needed to be sensitive to cultural issues as the team struggled to solve technological problems. The same is true for me. Art and creativity have been a big part of this book. I've gotten input from people from Africa, Latin America, Europe and Asia. Specifically, people have helped me who are from countries like Toga, Brazil, Costa Rica, Columbia, Ecuador, Serbia and India. I've spent countless hours so this book has a great cover, interior design and illustrations— to help people understand the exciting breakthroughs in the area of brain science and positive psychology. This book is a global STEAM effort!

The STEAM engine of progress

The STEAM fields are driving the progress I described earlier. Science is creating the stuff and business is selling the stuff— and investing in the science. It happens all around you. Look at everything around you in your residence and ask where it came from. There is a supply chain of companies working hard to satisfy you, the consumer! If you are not part of that progress, you are getting left behind.

Here is one barista's vision of the STEAM engine of progress in the little coffee shop she manages:

"I used to think business majors in college were the 'slackers.' Now I see the chain of people involved in providing a cup of coffee and I'm proud to be a part of that. Farm workers pick the coffee beans in tropical countries—they pick at just the

ANOTHER NOTE

Companies making progress are free to do so. Freedom and democracy are empowering this never-before-seen wave of progress since the early 1900's. You are part of this wave when you live your life to the fullest with a positive attitude. Enlightened selfishness works! Wake up! Open your eyes! Be grateful to be a part of Western Civilization, the greatest culture in history. Never has a culture created this kind of progress for humanity. I'm just stating the obvious.

right time. Then there are the companies farming the beans, transporting them, roasting them. Science is used to test the beans. Technology is used to roast them. Art is used to sell them. People all along the way are doing a good job so we can have a great quality product. Everyone is earning their money in the process. When I brew up a great cup of coffee and give it to a policewoman, that may give her a lift tonight for the night shift as she patrols our streets and keep us safe. I'm so grateful to be part of the whole coffee shop process. It's making our lives better and giving lots of people jobs along the way."

The global movement of optimism

Most anyone can learn a positive attitude and the results are amazing—all over the world. Martin Seligman, PhD, author of "Learned Optimism," and a leading researcher in the field, has taught optimism for decades at the University of Pennsylvania. He shows a positive attitude paves the way for success and satisfaction in life in this open-source article.[11] While positivity is a global force with global results, it is overshadowed by the global movement of pessimism which grabs most of the headlines in the media.

Here are some specific examples from **hundreds** of studies showing positivity makes for a better life. University students and administration in Sydney, Australia harnessed this kind of optimism and reported an enhanced educational experience.[12] They were more engaged in activities for women, minorities and Muslims, as well as taking action in sustainability projects. Now there's progress in some social justice issues! Researchers from the University of Padova, Italy and the University of Lausanne, Switzerland showed that a positive attitude strongly supported coping with work stress and feeling satisfied with one's life in Europe.[13]

Researchers from universities in Kentucky and Illinois surveyed college students to see what helped students thrive, feel good about themselves and have low levels of stress. The factor making the biggest difference: optimism[14]. Similar studies show positivity working in Turkey, China, Russia, Central

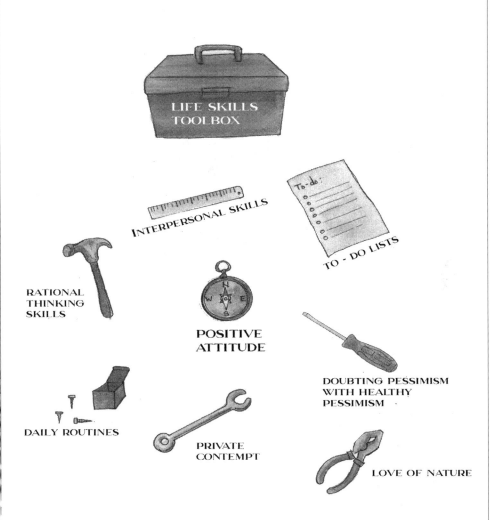

FIGURE 1.0.9

The toolbox of skills of positivity. By Esther Phingmoo.

and South America. The list goes on and on. Type "optimism" in a search engine for scientific journals and see for yourself. Local libraries can offer access to these search engines. Google scholar also works but often you can only view a summary of the article.

Positivity can be learned and it is worth it. What are you waiting for?

The Promise

Positivity can be learned. Positivity is just an attitude with a lot of tools. I'll teach you them in this book. When you finish this book, you will know dozens of quick, practical ways to put positivity into action to make progress on your dreams. Your toolbox of life skills will have grown. You will be able to catch pessimism and stop it from ruining your attitude. You can take the positivity quiz after each chapter you read and see if your positivity has grown. My guess is you will see steady progress in growing your positivity.

JOURNAL YOUR LEARNING HERE:

Forward: book organization

Principles and what they do for you

There are six principles of positivity. It is super helpful to remember them.

Knowing the six principles will change your life. Just jogging your mind and recalling them is like remembering a password for an app on your phone. Put in the password, then the app opens and you can use all its powerful functions! Boom! The I SHALL acronym does that for you by summarizing the six essential elements of positivity:

- **Initiative**—show it because that's how things get done.
- **Setbacks**—they are temporary and something to learn from.
- **Hopefulness**—feel it because your goals are worth it.
- **Accomplishments**—take them personally because you did the work.
- **Let go**—of caring for what you can't control.
- **Learning**—we learn from setbacks and accomplishments, its what life is for.

Now that you remember the six essential features of positivity, you can use them. There is a chapter for these principles so you can learn them in more depth. Then in books 2 and 3 there are many more stories so your grip on a positive attitude becomes even stronger and more tenacious. Stories make the dynamic power of each principle come alive.

In all three positivity books there are over 130 stories illustrating dozens of inspiring skills. You'll find yourself automatically using tips and techniques in the stories after you get in a habit of reading the book every day for a week or so. For those wanting even more detail in how to apply these techniques, I have created a video education program. For more details on this, see the back of the book or go to harrisjensenmd.com.

Oddly enough, many stories are about people reading this book before it was published. For several years I shared a digital working version of this book with dozens of people to see what ideas worked and which didn't. You'll read the results.

Life skills and what they are good for

Life skills empower each principle. They come from your experiences, not some textbook. The more life skills you have, and the more often you use them, the more powerful you are to live your best life. The six main life skills that empower the basic principles of positivity are:

- Communication skills (to connect with others)
- Time management skills (to be efficient)
- Task management skills (to become reliable)
- Asking for help (so you get help)
- Support system (the help)
- Openness to feedback (so you understand the help)
- Life organization skills (so you act on the help)

Tools

Tools help these life skills work. Here are a dozen tools used in this book to empower your life skills so you can live your best life:

- Mindfulness skills
- Perception skills
- Life lesson stories
- Daily habits
- Attitudes
- Rating scales
- Fun facts
- Action steps
- Jump starters
- Metaphors
- Icons or symbols
- Sayings
- Pro tips
- Myth busters

Overview of chapters

The **Preface** briefly reviews how positivity saved me from pessimism. Forward describes how the book is organized. Chapter 1 is **Why you need positivity**. It reveals how positivity can save you from pessimism—and help you tap into your awesome potential. Without a positive attitude you might give up on trying to live your best life because you randomly fall into a pessimistic attitude without knowing it. That happens all the time. Chapter 2 is **Why I am qualified to teach you positivity**. This shares the story of how I started out in life as a first class pessimist from a broken family. I could have easily gone into poverty or worse. Positivity saved me. Later I learned brain science and for more than 20 years I've taught positivity to thousands of people as their physician and psychotherapist—and seen them live their best life. Chapter 3 dives into the details of this powerful attitude with **Six principles for positivity: a deeper look**. It shows you step by step how to apply life skills to transform your life. In the **Appendix**, rating scales give you a perspective for how positive or negative you are now about yourself and your future. You can see your progress by taking these quizzes before and after reading the book.

Where did all these ideas come from? Here is an overview of that. For 25 years I regularly work with about 500 patients at any one time, seeing 80 per week or 4,000 visits per year. Each time I see someone, I ask something like "How has your past month been for you?" Then they reveal what they have learned to use to make progress in their life, whether it has been from me or another therapist or a self help book. Then I keep notes on what those tools or life skills are that they are using. Finally, I transfer those notes into this book. So you are reading a doctor's "brain dump" of 25 years of what has worked for thousands of people to make progress in their life.

There is a fault in this book. I tend to repeat certain ideas over and over. But each repetition is like peeling off layers of an onion: you are getting deeper insight (in your heart and mind) into how things really work with positivity. Be patient with me!

JOURNAL YOUR LEARNING HERE:

FIGURE 1.1.0
Your brain is born to be positive. By Toso Borkovic.

1

Why you need positivity

FIGURE 1.1.1
The paths of pessimism and positivity lead to different outcomes. Take your pick! By Esther Phingmoo.

Pessimism and positivity got into an argument today about positivity and it went like this:

It's elitist
>**No, it's for everybody**

It's propping up a sick culture
>**No, it helps you succeed**

It's making other people money
>**No, it cuts down on oppression by empowering people**

It's too hard to learn
>**No, just learn a little every day**

It's too hard to do
>**No, it's just reorganizing what you do everyday**

It just won't work for me
>**No, it's based on what works for everybody**

I won't remember it to apply it
>**No, you'll get better as you practice it**

I won't every get it perfectly right
>**None of us do, we just practice**

Positivity made her an Olympian!

Brazilian Rachel Salinger knows all about how powerful a positive attitude is. It took her from a small town in Brazil to the 2000 Olympics in Sydney, Australia—where she won a bronze medal!

"You need to have an attitude for everything in life," Rachel confesses. Would she and her team have won a bronze medal without paying attention to their attitude? "No way," she said.

"We were playing against the very best teams in the world," she explained. "Cuba, China and America. All were very strong. We played against Cuba and lost!" That meant they had just one more game to play for the bronze medal. It was easy to focus on their loss to Cuba. But that would be bad for their attitude.

In international tournaments, some teams will say bad things to the other team to shake them up, she noted. They had to be pessimistic about those other teams—they had to resort to dirty tricks to try to win. They were trying to win by damaging the other team's attitude. She won't say what team did that. "Also, when other teams think they are better than you, you can take advantage of that," she said. So there are mind games going on in Olympic volleyball.

"You have to keep good posture and good attitude and say, 'OK, I got this. I can do it,'" she said. "But if you slump your shoulders, look down, people will take advantage of you." You also must work with your coach.

After the loss to Cuba, their coach had a talk with the team. "Don't be upset," he said, Rachel recalls. "We don't have time for that. We still have a chance to win. Let's get together and fight." For ten years she'd sacrificed to make herself the best volleyball player she could be. Now her coach asked her team to make one more sacrifice to save their mental and physical energy. They would skip the opening ceremony in the Olympics.

Since the age of ten she'd dreamed of going to the Olympics and being in that ceremony. "I came from a simple family," she said. They didn't have a lot of money. But her family strongly encouraged her work and attitude. "If you work hard, you can go far," she said her family taught her. "If you work hard and prepare yourself every day, it's possible for anybody to achieve their big dreams."

The time for the big game arrived. Her coach gathered the team together. "Save energy," he said. "Keep concentrated. The whole world is watching." And he sent them onto the volleyball court where they won in a game against the United States! She'd won the bronze medal!

Rachel's story illustrates the power of positivity. Individual achievement is often part of a group achievement. The team had a healthy positive attitude about their chances for a victory. They also had a healthy pessimistic attitude that other teams would not compete hard enough to win. Raquel guarded herself from dwelling on setbacks—that would lead to an unhealthy pessimism about her chances of winning. She and her team braced themselves for a tough game against the USA. They did not fall into the trap of having an unhealthy (and unrealistic) positive attitude that it would be easy to win against the USA.

This story illustrates that there are four basic attitudes when it comes to positivity. If you use healthy positivity and healthy pessimism—and don't let yourself fall into unhealthy positivity and unhealthy pessimism—you can go far in life. You can even go to the Olympics!

Today Rachel continues to pursue her passion of volleyball, as a volleyball coach in the USA. Her students continue to learn attitude is a big part of a winning a volleyball game.

There are really four kinds of pessimism and positivity—and you need just two of them

The main focus of this book is to get positive about two things: yourself and your future. OK. But let's not lose sight of something. There is such a thing as being too positive so you forget to consider potential bad consequences. That is called unhealthy positivity. And then there is positive thinking that is actually good for you. That I call healthy positivity.

On the other side of the fence is pessimism. But actually, there is a pessimism that considers problems so you are ready to deal with them. That is called healthy pessimism. It is actually very useful, especially for dealing with addictions. Then of course there is unhealthy pessimism. It is unhealthy because no matter what you do, it doubts you and your ability to make any progress on your dreams. (The crowd can "Boo!" now.)

Knowing about all four forms of positivity and pessimism is quite a witty feat. You can use them all to your advantage to make progress in your personal life. I've done this for 20 plus years and it has made me a better doctor.

The Four Attitudes

An alcoholic tells me, "I just had one drink but I can handle it." My response: Do you think you're being overly optimistic? (Unhealthy positivity). Another man says "My girlfriend dumped me for some other guy. I'll never find someone for me." My response: Do you think you're being a little too pessimistic here? (Unhealthy pessimism). "I got rejected by four graduate schools to be a nurse practitioner—but now I am broadening my search to physician assistant and other medical related schools." My response: How creative. I loved how you learned from a setback and changed your focus. You're going to do well. (Healthy positivity). "I'm sick of smoking myself to death! Those cravings for cigarettes would never have happened if I never smoked to begin with! I quit smoking for good and threw all my cigarettes out! One cigarette creates cravings for cigarettes that last for weeks months." My response: My how you are pessimistic about the potential of one of the most addictive substances known to man to get you hooked! Good job. I'm pessimistic too about cigarettes. That's why I don't smoke. (Healthy pessimism).

You might be wasting your potential with limiting beliefs

It is a life skill to be able to spot your limiting beliefs. Limiting beliefs are one way pessimism can take over your mind. Positivity helps you replace limiting beliefs with empowering beliefs. In the moment of my career crisis, I felt stuck like my feet were in cement. The stagnation felt as real as rain. If I could go back in time, what would I have told myself? "My friend, you have some beliefs that are seriously holding you back. And you don't even know it." I felt I was limited by my past and many limiting beliefs. Here are some of my limiting beliefs and how they were replaced with empowering beliefs:

- Limited by my income…if I make less I can spend less while I increase my value
- Limited by my status…but I won't care about status, I'll increase my value
- Limited by how not cool I am…I'm leaving the culture where cool counts
- Controlled by my problems…I am driven by my accomplishments
- Limited by other people's problems…I'm prioritizing taking care of myself now
- Unable to learn new things…I'll stop at nothing to learn all I have to learn
- Always going to be what you are now…Every day I'll change a little to prove I can
- Never going to get help from others…I'll form powerful alliances with people
- Only going to do what you do now…Every day I'll be doing something new
- Never going to move to new places…I'll move wherever I have to in order to succeed
- Never going to make new friends…If I don't have friends in a new place, I'll be a friend

These are limiting beliefs and their replacements. It is a life skill to correct limiting beliefs with empowering beliefs. There is an art to these kinds of affirmations, of course. You state what you are going to do, not what you are going to avoid. Affirmations are ways of doing just the opposite of what a limiting belief used to make you do. Affirmations help to unlock your potential—in a big way.

All these limiting beliefs make pessimistic assumptions, such as: you won't take the time, set goals, learn from setbacks, pile up accomplishments, etc. But you will if you choose to. Struggling with some overwhelming limiting beliefs that you can't change?

You can challenge limiting beliefs with one of the most powerful words in your language: maybe. As in, "I'll be limited by my past, maybe." Or, "I'll be limited by my income, maybe." Challenge those beliefs that limit you. What have they done for you? You can stick with them. But there are also so many other beliefs to choose from. Tap into your freedom to question your limiting beliefs and liberate yourself. Use your freedom to pick the empowering beliefs that help you live your best life. I did.

I thought I was limited by my past and by many other things too—but at first I had no idea that the cause of that limitation was not the thing itself, but the limiting belief.

"What if judo"

As you might be figuring out, positivity is made of dozens of life skills. Another common hurdle from pessimism is "what if's" that can lead you down the "what if" rabbit hole. By rabbit hole I mean a pattern of thinking that feeds into a self-defeating pattern of thinking, feeling and acting. If you are in a rabbit hole of pessimism you are going to feel more helpless and defeated, and you won't know why. Until you use the life skill of recognizing that you are in a rabbit hole.

You might think, as I did, "What if my past does control me?" or, "What if I can't let go of the trauma?" or, "What if I can't learn new things?" What if, what if, what if...it will never end. Our imagination is limitless in its ability to imagine new things...for better or for worse. And in this case, it just imagines the worst. Of course, this way of thinking is just pessimism. You can tell you are thinking pessimistically if you are taking setbacks personally and not learning from them. Or if you are just imaging the worst that could happen and then obsessing about that. Now that you have learned how to identify a thought as pessimistic, you can reject such thoughts.

What do you do to a pesky, negative obsession? Use the life skill of what if judo. To this, "What if I can't escape my past?" Say this, "What if I can?" To this, "What if I can't escape poverty?" You can ask this, "What if I can?" Or if you feel, "What if I can't make new friends?" You can say, "What if I can?" As long as you are good at questioning things, and most of us are, question the thoughts that limit you. What an excellent empowering life skill.

The real question is: what are the limits on what you can learn? If you can learn solutions to a problem, then you have a chance to overcome it.

Three kinds of limitations on our potential

There are three kinds of limits on our ability to learn to make progress: biological, psychological and social. Let's take a closer look at these.

Biologically, we are limited by the chemistry of our physical brains. Our brain uses more than 200 chemicals to send signals, as well as dozens of different electrical wave patterns. So not very limited there. And when it comes to mechanical connections your brain is hard to beat. Your brain has from 4 million to 40 million times more nerve to nerve connections than there are stars in the Milky Way Galaxy. That applies to everyone's brain—of every age, race, sex, nationality, past, economic status, religion and ethnic heritage. EVERYONE. And with proper daily habits and exercise, adults can actually boost their connections—their IQ. The memory center expands 10% with exercise. So there are biological limits but you can increase them. I did.

There are biological conditions that limit the brain, too. But now we have treatments. For migraine headaches, new sumatriptan medications and meditation provide relief. For depression, we have new antidepressants, including some provided by intravenous therapy. For anxiety we have dozens of new medications and psychotherapies. For addictions, we have half a dozen new medications. The list goes on and on. The expanding new biological treatments for biological conditions put ever more power at your fingertips. Just ask your doctor if you think you have a brain condition—so it doesn't hold you back.

Psychologically we are limited by our thinking, but now you know you can control, guide and change that thinking in many ways. You can change your psychology by reading this book and learning dozens of ways to break down barriers to your

YOUR BRAIN HAS CONNECTIONS EQUAL TO THE STARS IN 4 MILLION MILKY WAY GALAXIES

AND PROCESSES SIGNALS EACH SECOND EQUAL TO 400 MILKY WAY GALAXIES ...

FIGURE 1.1.2

Your brain is like millions of galaxies. By Esther Phingmoo.

progress. Just being aware of them is a game changer. Then you can use those life skills to transform your life.

Socially we are limited but that, too, you can change. You can make new friends, move to new towns or countries and change how you relate to the people you know. The microbiology lab job I got, that was key in getting me into medical school, came about when a friend named Rob suggested I talk to a friend of his, a physician Dr. Andrews. Dr. Andrews referred me to the microbiologist and the rest is history. I widened the limits of my social circle. I got into medical school.

In the stories in this book, people use life skills to "massively" push back the biological, psychological and social limits that are holding them back. You are a lot less limited than you think.

The massive push back

One woman found defeat in three different countries for her goals—but pushed back and solved her problems. Her family couldn't find adequately paying jobs in Columbia, so they pushed back against those odds and moved to Canada. Later those jobs dried up. So they moved to the United States. She graduated high school and got hit with a severe medical condition. Her family couldn't afford her medical care. She pushed back against the adversities and travelled to her home country of Columbia and got the care she needed. She couldn't find the job opportunities she wanted in Columbia—so she pushed back against the problems and returned to the US for the income she needed for her life goals. Not everyone can move to different countries to solve problems. But this story highlights just how far people can go to keep pushing for the progress they want in their life. If a country fails you, try to move to another country.

You can't change your DNA. That's what people mean when they say, "Oh, I am what I am. This is me. I've been messed up and that's how I'll always be." That is a limiting belief. As I will show below, your DNA and brain are fine. If you are feeling stuck it's because of how you are using your DNA. You can change how you use your DNA. You can change how your DNA is activated in your brain—by exercise that elevates levels of nerve growth factor—and by a positive attitude.

Nerve growth factor is a game changer for people wanting to change their brain quickly using exercise and positivity. Within several hours of getting nerve growth factor—literally thousands of connections grow on a single nerve taken from a chicken egg. If that can happen for a nerve from a bird brain, the same is true for your brain.[15]

What if our brain wasn't limited? What if it could change? What if it had boundless abilities to learn new things? Would that change how you thought about yourself and your world? What kind of new connections do you want to make in your brain so you can pursue your dreams? What kind of new connections do you want to grow in your brain's positive attitude center, the rostral anterior cingulate cortex?

There are biological limits on your potential. Let's explore the amazing biology of your own brain. The biology of your mind just might blow your mind.

Unlimited potential

How can you learn to have a positive attitude? Just ask yourself to focus on your goals and get excited about your potential. Everyone has an amazing potential to benefit from a positive attitude. Is there a lot to learn? Yes. Can it get complicated trying to pursue your dreams? Sure. But you have tremendous information processing power sitting there right between your ears. Let's look at your amazing potential.

Your brain comes loaded with potential in terms of three things:

- computing power (calculations per second)
- speed (distance per second)
- connections to different areas (length of wiring)

In all three areas your brain beats most computers in the world! Look at the numbers.

WITHOUT NGF   WITH NGF (2 DAYS)

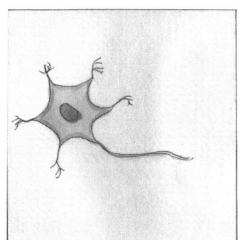 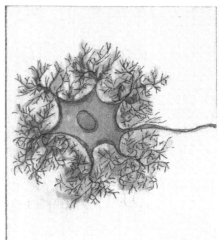

FIGURE 1.1.3
Nerve grown with nerve growth factor for two days.
By Esther Phingmoo.

THE BALANCE OF COMPUTING POWER

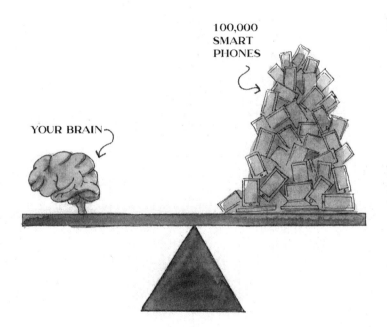

FIGURE 1.1.4

Balance of computing power: your brain can process information as fast as 100,000 smart phones. Nice! By Esther Phingmoo.

Computing power

The human brain has more computing power than you can imagine. But I'll ask you to try anyway. First let's compare the brain to a smart phone. An iPhone 12's A13 bionic processor has 11.8 billion connections.[16] Your brain has it beat by 100,000 times.

Your brain has more "on/off switches" than all the computers on Earth

Your brain has approximately 880 trillion (8.8×10^{14}) connections[17], equal to the connections in about 100,000 iPhones. Your brain is like 100,000 cell phones, each of which is making 1 billion phone calls per second. All those connections come from just 30,000 genes in your DNA that create about 88 billion neurons. That's about 10 times more than all the people on Earth. And each nerve has about 10,000 connections. Add up all those numbers: 88 billion (9 zeroes) multiplied by 10,000 (four zeroes) equals (add the zeroes—9+4=13 zeroes after "88") and it equals 880,000,000,000,000 or 880 trillion.[18] So there are 880 trillion connections in the human brain to process information. Lots of computing power!

Stephen Smith, PhD, a professor of molecular and cellular physiology, used new technology to image connections in a mouse brain. Based on his 2010 study at Standford University Medical Center in California, he concluded that in just the thinking part of the human brain alone (the cerebral cortex— just part of the brain) there are as many nerve to nerve connections as there are stars in 1,500 Milky Way Galaxies. (Source: Science Daily, 11/17/2010, "Stunning details of brain connections revealed." https://www.sciencedaily.com/releases/2010/11/101117121803.htm) Dr. Smith also estimated that there are about 1,000 "on/off switches" in each of those neuron-to-neuron connections. That means, he said, there are more on/off switches in one human brain, than all the on/off switches in "all the computers and routers and internet connections on Earth." (Internet search: number of connections in the human brain). Your brain even has **artificial intelligence**

FIGURE 1.1.5
Positivity releases the potential in your brain, like a match does
in lighting a candle. Pessimism is like the candle on the right.

beat in terms of self-awareness, creativity and "big picture" problem solving.[19] You are loaded with computing power!

Complexity

Looked at another way, the connections in your brain are equal to 4 million times all the 200 million stars in the Milky Way Galaxy.[20]

Speed

Look at the speed of information processing in all those connections. If your brain raced your phone, your brain would be 100 times faster. Your phone processes data at 1 billion signals per second. All of your neurons put together are a rocket by crunching data at 100 billion signals per second.[21]

Internet brain

As it turns out, your brain isn't like a computer; it is like thousands of computers connected to each other. It has countless areas processing specific kinds of information (like sight or sound) and then these areas are wired together with nerves. Wiring between connections adds to computing power. Your brain is massively wired, connecting thousands of areas so they can talk to one another. You have an internet in your head with a lot of wiring.

Your well wired brain

The wiring in your brain would roughly stretch around the Earth. A laptop computer's processor, such as what you might be using now to read this book, has about 18 miles of wire just 7 nanometers thick. The wiring in your brain is more than 1,000 times longer. Your brain's nerves stretch out to a length of 24,840 miles, just 61 miles short of the circumference of the globe at the equator (24,901 miles).[22] Not bad for something free! You can make great changes in your brain, and in your life, with that much wiring.

Your brain's memory center, the hippocampus, grows 4 million new nerves per day, so you can learn and adapt to new experiences. Each of those nerves has thousands of connections. So each day your memory center might be growing as many connections as there are people on earth (8 billion).

Your brain is stronger, faster, more complex and more adaptive than your average computer by at least 100 times. Let's get busy tapping into that potential!

Positivity is a natural part of you

Pessimists might say positivity is something hopeless that people just make up in their heads. But positivity helps people survive and thrive and there are actually two areas in the brain dedicated for positive thinking. Researchers at the New York University Center for Brain Imaging published results in the scientific journal "Nature" showing the physical location in the brain for positive thinking.[23] The brain's fear center, the amygdala, becomes a center for optimistic thinking when it joins up with another area in the brain called the **rostral anterior cingulate cortex** (RACC). Every person has this "dynamic duo" in their brain for thinking positive. The cingulate cortex is the brain's internet or superhighway, allowing hundreds of areas on the right side of the brain to communicate with hundreds of areas on the left side of the brain. The lower part of this, the RACC area, is uniquely positioned in the cingulate cortex and next to the rational thinking part of the brain (cerebral cortex) and other emotional areas of the brain. The RACC is located at the intersection of thoughts and emotions and the brain's internet.

Everyone has these two brain centers for positivity. Science shows optimistic people tend to be more successful in their life than pessimistic people. The question then is how can you promote more of this good attitude?

If you say "I'm going to be more positive," your mind might cooperate for a few seconds or minutes, and then it will likely wander from that attitude. An attitude is a pattern of how you think and feel about something. What should you do when your mind wanders? Remind yourself of your dreams and your potential. Then ask, "What kind of attitude do I want today for chasing my dreams?"

Positivity unleashes your potential

You have a right to choose the attitude that is right for you. When you choose optimism, or positivity, you are choosing an attitude that is focused on using a whole toolbox of skills to help you succeed in pursuing your dreams. Why? It says keep going, keep focusing on your dreams and your freedom to choose the attitude that best works for you. Put your happiness first. The science is clear on positivity. Positivity can be measured in a statistically valid method[24] and separated from pessimism.[25] Positivity improves outcomes in medical conditions ranging from cancer[26] to heart disease[27] to chronic pain.[28] Positivity can protect people against getting depression in cross cultural studies such as those done in China.[29] People living with a positive attitude, according to scientific studies, have better:

- Grades in school[30]
- Job satisfaction[31]
- Job performance[32]
- Financial intelligence and well being[33]
- Presentation of accomplishments at work[34]
- Post traumatic growth[35]
- Health[36]
- Relief from addictions[37]
- Longevity[38]
- Satisfaction with their life[39]
- Positivity or optimism is present in every country in the world and **massive surveys of almost every country in the world** show the more optimistic you are, the more rewarding your life will be.[40]

FIGURE 1.1.6
Positivity unleashes your potential by "chewing through" the mazes in our mind—created by self doubt. By Toso Borkovic.

Let positivity change your history!

Positive thinkers have many successes in life. They are the "go getters"! A positive attitude will help you have more success in: sports, school work,[41] physical and mental health, family life, getting hired, earning an income, achieving status[42], coping as a minority,[43] overcoming bias and succeeding while minimizing the impact on the environment, according to a host of studies.

Positivity has changed world history!

An attitude is a way to focus your thoughts and actions. By definition, a positive attitude means you are focused on being excited about achieving your goals. It's the perfect attitude to help you unleash your potential. But is that what history says?

Absolutely, yes.

Positive thinking (i.e., optimism) in its modern form started with the European philosophers of the Enlightenment such as Descartes, Leibniz, Kant and Hume in the 17th and 18th centuries.[44] These philosophers believed that mankind could cure many of its problems with democracy, science and technology. In America, the Founding Fathers shaped a government so that representative democracy and religious freedom could help individuals prosper and have more individual liberties. Many cultures have a similar history of being focused on what improves people's lives in that culture.

Modern history documents amazing progress because of these progressive ideas.

In practically every country, in every decade since World War II, people are prospering! If you see a teacher, tell them the good news that education is changing history! The following facts document the success of education and the communications industry to improve people's lives. According to "Progress: Ten reasons to look forward to the future," by Johan Norberg, a Book of the year by The Economist magazine, we've seen progress around the world since about 1900 with dramatic drops in:

- Childhood mortality
- Maternal mortality

- Bacterial and viral diseases
- Famines
- Domestic violence
- Wars

Vaccinations alone have saved hundreds of millions of lives, according to Steven Pinker in the book Enlightenment Now (page 64).

I'm willing to bet you haven't heard much of this good news. I hadn't either until I did my research.

History shows there have been increasing levels of prosperity, safety from violence and relief from diseases in almost every country since the 1950's. This has never happened before in history. Harvard Professor Steven Pinker documents in painstaking detail how education, science and democracy have pushed this progress. His book, "Enlightenment Now: The Case for Reason, Science, Humanism and Progress" details hundreds of references to establish these facts.[45] In another book, he documents the steady progress of a "humanitarian revolution" all over the world to make the world safer in terms of wars, unjust punishments, slavery, racism, sexism, animal rights and discrimination based on sexual orientation. Forward thinking people made this happen by being focused on humanitarian goals.[46] Education, science and democracy are winning the war for peace and prosperity. This is the biggest story of the 21st century and somehow many in the media have missed it. But you are in on the scoop!

Despite all these facts, it can be hard for us to feel positive action is making the world any better. Human psychology is biased to feel the world is scary and ignore the facts, according to Dr. Hans Rosling,[47] TED talk presenter and former adviser to the World Health Organization.

Positivity is erased by pessimism

Unfortunately, positivity has an enemy: pessimism. Pessimism can negate positivity in the blink of an eye. For that reason, it is important to know the difference between pessimism and positivity. If you don't, it is easy to let pessimism undo the progress you've made with positivity. It happens all the time. As a therapist for more than 20 years, I've heard these stories many times. Pessimism is like a "goat" that can literally "chew through" and ruin months of hard work on your part. Pessimism is like a goat in your garden of positivity. Of course, I am referring here to unhealthy pessimism, not healthy pessimism. On the other hand, healthy positivity can also be like a goat that chews threw the "maze in the mind" created by pessimism! Keep pushing back against unhealthy pessimism! Keep him out!

A quick way to separate positivity and pessimism is to see how you deal with a setback. That's a dead giveaway. If you're taking a setback personally, you are reacting with pessimism. If you take it as temporary and something to learn from, you are acting with optimism and positivity. Let's take a closer look at the three qualities that separate positivity and pessimism.

Positivity has three essential qualities

Positivity is an attitude that helps you make progress on your individual goals so you can have more happiness and freedom. Pessimism thwarts this progress. Three qualities separate these two attitudes. These three qualities are like a candle, a wick and a match. Set apart from each other, nothing happens. But when the match lights the wick, the candle now becomes a source of warmth and light. So it is with positivity. Here are the three essential qualities of positivity:

1. Acknowledging accomplishments. Every day set goals. If you ignore your accomplishments, then you'll feel like you are not even getting any accomplishments (big surprise), so you'll quit trying to make accomplishments. Don't ignore your accomplishments! That is being pessimistic. **Take your accomplishments personally!** That will feed into your positivity and, ultimately, will help you have more accomplishments.

2. Using setbacks as opportunities for growth. Not everything is going to go your way every day. That's ok. You're going to have setbacks. But don't dwell on them. Setbacks happen, they are part of life, so get upset briefly, learn from them, get energy from them, then move on. You've used them up for all they are good for. If you dwell on setbacks, then in your mind the setbacks will get bigger in your imagination, creating a feeling of a greater potential for more setbacks in the future. **Don't take setbacks personally.** They are to be expected.

3. Learning. Positivity is interested in learning from everything that happens around you. Pessimism gives the mindset that problems are bigger than people and people don't matter. Pessimists don't learn from their mistakes, and they go on to repeat them. Positivity teaches you to focus on your goals with to do lists and notes in planners, because you matter, your time matters and your life matters. Furthermore, when you write things down it helps you learn from those things. You can study them if you write them down. Gotta love that positivity! Pessimism distracts from learning. Positivity's advice? **Learn from everything.** This is the driving force of progress in the world: to learn from everything. Use science and democracy to overcome problems like disease and violence, and make the world a better place.

How to stop pessimism from erasing positivity

Pessimism doesn't sound that bad. You just think problems are bigger than you. You take setbacks personally. Who hasn't done that? You feel you can't learn from things. Again, who hasn't had that feeling? This mindset leads to a world of troubles. It can lead to mental illness.

If you take setbacks personally, you may go on to compare yourself with others. That just throws salt on the wound. Who cares what others are doing? Life isn't a popularity contest. But if you keep comparing yourself to others it will feel that way.

Taking things personally often leads to becoming a people pleaser. People pleasers feel guilty if they don't do what others

PRESCRIPTION FOR POSITIVITY

want them to do. Not learning from things often leads to self-blame. We all tend to do that from time to time. But when you are focused on learning from things, you ask the question, "How did blaming myself work?" "It didn't do any good." "Oh, OK, I just learned it's a waste of time." The problem with self-blame is it is guaranteed to fail, every time.

"I'm a screw up," you might say. This is a character assassination comment. It is a blanket statement that you are a bad person, instead of recognizing that everyone has some good and bad in their character. No one is perfect. No one is all bad. Also, this kind of comment doesn't help you know what to change. It doesn't zero in on the actions that caused the trouble—and the actions that can be changed next time.

Instead of "I'm a loser at relationships," say, "I'm afraid of intimacy and need to work at being comfortable with those kinds of conversations." Now you are focused on what you can change and can control.

How positivity naturally grows

It is natural to wonder when you are going to turn your setbacks into opportunities for growth. Try writing down what you are going to do to learn from a setback—and write it on a to do list. Doing so means you are really making a commitment to improve yourself! People hesitate at writing things down but that hesitation makes them weaker.

There is a natural flow to what happens when you set goals and work for your future. First you write items to do on a piece of paper. This is a to do list. Write items systematically the same way every time (from left to right): check circle, number, period, due date, then the item as a 5-10 minute task. Make them line up in a vertical column. Write in the list every day and check items off every day. This is like a leaf unfurling and working and feeding the larger vines of your life.

Now you are getting some momentum. One action leads to another action. But just when are you going to do these things in your to do list? To organize this, I recommend people write down what they are going to do and when they are going to do

FIGURE 1.1.7
How positivity naturally grows like a vine.
By Esther Phingmoo.

FIGURE 1.1.8 The leaf of to do lists. By Esther Phingmoo.

it—in a daily planner that has a line for every 15 or 30 minutes from 8 am to 8 pm. You are creating more orderliness in your life as you take control of your time. Don't forget to write in things to do for fun too! Mix "energy booster" activities with "energy draining" activities so you don't burn yourself out. This is called pacing yourself. Exciting things are happening!

The orderliness of to do lists and daily planners are like the structure of leaves and vines to support the larger plant of your

FIGURE 1.1.9 The leaf of a planner. By Esther Phingmoo.

life. When I learned this at summer camp at 15, the to do lists were already written out as requirements in merit badges. I just had to do them in little bits of free time I would have during the day. I would scribble down what I was going to do that day on a scrap of paper that worked as a daily planner. Now you are imitating the orderliness of plants in the natural world and helping yourself grow just like that vine does. A little progress every day makes for big progress in the long run.

FIGURE 1.1.10 The leaf of advisers. By Esther Phingmoo.

Get power in numbers

At some point along the way, you will likely run into a problem that you don't know how to solve. Now is the time to build up a circle of advisers. These are people who give you information or teach you skills to solve problems. Be hungry and excited for this learning! These advisors support your independence and self-reliance. They don't actually solve the problems for you, that's your job, but they show you easier or more effective ways to get things done. Again, knowledge is power, and positive thinking people are knowledge hungry.

All this naturally happened for me at summer camp. I would finish chores and return to the circle of a dozen tents that was our staff area. It was in a small clearing in the woods. I heard other boys talk about their problems and challenges and find solutions. They laughed and joked about their problems. "I thought that requirement for a merit badge would be tough. Now I see it will just take a half an hour." "Yeah, it will be easy. But I still think you are going to whine about doing it like a sick cat! Ha ha!" And so we would kid each other about our little setback, like complaining that a task took half an hour, so we wouldn't take it personally—in fact we would laugh at it.

The staff area was a place for automatic encouragement to stay excited pursuing your goals. If you wanted to earn a certain merit badge there was someone in the staff area with all the answers. Where to get the book to read, how to practice the skills, and who could teach you the "hard to learn skills." Finally they would tell you who could test you on the merit badge so you could "earn it." They knew because they'd done all these things in the past year.

We all wanted one day to become an Eagle Scout and knew we needed to encourage each other. Over the next several years most of us finally did get that rank. A little progress every day worked! Along with lots of encouragement from one's "circle of advisers." In time, those staff members that were 15-17 years old then, achieved other things too: they became fathers, doctors, lawyers, business owners, railroad men, even a Coast Guard sailor.

Not by accident. They in their own way stayed focused on their goals and worked their to do lists and planners so they got their work done on time. And their long range planning on their month to month calendars had their bigger professional goals so they were achieved as well.

All this orderliness and self-discipline was fun at summer camp. The focus every day was the same: just make a little progress every day—it's fun. This was the sum of the positive attitude as I knew it at summer camp at Lake Metigoshe in North Dakota. It's still true for me today.

FIGURE 1.1.11 The leaf of positivity. By Esther Phingmoo.

Pessimism can infect positivity

Working to make dreams come true can be stressful. If things go your way on a task, and it works out, that's an accomplishment! Good job! But things don't always go your way so sometimes an effort will flop. You won't succeed. And here all your progress can come to a crashing halt! You could give in to the temptation to dwell on the setback. But that would be demoralizing. If you obsess on your potential to fail, failure will feel more likely to happen. On the other hand, if you obsess about your potential to succeed, then that will loom larger. You have the choice of what opportunity to dwell on: to succeed or fail.

This insight will help you keep motivating yourself and not become self-defeating, which is what pessimism does. One

FIGURE 1.1.12 The leaf of reject pessimism. By Esther Phingmoo.

woman put it this way. "The most powerful thing I got out of your book is when I get up in the morning, the first thing I think is, "What kind of attitude do I want today? If I'm already negative, I reject it." Just that simple question prompts her to use her RACC to take charge of her life. I mean you have a positive attitude center in your brain. Why not use it? It is like having a thumb and deciding to use it to get a grip on things. Life suddenly becomes so much easier. Now you can imagine things you want in your life and pursue them. But what goals will you choose for your life?

FIGURE 1.1.13 The leaf of life goals. By Esther Phingmoo.

Life goals and life organization

You have goals and ambition. Maybe it is just that someday you want some goals and some ambition. OK. Where are you going with those treasures? In the direction of your dreams. Let's say you have life goals, such as to start a family, start a career or get a dog. Great! Write them down somewhere. Think about them. Dream about them. Pray about them. Every day do one small thing to make progress in the direction of that dream. When you pray, give the ultimate future results to God. Now you don't have to worry about them. Something different will happen than what you want, but that is OK. God might change things. Or things might just happen that you don't want.

It doesn't matter at this point. You are moving forward and adapting as things change. You are growing in maturity and in technical skills. You are becoming more passionate. Your life goals are pulling you forward in your life. When you make an accomplishment, it means something because it is bringing you closer to seeing your dreams come true! In this way, your life goals are constantly energizing your life.

Money and your dreams

(**FIGURE 1.1.14** The leaf of financial budget. By Esther Phingmoo).

Good things don't usually happen by accident. For your dreams to come true, your life needs to be organized and make financial common sense. For example, to get your own bike you need a place to store it and money to buy it and a bike lock to protect it. Otherwise, your bike could get damaged or stolen. Once you get a bike then you can perhaps bike to work. That might allow you to travel farther for a better paying job. Your bike has added value to your life. Let's say you eventually get that job. You did research and found the job opening and succeeded in the interview. You got hired. You are now a higher value person than before the bike. Good for you! Take pleasure in having the cleverness to make things work out financially for yourself. You have invested wisely. The dream of getting a bike so you can get a better job has paid off.

Some dreams propel you to set goals and get happy from overcoming obstacles as you pursue those goals. Your happiness depends on you. You are happy because of things you control. What you learned while overcoming a challenge. What you experienced working through a tragedy. You can only control your thoughts and your learning and to some extent your experience. Make your happiness depend on what you can control and you are going to be a happier person all around. But also pay attention to the financial value of things. Avoid the attitude that you must spend money to be happy! That is the road to financial ruin! Make up your mind you want to become more financially valuable to people by helping them solve big problems with the big things in their life: relationships, business, possessions, home, and health.

This was the attitude of Ben Franklin, the first optimist in America. He inspired me because as a teenager he had to deal with hard times like I did. Somehow he always found a way to bounce back from hard times. As a teenager he got a low paying job at a printing press. Rather than grumbling about living in poverty, he took it as an opportunity to meet successful people who came to the printing press to order books and newspapers and announcements. He found some powerful people were "flakey," but others were reliable and industrious. He found as he helped others succeed, sometimes they helped him succeed. Soon he impressed so many people with his hard work he had his own printing press!

Do an internet search of "Ben Franklin inventions" and "Ben Franklin sayings" and you can see how he was working to help others succeed as he continued his own success—by hard work and ingenuity. You can live your life this way too. Meanwhile, keep track of your money. Be thrifty. Franklin lived this way. Franklin was so careful with his dinner ware, he used the same knives, forks and spoons for many years—while others wasted money buying "new" dinnerware every few years. Franklin was also optimistic that he could find more efficient ways to get things done and that would make him more valuable. History proved him right. He is credited with inventing the lightning rod, flexible catheter, bifocal glasses, political cartooning, the Franklin stove, swim fins and an extension arm. He discovered public street cleaning methods. He helped establish America's first: volunteer fire department, liberal arts college, public hospital and circulating library. (See visitiphilly.com).

Get your life organized

FIGURE 1.1.15

"Getting your ducks in a row in your life" means organizing the different areas of your life so they work together. Like a flock of ducks swimming together. By Esther Phingmoo.

Success takes focus. Franklin found success takes making all the different parts of your life work together. This means organize your personal and school life, but also take care of your physical health and relationships. Franklin did all that as he notes in his free book, "The Autobiography of Benjamin Franklin." Visualize how your success might happen and make everything in your life work for that success. To succeed in a career, you will need an education. To succeed in school, you will need great daily routines with to do lists and a planner guiding your way so you don't fall behind in your studies. You may wonder how you are going to afford school. You will need to have done your research and have a budget to finance your success. Ben Franklin was poor when he was young so he taught himself math and other languages, with a study partner. If you are trying to teach yourself something, let's say English, get a study partner who will hold you accountable to do your homework and you'll make more progress.

Once you establish you have the time and energy to succeed, you will need to reject surfing on social media too long—that might make you fail in school. You will need to control your spending so you can afford to pay for education whether it is online or in person. You will need to be organized about your priorities and what you need to succeed. Reject any action that could put your success at risk. This kind of life organization can be so meaningful. I can remember feeling so happy when I realized I had a chance at getting accepted into medical school if I stayed focused volunteering in a hospital on weekends and working in a microbiology lab washing test tubes. Working long hours in your private endeavor can be draining. Don't forget to tap into the energy in your culture that celebrates personal renewal. I charged my batteries by going to church. I once sang in a public Handel's Messiah choir. I camped and fished with friends. All these things "charged my batteries" so I could keep pursuing my dreams.

Cultures celebrate positivity

Most cultures have holidays that celebrate times of renewal and the promise that a person can have a new beginning. Use that energy to charge up your positivity. Holidays around the world that celebrate the promise of a new beginning include Rosh Hashanah, Baba Marta, Christmas, Easter, the festival of Ostara, Nowruz, the Songkran Water Festival and New Year's Day.

FIGURE 1.2.0
The inner conflict: pessimism versus optimism.
This is what I was caught in, until I met The Good Professor.
By Toso Borkovic.

2

How I learned positivity

FIGURE 1.2.1
The Good Professor.

A meeting by chance in a back alley

Life's path has its twists and turns. We plan for one thing and life gives us another. When something happens by chance, take advantage of it. I have a friend Steve who found his career in Geology when he graduated college with a degree in English and got a job editing articles for a geology journal. He found himself fascinated with geology. He got a master's degree in geology and has happily worked in the field ever since.

My path has had its twists and turns as well. I was a pessimist as a teenager but I had a stroke of good luck one cold spring day when I met a very optimistic classmate named Jim in the alley right behind my house. He and I went to the same school in 9th grade.

Why was he in the back alley? And why was he behind my house? That was weird, I thought. And there was something in his hand. As I got close I could see it was a cigarette. He was back here so the police wouldn't catch him smoking.

"Hey," he said, greeting me.

"Hey," I replied.

"You like fishing?" he asked. He knew I did.

"Yeah," I replied.

"You like canoeing?" he asked.

"Of course, you know I do," I responded. "I live for that stuff."

"How would you like to volunteer for summer camp?" he asked. "They pay you a hundred dollars to canoe and fish as much as you want." Getting paid to fish and canoe? That sounded great to me, but I said I'd think about it. I was a pessimist.

"You first have to join a Scout troop," he informed me. "Want to join my troop? It's pretty fun."

"Maybe," I replied, smiling. "Do you want to quit smoking?"

"Maybe," he replied, smiling right back at me. I later joined the troop and he kept on smoking.

FIGURE 1.2.2

The Good Professor in his element. He loved adventures in the outdoors and passing on his skills—and his stories!

Positivity Takes Risks

We walked down the alley towards his house. "I'm going to be an Eagle Scout one day I think," he blurted out. "I'm in this troop where all kinds of guys are getting merit badges and becoming Eagle, so why not me? But this summer I want to get away from home and volunteer where I can canoe and fish every day. Maybe you could join me," he said.

I'd never been away from home that long, I thought. That would be a risk. That would be scary. I didn't like scary. But he said I could join him. We were friends. So at least I'd know one person. And if I didn't do it and Jim had a great summer I would feel so left out. That would be bad.

I took some risks

"I'll check your troop out," I replied. Which I did the next week. A week later, Jim and I filled out the long application form to be a volunteer called a CIT or "counsellor in training." "What does that title mean?" I asked him.

"You help out with stuff but it's like you don't have any responsibilities. You're not a real counsellor. Just a helper."

"Oh, OK," I replied. "So I'll be a CIT."

"Yes," he replied. "And it's pronounced zit,'" he said with a laugh. "We are not real high status."

I laughed and said I'd had a zit in the past, but "I've never actually been called a zit." A "zit' is another word for "pimple."

"This is your big chance," he said with a chuckle. I took it. I mailed the application in and waited. I waited four nerve wracking weeks. Finally a letter with "Scout Camp" on the envelope came in the mail. I opened it and it said I was accepted!

June rolled around and Jim and I went to summer camp. Every morning started with a circle of staff people in front of the flagpole. I waited for the camp director to say, "OK you zits can do what you want." But it never happened. We were told to haul tents, cut trees and clean outhouses. And here Jim said I was going to get paid to do whatever I wanted. What a disappointment! But all the boys seemed happy to do rough work. I jumped in and found it was fun. Their positive attitude was rubbing off on me.

One morning, at the usual flagpole meeting, the camp director said he had a special announcement. "I like bird watching and I'll be taking a hike to identify birds at 5:30 tomorrow morning. Anyone who wants to can join me. We'll meet at my office door at 5:30 sharp!"

I'd never been able to identify birds except the common robin, so I jumped at the chance to learn some tips, especially from someone who was a college professor. Secretly I'd been frustrated that I hadn't learned to identify many birds. Birding sounded easy, but the birds flew away before you could get a good look. So how could you identify them? That left me feeling hopeless. But taking a walk with a professor also felt like a risk. Professors are smart. What if he made me look stupid? The idea of taking a walk with a college instructor sent my head spinning. This chance was amazing. This would have never happened unless I took the risk and joined Scouts. All I had to do was get up at 5 am. That would be pure agony. I wasn't a morning person.

I got up at 5 am anyway in the cold and damp darkness and met the camp director at 5:30 am at the door to his office, which was in a large cabin. "Looks like you're the only one here!" he said with a laugh. "Let's go!" Wow, I thought, I am one on one with a college instructor. I am so lucky. Or am I? I was always doubting things.

We walked down a forest trail and I saw a bird. Just a flash of feathers and brown. "What was that?" I asked.

"Don't know," he replied, smiling. I was upset at myself. I tried and failed to identify the bird! Same old story. I felt like I couldn't get anything right.

Setback after setback: time to quit?

"Doesn't matter," he said. "There will always be another bird." That was weird, I thought. Suddenly there was another flash of brown. And gone. I couldn't see anything. He looked at me and waved his hand to say he wasn't able to identify it either. He kept walking. He smiled and flipped up his heavy eyebrows like there was nothing wrong. I hurried to catch up.

Wave off setbacks constantly

Then there was another flash of feathers and he smiled and shrugged his shoulders and moved on like nothing happened. I saw only failures, which I took personally, and he just waved them off like they were nothing!

At a turn in the trail he snapped his binoculars up to his eyes and a bird stood still for one second and flew off.

"Ha! Yellow warbler," he gushed. "Slender little bird, yellow all around, nothing like it!"

FIGURE 1.2.3
The elusive yellow warbler. By Esther Phingmoo.

Setbacks lead to learning

With birds, he said, you just needed to spot two or three key points and you could identify it. If a bird is small and yellow all over, it's a yellow warbler. If it is small and has a red breast, it's a robin. If it is big and black all over with a big bill, it's a crow. Simple, he said, with a wave of his hand. It made sense to me.

A few seconds later he saw another bird and pointed and hissed, "What is that?"

I saw yellow all around in a slender bird. "Yellow warbler?" I replied.

"Correct!" he said, glancing at me in the eyes. "Ha! Good job!"

Setbacks energize you

The sun rose a little higher and the bird chatter quieted down. So the good professor pointed out some other items in an impromptu teaching session. Tall white barked trees lined each side of our trail. He pointed to one and said, "See the black spots on white bark? That is a quaking aspen." We walked around a bend in the trail and he pointed to another tree with white bark and black spots and asked, "What's that?"

"Quaking aspen," I said tentatively.

"Exactly right!" he said. Then the thought occurred to me, "I am being quizzed on the fly by a professor I don't even know and he could make me look really stupid. I should be

FIGURE 1.2.4
The Good Professor doing what he does best. Whether around a campfire or on a hike, Professor Curtis had a way of enjoying an adventure—immensely. It was even better if he could teach someone something, such as helping a young boy believe in himself.

scared as hell!" The fear energized me. I thought of running back to my tent. That is what I had done in my life. When things got tough, I quit. But I saw how the professor kept moving forward down the trail. I chose to keep going. The fear energized me to act positively—and see what was around the next bend in the trail.

He was testing me to teach me

I felt scared being tested by a college professor. But I also felt like he was rooting for me, going out of his way to teach me something I had always wanted to learn. The trail took another turn and the professor stopped and pointed down at a yellow flower growing in a marsh. "See how the yellow petals circle around and the middle of the flower has a certain look to it?" he asked.

"Yes," I replied inspecting the little flower.

"Now it's growing in a marsh and it's a marigold. What do you think it's called?

I thought a moment and gingerly offered a response, "marsh marigold?"

"Right," he replied, not looking at me but walking fast down the trail, binoculars in hand, scanning the treetops for birds. We stopped.

He saw something and brought the binoculars up to his eyes. He studied something in the trees. I was relieved. This oral exam business was making me feel stressed even though I was passing with flying colors.

The dynamo of the inner dialogue and outer dialogue

The outer dialogue: "So what brought you to summer camp?" he asked while still studying that tree, like he was reading a book.

"Me?" I asked.

The inner dialogue: "I can't let out my dirty secret that I just joined camp to get paid to have fun. And this testing now is pure torture."

The outer dialogue: "Yeah," he replied after a moment, "Why did you come to camp? Don't you want to earn a lot of merit badges like the other boys are doing?"

The inner dialogue: "I'm so afraid to fail. But it might be fun to win at something. I just lose at everything." There were the voices of pessimism and optimism at work in my soul. A lump formed in my throat and my mouth turned pasty dry.

The outer dialogue: "No, merit badges are pretty tough," I said, putting on a confident face, "but I thought it would be fun to see how other people do it."

The professor nodded and continued to study that tree like it was a textbook.

"You'll succeed at anything you put your mind to"

The professor cleared his throat. "Well, you made progress identifying that bird, that's progress in the bird watching merit badge," he began. "Then you identified a tree by its bark. That's progress in the forestry merit badge. And a few minutes later you identified a flower by its appearance and habitat. That's progress in the botany merit badge."

I saw where he was going and I didn't feel comfortable with it. I thought of myself as a flake and a quitter. He was challenging the only way I knew to look at myself.

"Well," I replied, "so what? I mean, whatever." I was trying to get him to quit asking me questions.

"In half an hour you made progress in three merit badges and if you keep that up, you will earn all three, I guarantee it."

I stopped to take in what he said. He also stopped.

"If you keep focusing on making just a little progress every day," he announced, "you'll succeed at anything you put your mind to." He chuckled to himself at his discovery about me and went back to birdwatching.

My world turned upside down. I quickly tried to find something wrong with what he had said. I searched through every word he said to find a mistake. I was shaken by a realization. There wasn't anything wrong with what he had said. That could only mean one thing.

He was right.

FIGURE 1.2.5
I'm finally smiling with a little positivity. By Esther Phingmoo.

I Accepted Guidance

At the end of our walk, my camp director said good-bye and walked down the dirt road to his cabin and I walked up the foot path towards the staff area. There my tent was pitched in a circle of a dozen other tents.

I kept thinking about the walk, however, and had to stop along the path to think about what had just happened. He had silenced the doubts that had ruled my world. He delivered evidence I couldn't doubt. I had done the things he said I did. I identified that bird and tree and flower. I couldn't deny that. I thought it was stupid. He thought it was amazing and evidence of something even more exciting. My potential, which I had thought was nothing.

"If you keep focusing on making just a little progress every day," he had said, "you'll succeed at anything you put your mind to." He'd chuckled like he knew a secret, a secret about me. I was having trouble believing what he said but I couldn't doubt it either. I was so confused. I felt like now my life could go one way or another in the blink of an eye. I had to think about it some more.

An Epiphany

First off, I didn't really believe what I just heard. Me and "succeed" in the same sentence? Nobody talked to me like that. I doubted what he said but I just couldn't defeat his reasoning. I tried again and failed. As I stood there on the path and tried to make sense of what the camp director had said, something dawned on me that was just as real as the tall aspen trees that towered above me.

He was right.

If I made a little progress every day, and I could succeed at all kinds of things. I didn't have to be perfect. Make just a little progress every day on an organized project and good things will happen. I had control of that. That is how success works.

I got some hope

"Cool!" I said to myself. "I have a little hope after all." I gave myself permission to feel that hope. Just a little. Change is scary. I felt something heavy fall off my shoulders. I got a spring in my step as I walked those last few yards of the trail into the staff area, which was a small clearing with a circle of tents. My buddy Jim greeted me with a smile. "How was your hike?" he asked. I'd told him earlier about the hike. "It was cool," I replied.

Jim had invited me to join the camp staff a few months earlier. I was feeling bored and lonely then. Now it was a different story. I was getting a vision for my future. I could be successful!

Positivity Makes Dreams Come True

I told my friend Jim about the idea that a little progress every day lets bigger things come true. He said it sounded great. A little progress everyday became my mantra. I thought about it when I went to sleep and when I woke up and all day long. Every day I made a little progress on some merit badge. I set goals, had setbacks, shrugged them off, had accomplishments and gave myself credit every day. I didn't keep track of my failures, only my accomplishments and what I learned from my setbacks.

By the end of summer, "a little bit of progress" got me 14 merit badges. John saw me get my Eagle Scout badge two years later with that attitude. And 15 years later he saw that attitude help me graduate from medical school in North Dakota and later from residency in Minnesota. "A little bit of progress" has been part of my medical practice for 20 years now. I'm using it right now as I write these lines.

A little progress every day works.

A little progress every day and you can succeed at all kinds of things. You just need the right attitude and organization for this method to work like magic. You can also benefit from this amazing attitude.

FIGURE 1.2.6
The path of positivity. By Esther Phingmoo.

Throughout our friendship, John helped me remember to brush off setbacks. He was always able to teach me something from a setback that I thought was hopeless. He naturally took accomplishments personally and I had brushed them off. We were polar opposites in that way. That made him the cure for what I didn't even know I had: pessimism about myself and about my future.

Discussion: the elements of optimism

All the elements of optimism were there in the walk with the Good Professor.

- Having **initiative**: we met at 5:30 am. That took some dedication!
- Setting a goal: we would identify birds. Dealing with **setbacks** by learning from them.
- Being **hopeful**: the Professor looked at the hike as a chance to learn.
- Enjoying **accomplishments:** we managed to identify birds and he relished those successes. I didn't know what to think.
- **Letting go** of what you can't control, like birds flying away. But **learning** from setbacks, like the idea two field marks can identify most any bird or plant.

As you can see, the Professor's positivity was more than just a "looking up" attitude.

John deeply loved learning

The Professor loved learning, which made sense; he was a college instructor. But he deeply loved learning. He saw it as part of his life's purpose. He loved learning about nature, history and literature. That was why he taught art and literature of the American West at the university in my town. More and more I caught on to his sunny attitude as I saw it each day for the seven weeks of summer camp, in good times and in bad.

At the end of summer camp, the Professor's positive outlook became my attitude. It worked great. I could identify most plants and animals I saw. I earned 14 merit badges. I saved a troop in the middle of a lightning storm. I was off and running with my own version of being brash and daring and not caring about failures. Why should I? There was an accomplishment around the corner if I just kept going. I had a stack of merit badges to prove it.

John laughed at life

John's joyful optimism had some other things too. Jokes. He would tell jokes on himself and his friends. He loved irony and parody. Life was full of ironies, I found out. Like we love nature best when we have the comforts of civilization like a camp stove or a pair of binoculars. Life was also inspiring. He once stopped paddling the canoe we were in. I turned around to look at him to see what was wrong. He pulled his pipe out of his mouth and pointed it forward and up at a soaring hawk with a bright red tail. He shook his head in amazement. "Now wouldn't you look at that," he said. "Beautiful."

John let nature inspire him deeply

The Professor let himself feel inspired by nature. He felt closer to nature if he could identify a bird or plant. He also found experiencing nature's beauties to be profound. He believed art and literature helped a person experience more of the wonder of nature. Wild sweeping clouds were a "Bierstadt sky," referring to the 19th century painter Albert Bierstadt. To express the experience of seeing a fog shrouded lake in the forest, quiet and serene, he quoted Henry David Thoreau. "In wildness is the preservation of the world," he said.

One morning, he saw a pink splash, like a watercolor, sweep across the eastern sky. He gestured at the sight and said, "Ahhh! The rosy fingered dawn!" I thought he invented that phrase. Years later I found out he was quoting the Ancient Greek writer

FIGURE 1.2.7

A little progress every day works. Patience, however, is required to make that work. By Toso Borkovic.

Homer from his book *The Odyssey*. John did this spontaneously, from his soul, drawing on famous artists and writers to express how he felt. I saw all this and didn't know what to think. But as the years went by I started to do the same thing. Nature was inspiring me more deeply as well.

John had a deeply adventurous attitude

To further power his positive attitude, John was self-disciplined with a belief he could win at anything. In the military, he had swam down rivers at night on training missions. After that, everything else felt easy. The biggest problems could be broken down into smaller tasks that could be completed as a matter of routine. And he loved routines. He liked using to do lists and being organized. He loved to challenge himself to do something he hadn't done before. He was always looking to improve himself—and others like me if they were interested. He reveled in history, especially enjoying reading about great adventurers such as Lewis and Clark. Now I see all these as qualities of a positive attitude.

John had a rebellious side

While John understood the need for authority, he wasn't afraid to challenge it from time to time. Soon after he was hired to teach English at the local university, he drove by the courthouse and saw a Christian cross on it. He thought there should be a separation of church and state and later persuaded the local authorities to take the cross down. So John was in his own quiet way a professor but also a civil rights person too. Now how many college professors have done this? That speaks volumes about his commitment to truth and great principles, like the separation of church and state. He was a man of character and boldness.

John had great devotions

The Good Professor was a man of great devotion. This quality showed in how deeply he cared for the Scouts at summer camp. He took the time to plan out all the activities each day to give every boy the best chance for success. He showed the same kind of passion for teaching freshman college English, which he did for nearly 30 years at the same university. He actually wasn't a full professor but an associate professor. Likewise he was a devoted friend. He had many friends for 20 or 30 years. He was my friend for more than 30 years. How many people nowadays have such deep devotion to others? Not many.

A measure of a great friend is also that he knows your soul. He cheers you on to succeed in your dreams because he knows what all your hopes and dreams are. Not many people get the chance to have a great friend like that: actually it is quite rare. I'm so grateful I had a great friend who knew my soul and I knew his.

Another measure of a "soul brother" or "soul sister" is they will share in your great devotions. Our devotion was for adventures. We fished in Canada where we lived in a teepee. On that trip, John argued with the Border Patrol and that almost got us all arrested! We canoed the Boundary Waters in Minnesota and ate pancakes with fresh wild blueberries. We fished for salmon in British Columbia where he almost drove our boat into another boat full of fishermen! Also on that trip, our brakes went out on his car and we almost hurdled into the Pacific, but a passerby reminded me to use the emergency brake! The adventures never ceased with the Good Professor. We caught trout in Grand Teton National Park and walleye in North Dakota. At a mountain man rendezvous in Manitoba we ate buffalo roast and danced with native people in a pow wow— where John advised me not to be too friendly with a certain native woman dancer. (She's married, John advised me).

We canoed in Yellowstone National Park and hiked in the Badlands where Teddy Roosevelt had his ranch. The West was a place that filled our imagination. Antique shows took us to Washington, Montana, South Dakota, Wyoming, Minnesota and Wisconsin. Every trip was planned. Every trip had things go wrong. Every trip was a measure of our devotion to the endless quest for an adventure.

When I started to learn positivity, however, I did not have much devotion to myself or anything else. I didn't take my failures with a sense of humor—I had the bad habit of quitting after taking my setbacks personally. That is why John's positivity was such a revelation to me. Because he brushed off setbacks he could charge off on adventures all over the West and Midwest. Me? I was still taking setbacks personally and stewing about them.

Before meeting the "Good Professor" I was a quitter

FIGURE 1.2.8
The Good Professor and I at my medical school graduation at the University Of North Dakota School Of Medicine, in Grand Forks, ND. He didn't want his picture taken!

Quitting feels like the easy way out

Summer camp made such an impact on me because, like many young people, I was a strong pessimist about myself and the world. Growing up, I acted positively towards other people, but I was quite pessimistic on the inside. Before camp, I hadn't learned how to foster an optimistic attitude, so I was pessimistic. It often takes a guide to show you the basics of positivity, like this book. If you have someone in your life who seems to be living with an optimistic outlook, you can ask them for help in cultivating this beneficial attitude.

In my youth, when things got tough, I quit. That was a simple action to take. If the going was good, I was in. When the going got tough, I quit. When church choir got tough, I quit. When I stumbled on the stairs at a recital, I quit piano lessons. The same thing happened for saxophone, painting classes and Cub Scouts. I quit Cub Scouts. It was too tough. At every setback, I took it personally and I quit.

Quitting was an escape from failing. Or so I thought. In reality, quitting just trades one problem for a bigger problem. Habitually quitting leads to a negative outlook. Problems feel unsolvable because you have always quit instead of learning the skills to solve them. You become a pessimist.I was a pessimist but I thought of myself as an optimist. I was confident about some things that were easy for me. Fishing: put a worm on a hook and drop it in the water. Catching tadpoles: wade in a pond and sweep the water with a net. Hiking: pack a lunch and start walking. I was positive about activities where I knew how to succeed. But if I wanted to learn something new, I was not prepared to keep going when my plans didn't work perfectly.

I let fear be my guide

Anything that got tough—I quit. That is how I became a quitter and a pessimist without even knowing it.

More than anything, I wanted someone to look up to, someone who saw life as a fun adventure. I wanted someone to show me how to take things one day at a time with a carefree attitude. But everyone around me was full of worry, especially my parents. And they had a reason to worry.

My family was broken

A few months before that life-changing summer at camp, I felt so cooped up by rules at school and home that I was unraveling at my psychological seams. I was fidgety in classes. Homework felt like a prison sentence. I refused to do my chores. My mom had to remind me endlessly to take out the trash. I felt angry at what seemed like an endless list of do's and don'ts.

Part of the problem was my mom had chronic pain. That made her irritable all the time. Her arthritis kept her up at night with a sharp, stabbing pain in her back that led to depression. Occasionally she screamed in pain in the middle of the night. It was terrifying for my brother and I. On top of that, my parents divorced a few years earlier because of Dad's alcoholism. He stopped drinking but continued moody. Twice he had to go away to hospitals to be treated for depression with shock therapy.

Then when I was 13 Dad was diagnosed with a brain tumor. He had brain surgery and had to learn to walk and talk all over again. We were so glad he survived—but his personality changed. He argued and yelled at us, even in public. On top of that our family was doing poorly financially. We had to sell our house, leave our friends, and move across town into the smallest house I had ever seen. We changed schools.

I wondered why couldn't I have normal parents? Why was everything so difficult? Why was life so unfair? These questions privately burned in my brain. Some readers of this book may have similar catastrophes hitting their lives. I'm mentioning my adversities to show you positivity can help—even if your life has turned upside down.

Nature gave me an escape

I needed a release from all this stress and I found it in nature. I got in the habit of taking long hikes after school in the little patches of trees and meadows near my home. I lived in the Midwest prairie so there were few trees around. But in the spring green grass and creeks magically appeared where the snowbanks melted. Where there was water, you could find all kinds of wildlife. Birds, bugs, blooming flowers, it was all amazing

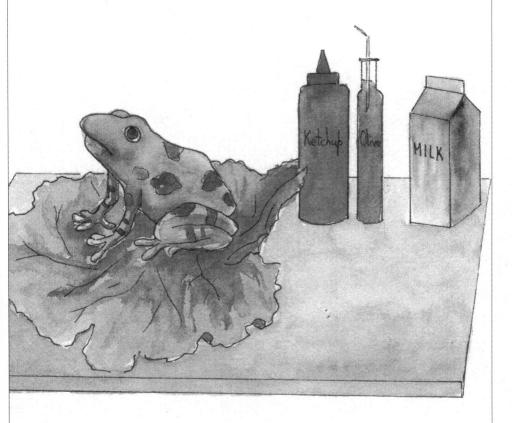

FIGURE 1.2.9
Frog on lettuce. By Esther Phingmoo.

after six months of white snow and cold winter. During one hike, I caught sight of something weird: something green and shiny in the grass. I crept up for a closer look.

It was a frog.

There was something wild about it. Wild and free. I liked that. I wanted to be that way too. So I did the natural thing. I scooped it up and put it in my coat pocket. I walked home with my new friend. I walked in the door and looked for a dark and cool place for my new pet.

That night Mom was cooking supper for her two teenage boys. She started to make a salad. She opened the salad drawer in the refrigerator and saw my little buddy perched on a lettuce leaf with its black, beady eyes looking calmly back at her.

Mom screamed.

I of course confessed to my crime and released the frog. I scrubbed the salad drawer clean. But things were never the same for me. I saw I needed a way to feel free and happy. I needed to feel like I had the potential to do something with my life besides just following rules. But I felt like I had no more potential to do something with my life than that frog had for his life.

I was stuck in pessimism and didn't even know it. I was saying no to anything my Mom or Dad said to the positive. I was stuck. What is often helpful when one is stuck is to get a coach or trainer or mentor. Then suddenly your life becomes much simpler. You just must do what makes your coach happy. In the end, however, you do all the things that it takes to make you happy.

I felt lost because sometimes I was optimistic, like when I went fishing. Then I felt happy and in control of my life. But that was because I was just focused on what I could do. Put a worm on a hook and cast it out. I was letting go of what I couldn't control—whether or not the fish would bite. And I was looking at life as an adventure. Boom! I was practicing positivity. But at other times I was pessimistic—and also didn't know it.

Now wouldn't it be nice if you actually knew when you had a healthy attitude and when you didn't? Then you would actually know what to do when you felt bad: change your attitude. Let go of the unhealthy pessimism and latch onto a healthy positive attitude.

Rating things gives you insight into those things. That's why we have speedometers on cars and thermometers in ovens. So why not with our attitude? People using these rating scales find it really helps them "fine tune" their attitude. They are better able to catch their attitude when it is "slipping" into being too positive or too pessimistic.

I first learned about positivity at 15, on that walk with the Good Professor. If I could go back in time and give myself a quiz on my pessimism, I would use the unhealthy pessimism rating scale here:

The unhealthy pessimism rating scale

Rate the following on a 1-5 scale: 1 is strongly disagree, 2 is disagree, 3 is neutral, 4 is agree, 5 is strongly agree. These questions assume you are focused on healthy activities in a negative manner.

1. I am **not** taking initiative today. ____
2. I **don't** take setbacks as temporary. ____
3. I am staying **hopeless**. ____
4. I am **not** taking my accomplishments personally. ____
5. I am **latching onto** what I can't control. ____
6. I **don't** take life as for learning. ____
7. I'm disappointed if I can't control everything and everyone in my life. ___

Total unhealthy pessimism score: ____

Here would be my pessimism rating at that time for each of the seven questions:

I-2, S-4, H-4, A-5,L-5, L-4, C-4=total of 24/35

> **DISCUSSION:** Any setback was mayhem in my mind. I melted like a snowflake when things didn't turn out just the way I wanted. S was a 4. My lack of hope was high. I was there to canoe and fish. I didn't have any hope of doing anything serious. H was an 4. If anything went well, I passed it off as dumb luck. I was a quitter. Life wasn't an adventure. It was so confusing and stressful. I needed to go fishing every day! L was a 4. But the next L is for learning and I was super excited to learn the names of animals and plants. That was a doorway to learning about their secret lives. I scored low here, a 4. That might have been my saving grace. That love for learning of mine is what saved me: it is what got me to go on that bird watching hike to begin with.

My camp director was so positive! He loved every opportunity to learn new things.

His positivity was huge! It was contagious and I was soon caught up in a positive attitude. It changed my life!

Again, wouldn't it be interesting if I could go back in time and rate his positivity? Well, as luck would have it, when you are writing a book you can do just that. I'll use the positivity rating scale here:

The healthy positivity rating scale

Rate the following on a 1-5 scale: 1 is strongly disagree, 2 is disagree, 3 is neutral, 4 is agree, 5 is strongly agree. These questions assume you are focused on constructive activities.
1. I am taking initiative today. ____
2. I am taking setbacks as temporary. ____
3. I am staying hopeful. ____
4. I am taking my accomplishments personally. ____
5. I am letting go of what I can't control. ____
6. I learn from life. ____
7. I can't control everything but I can improve my outcomes. ____
Total positivity score: ____

Here is my camp director's positivity rating:
I-5,S-5,H-5,A-5,L-5, L-5,C-5=Total of 35/35

>**DISCUSSION:** Setbacks were things he laughed at! It was a setback he had to get up at 5:30 am to watch birds and only one other person came to join him (me). He laughed at that! He was so hopeful he'd see some bird to identify even though there was no guarantee of that. A is for accomplishments and he reveled in helping me learn new skills in identifying birds! Learning was a fabulous experience for him! He let go of the worries of the world. In all, he was brimming with positivity and the challenges the new day offered him! That is why his positivity score was so high. That is why I got caught up in his positive attitude!

JOURNAL YOUR LEARNING HERE:

3

Positivity has many benefits

Feeling stronger

The world can feel like a harsh and unforgiving place. In the wake of life tragedies it is easy to feel damaged. A positive attitude has been shown to give "mental resilience," and can be used to reduce the post-traumatic stress soldiers experience from war. The following stories illustrate how life skills help people even after they feel damaged by challenging times. You may feel weak now, but these life skills will help you feel stronger.

Feeling fragile and "making memories"

Getting yelled at is no fun. It can make you feel fragile. But I think if someone is mean to you, then you can return that negative with a positive—doing something nice. This story is about how I did just that.

My friend Craig came with me on a trip into the mountains one year. We were elk hunting on public land in an area deep in the Snowy Range mountains, just west of Laramie, Wyoming.

After a long morning hiking on steep slopes, we walked back to my old camper trailer to rest. At the trailer I heard a loud roaring sound behind me. I spun around and saw my friend Frank, a man who was camping in the area, barreling at me on his four-wheeler. He stopped and dust shot up in a cloud.

"What the heck are you doing!" he yelled at me. "No visitors on this public land!" His face was red.

"We can fight about it," Craig said, who had a big problem with anybody yelling at him.

"No way," I protested. Before I could say anything, Frank spun his four-wheeler around and drove away. A few days later, Frank called me. He said in Wyoming some folks get ornery, but they get over it. I didn't ask any questions. I took this statement as an apology. I said, "OK."

"Listen Jensen," he grumbled. "My family is going hunting and if you hear us shoot, you call us. If we hear you shoot, we'll call you. That way we can help each other drag an elk out."

I agreed and said thanks. I felt a little bewildered. I'm from Colorado and sometimes us "Greenies" have a difficult time understanding people from Wyoming.

A week later I was back up in the mountains, alone. I heard a shot. I called Frank. He said his daughter had killed an elk. He asked if I could "hop up" and help them haul the bull out. An hour later I reached them, huffing and puffing. They were already pulling the bull out on a cart.

"You can follow us," Frank said. "You can see how a Wyoming family feeds itself." I walked along. I felt rather useless and tried to stay out of the way.

We got to a fence. They scooted the elk onto a four wheeler and started to buzz away. They left me behind.

"Hey Andy!" I yelled at Frank's nephew who was driving the second four-wheeler. Andy had a reputation for never having lost a bar fight in Laramie. His arms were as big around as my legs.

"Yeah," he said in a low gravelly voice.

"Can I have a ride?" I asked. "You're leaving me behind."

"Sure," he said with a tired look in his eyes. I hopped on and we roared across the meadow. I felt somehow like I belonged to them as we banged and bumped over the boulder studded meadow.

I felt myself sliding around on the four wheeler and got worried I would fall off.

"Hey Andy," I yelled over the roar of the engine. "I need to hold onto something or I'm going to fall off." He didn't slow down.

"Yeah," he replied.

"There's nothing to hold onto," I said. Silence. "I have to hold onto you." More silence.

There was a moment of just the engine roaring. "Ok," he yelled. I grabbed him around the midsection as we lurched straight down into a stream bed called Dry Creek. Dirt sprayed in the air. The four-wheeler pitched right and left. We burst up the far bank, the wheels grinding more dust into the air. On the level, I let go of Andy.

FIGURE 1.3.1

Facing someone else's negativity can be like facing down a tornado. But it can be done. By Toso Borkovic.

Then came another creek. I hung onto Andy. We pitched down, then left and right and then up. Back on the level, I let go of Andy. We raced across that meadow bouncing over boulders. Up ahead I saw fence posts in a tangle of aspen trees. Frank was there, watching our every move.

We neared the trailhead and everything slowed down. The trail was level and smooth. I don't know why I wrapped both arms around Andy. I squeezed him as tight as I could. He reached out with his right elbow to jab me off. A tire hit a rock. We pitched to one side. He couldn't let go of the handlebars or he'd lose control of the four wheeler. I couldn't let go of Andy. I held on for all I was worth. He tried to swing me off with his left elbow. He hit another boulder. He gunned the engine. He held onto the handlebars. I hung onto Andy.

In another second we bounced to a stop. I let go and looked up. Frank was looking down at us from his four-wheeler on a low hill. His face looked like stone. I felt a lump in my throat.

The question

"How was your trip?" he asked Andy.

Andy was silent.

I was silent.

"What did I just do?" I thought. "Am I going to die now?" I felt a breeze. A few aspen leaves twittered in the distance. I felt hollow inside.

"What did you do that for?" Frank barked at me.

Andy turned around. He stared at me. His face looked like stone too. My mind went blank.

"Yeah, what did you do that for?" Andy asked.

I tried to think. Nothing happened. I said the first thing that came out of my mouth.

"I don't know," I said, smiling a little. "I was just making memories."

They both gave me a blank look. They jumped on their four wheelers and sped off down a trail in the aspens and out of sight. A breath came into my lungs. I felt grateful to be alive.

➤**LIFE SKILLS:** persevering and doing something nice for someone who was mean.

➤**ACTION STEP:** do something nice for someone who is rude to you.

Feeling frail

Evette went to therapy to try to combat her depression. "Everything seems so overwhelming," confessed Evette. She had just started college and she missed her friends from home. She was adjusting to the newness of the campus, her class and her roommates in a strange building in a new town. Evette felt overwhelmed by the paperwork for classes and bills. It all is coming at her in a wave. When the panic was overwhelming, she skipped class, which only increased her sense of being overwhelmed.

"Like where do I begin?" she asked.

"Do you ever write things down?" I asked.

"My room is covered in sticky notes," she replied.

"Do you ever do stuff?" I asked.

"All day and I feel like I'm getting nowhere," she responded.

"We are going to take those two things you are already doing now—writing stuff and doing stuff—and simply organize them differently," I said. "Then you get to tell me how I did. All the pressure is on me. It's pass or fail and you get to grade me. OK?"

She nodded. I nodded.

"You really don't want to feel like you have to get everything done now," I replied. "Then anytime a new thing comes up, you'd feel like you had to do it immediately." She didn't look satisfied. "Hamsters on a wheel act like that," I continued. "What you want to do is get off that wheel. Then you'll have time to think."

She thought about that. "In that situation, the wheel is in charge of the hamster," I explained. "If the wheel stops, the hamster stops. If the wheel goes, the hamster goes. In your situation, all these things seem to be controlling you but that's because you haven't dropped back and looked at the situation from a different perspective."

She nodded. "But what perspective? I've got all this stuff to do."

Put your happiness first

"What do you want to get out of life?" I asked her.

"I want to be happy, I guess," she replied.

"Then put that first," I replied. "Give yourself enough time to get each thing done but add 50% more time so you don't have to rush." Rushing causes your body to release adrenaline and that makes your brain think something is wrong. Goodbye happiness even though nothing is wrong, I explained.

"You seem to like order in your life. You are dressed all stylish with your summer dress," I said. She nodded. "Then take that same fashion sense and organize your tasks so they don't organize you, like that darn hamster wheel did for the hamster." She smiled.

Together we organized her to do list. She numbered the items and gave each a priority. She would work on the top priority items today. There were only three. Each would take an hour. They involved reading assignments for three different classes.

"Let's make it fun," I said. We broke down each item into four, separate, 15-minute tasks so she could have four times more fun checking off items on her to do list. After every two items got done, she could take a break. "What's a fun five-minute activity that boosts your energy?" I asked.

"Petting my dog," she said. "Calling a close friend back home. Surfing on Instagram." I nodded.

"So now you'll use up energy for half an hour, then boost it," I explained. "You are riding the wave of your emotions—making them work for you."

Another way to boost your emotions is to picture your dreams in life, I said. "What's your dream?"

"I want to be a fashion designer," she said. "And have an apartment near a bunch of dance clubs. I like to dance." She looked online and found a picture of a group of women dancing in an apartment. "Perfect," she said. She set the image as the wallpaper on her phone.

"When you get tired and call your friends," I said. "Look at that picture and say, 'One day you will be mine!'" She nodded and smiled.

Staying focused in a long process

"Success seems so far away," she said. "It seems so long to take four years of college." I nodded.

"Is success an event that happens once and is over?" I asked. "Or is it more like a one-time event like a holiday like Thanksgiving—or like having a dog and with lots of feel-good moments?".

She said she understood where I was going. "Success is a process," she said.

"That sounds a little sterile," I said. "It's an experience, for sure. You feel it. It's happening because of all the steps you take. You are moving forward. There is a feeling of progression in your life in the direction of your dreams. Good things are happening now and there will be more to come. Like, well, like owning a dog."

To have success you must visualize success. Even if making a to do list feels silly, habits like that are building a foundation for success, I explained.

"What was your visualization of success?" she asked.

"I met Dr. William Sears in Southern California," I replied. "He wrote books and had his own private practice as a doctor. I wanted to be like him. I kept that vision alive through all eight years of my medical training. Whatever happened, I wanted to be making progress toward that goal. And here I am." "Cool!" she said. "When did you start to feel successful?"

I thought a few seconds. "The moment I quit my job and made a commitment to become a doctor. I told myself, 'Oh my gosh, it's starting to happen right now.'"

She thought a while. "I've seen fashion designers at work," she said. "My aunt is one. She has to do lists and a daily planner, so I see what you mean. If I start using them now, I am preparing for using them in my career."

Feeling more powerful

I smiled. "You're on your way," I said. "You're getting started like I did. Do you feel a little more powerful now?" She nodded but looked unconvinced. "The more you use these tools, the more powerful you will feel," I said.

"You forgot to ask me what grade I was going to give you!" she blurted out.

"I'm afraid of what you'll say," I said playfully. "What is my grade?"

She squinted her eyes in jest. "Pass," she said.

➢LIFE SKILLS: visualization and time management strategies to feel more powerful in your life.

➢ACTION STEP: visualize something small you can do today, do it, and appreciate the power of visualizing.

Feeling empty

Desiree sat in my office. She was seeking therapy to help with her sense of hopefulessness. "What is all this for?" she asked me. "I mean school and work and bills. What am I working for? I think about this stuff for hours. I feel so empty."

I was quiet. Those were all valid questions. I could also see she was in the clutches of Post Modernism philosophy she'd been fed by the media or schools. "I feel empty too sometimes," I said. "All the ruined habitat. All the animals that went extinct. The environment has really taken a beating."

More silence.

"What do you want me to help you with?" I asked.

"Well, I don't want to feel so empty. I mean, like, I am in a fog in lectures. I feel so lost. I'm such a loser."

"Loneliness is one thing. It is part of modern life because we are not always in some social activity like tribal people were. Loneliness is ok," I replied. "But then to call yourself a loser. That is a label, don't you think?"

"Yeah, that's kind of harsh," she replied. "I agree," I said. "You're a person, not a label. When you label yourself you kind of erase yourself and all the positive qualities you have. Not good. The philosopher Soren Kierkegaard said it doesn't feel good when people label you. He said, "When you label me, you negate me." What do you think about that?"

She paused. "I guess I won't do that again," she responded. "Wow, what you tell yourself can have a big impact on your emotions!" "It sure can," I said. "That's cool you're open to being more considerate towards yourself. Cool." "Yeah, thanks," she said.

I looked around the office briefly. My dog walked over and laid on her feet. I moved to get him away, but she held up her hand. "It's ok," Desiree said. "He's so sweet."

I put away my laptop for a moment. "I've been lost before," I said. "It was pretty scarey like what you're going through. I was hiking in the fall with my buddy Ken. It was after sunset. Getting real dark. But it was OK. The sky was clear, the stars were coming out. I could tell where I was by the Big Dipper in the west and I knew if I just headed east I'd hit a fence in half a mile. Then turn right and follow the fence to the truck. Boom. Done. I'd be home in an hour." I paused.

She looked at me. I waited for her response. "And..." she said, smiling.

"Fog came up from below," I said. "First I lost sight of ranch house lights in the east. Then the stars went out. The fog swallowed us up. I'm actually afraid of the dark and afraid of getting lost. Now I had to deal with both." "What did you do?" she asked.

Feeling lost

"I lost track of my buddy and yelled for him. He was right next to me. I said, 'Ken, don't tell anybody this, but let me hold onto your elbow and get me the hell out of here." He said, 'We're OK,'" I recalled. "He had seen this before. He always looks back when he's hiking in, so he knows what to look for on the way out." We walked beside a line of trees to a fence and turned right, following the fence.

One terrifying hour later, we were back at the truck.

More silence. "It sucks when what you're counting on isn't there when you need it," Desiree said.

"You've been focusing on what's scarey like I did when I was lost," I said. "You feel empty as a result. But I am seeing a person who wants to feel she can live a meaningful life. It took initiative to come and bear your soul to a stranger. That takes courage. Hell, all I had to do was hold onto my buddy's elbow." I laughed at my story.

Hesitatingly, Desiree asked, "So maybe I should look at what I can do and believe in that?"

I nodded my head. "I think I've been trying to believe but everything seems so meaningless to begin with," she said. "Pointless. People are so selfish. The system is screwed. Society is so messed up." She nodded. I could see she was caught up in the philosophy of Post Modernism without knowing it. That philosophy says that Western Civilization is headed to ruin. Some people even say Russia and China share this philosophy. Western Civilization is crumbling around us. It is a narrative that sells a lot of expensive college textbooks to naïve students who are never even taught what Post Modernism is—or the facts for and against it.

"Those are all interesting ideas," I said. I shrugged my shoulders. In her I saw a reflection of myself in my mid 20's when I believed all the things she just said and those beliefs made me feel hopeless too. I could see her identity was wrapped up in Post Modernism ideas. Challenge them and she will take it as an attack on who she is as a person.

"Yeah," she said.

"What are some other ideas you've been thinking about while feeling so empty?" I asked.

"Pollution is terrible. Global warming is awful," she began. "Corporations are screwing the planet and there's like nothing we can do. I feel so helpless. I mean the planet is dying."

"I happen to agree with the idea that the environment is in trouble," I replied. "But I'm not a pessimist about environmental problems. I'm an optimist. I think people can make a difference. I've been a conservationist trying to help fight those problems since I was a teenager living in North Dakota. Because of my conservation work that I did, The North Dakota Wildlife Federation gave me an award called State Conservationist of the Year and I'm still proud of that. The award showed that an individual, even a teenager, can make a difference."

"What did you do to make a difference?" she asked. She was asking for evidence that positivity works.

Obsessing on losses can make you feel empty

"I put on workshops to teach people the names of plants and animals. I raised money for conservation groups. I didn't feel hopeless. I was focused on how nature could gain something from my efforts in education. Something was better than nothing."

Stoney silence. I was challenging her belief system that she was hopeless and she wanted nothing to do with that! I've been there, so I backed off and mentioned something about the weather.

"Well, what else can I do?" she finally asked. I could see she was hurting.

She looked down at my dog Sammy lying on her feet. She looked up. "What causes feelings of emptiness?" she asked.

I said I thought some feelings of hurt or emptiness are normal for being human. Existentialist philosophers said some feelings of emotional pain are part of being human like having a heartbeat. But if we keep focusing on thoughts of loss, that is going to create even more sadness and emptiness than there needs to be.

"I care about global warming," I said. "But that doesn't mean I need to think about it all day to show I care." "Well I think about it all day," she said. "Are you helping the situation by doing that?" I asked. "No." "I think you might be creating more heartache for yourself." "I think your right." "You might be right. But what else can you do?"

Set a goal for your mental health and your caring for the environment, I suggested. "OK I want to be happy in general, but sad for nature's global warming."

Our mood is like a lake that is filled by the streams of our thoughts for the past week or month or six months, I suggested. "Look at negative thoughts like muddy water going in the lake. A little is ok, but too much and it will cause lake life to suffer."

"How do I stop negative thoughts when they add to my stress?" she asked.

There is a technique called thought stopping, I replied. You stop one mental activity, thinking, by replacing it with other mental activities. One such activity is called grounding.

"You are familiar with your five senses?" I asked. "Yes." "Then to stop negative thinking or rational thinking that is just getting too repetitive, just go down the list of your five senses. Say this: This is what I am seeing (then focus on it), this is what I am hearing (then focus on that), this is what I am smelling, this is what I am touching, this is what I am tasting. All these things are happening now. You are so busy focusing on what your senses are taking in now, your mind doesn't have room to also focus on that obsessive thinking."

"Cool," she said. I had her role play. She pretended to be obsessing on how global warming could kill all life on the planet—an irrational catastrophic thought she occasionally got stuck in her thinking. Then she went down the list of five senses and "crowded out" that obsession.

"It worked!" she said. "Even though it was just a role playing." "Good," I said. "How does it feel to put your happiness first and cut out some self-destructive thinking?" "It was fine." "Do you see how you can care about nature and also care about yourself?" "Yeah. This seems so balanced. I just didn't know the grounding technique but now that I do I'll have to use it." "That sounds excellent," I replied. "The good life is the life of balance." "Yeah I get that," she said.

Experiencing self acceptance now

Several weeks later Desiree came back for a follow-up visit. That is how counseling visits work. We talk about an issue. Get insight perhaps to a cause of some of the pain. Then explore and see if a thinking skill might help to lessen the pain. If it does, then the patient might be asked to practice that skill to gain more mastery. In the end the patient and the therapist make a commitment to keep working together for the patient's benefit. Out of that commitment, the patient often gains deep insights into themselves and life in general that helps them chart more successes in their life. The patient grows in maturity by experiencing what it is like for someone to make a commitment to be there for them through thick and thin—no matter what.

I thought Desiree would be eager to talk about the grounding technique but all I could see was her face was tied up in knots of pain.

"I'm so F'd up," she said. "But I really like your dog. Can I pet him?" Tears came down her cheeks. She sat down on the floor.

"Sure," I said. She leaned over as Sammy walked over to face her. He was already headed her way when he saw her tears coming down. Some dogs have an instinct to console people who are hurting. My dog Sammy, a Labrador, has a way of soothing people's hurts like he is a human himself. Sammy put his head down, inviting a hug, then looked up and kissed the tears off her cheeks.

"Ohhh," Desiree said. "That is so darn sweet."

"I would agree," I replied. I don't like to talk about my dog and how he comforts people. People don't seem to need an explanation. Honest affection needs no explanation.

Meditation can quiet the voices in your head

"I'm just so messed up," Desiree confessed. She put her head down and pulled a piece of paper out of her book bag. She said she wanted to read something to me. "My roommate is so together. She has a major. She has a boyfriend. She has a car. She always seems so happy. I got none of that. My life is just crap, you know? It would be nice to have a boyfriend, I guess. But most guys are terrified at any kind of commitment, you know. Sometimes I just feel so lonely. I got drunk this past weekend thinking about all that. Like at the rate I'm going I could be single my whole life. Thinking about that just made me feel worse. Like what can I do? I just get so down on myself. I think I'm pushing people away."

I took some time to take in what she'd shared. I thought of how many times I had similar thoughts in college. I told her that took a lot of courage and honesty to share those things. She nodded. She looked at her feet.

"I figured out sucky things happen," she said. "Ok. I get it. But then I start getting down on myself. You're ugly. Your fat. Nobody likes you. Nobody will ever like you. This is just so much self abuse. I go to bed. I try to shut off those voices in my head. Nothing works. What can I do? I just want to shut off that noise so I can get to sleep at night."

I thought of the grounding technique. But that didn't deal with self acceptance. We could have explored childhood experiences. She wanted a technique that worked now.

"What can I do?" she asked.

Three step meditation

"Meditation," I said. I showed her how to do three focused activities with her senses. She focused on: 1. the shape of leaves of a plant in my office, 2. the shades of green in each leaf, and 3. the subtle changing temperature in the front part of her mouth as she breathed with a partially open mouth. It got cooler when she breathed in and warmer when she breathed out. It was constantly changing.

"Practice this for 30 seconds. I will too," I said. "Then I will ask you what your experience was like. We'll see if you got out of this echo chamber of negative thinking in your head."

Thirty seconds went by. "How did that go?" I asked.

"It was peaceful," she said. "But I kept thinking about Sammy!" She laughed. Sammy was half asleep on his dog bed across the room.

"What happened to the echo chamber of pessimistic thinking?" I asked.

"Not there," she said."But what am I supposed to do—meditate all day?"

"That's an idea," I joked.

"No, the negativity is back," she said. Her face tensed up.

"Did you escape the rainstorm of negativity for a moment while you meditated?" I asked. "Yeah," she said. "It was nice." "And was that valuable?" I asked.

"Yes," she replied.

"Did you gain something in that moment?" I asked.

"Yes," she said. "For the first time ever I could shut off the fire hose of negativity in my head. That was cool."

"Awesome" I said. "Now, a trick question. What is the right way to do this meditation?" "Well you do three things…" She paused. I raised my eyebrows and frowned slightly. "There isn't a right way," she said. "You never said there was a right way." "Correct," I replied. "Meditation is a tool like a hammer. It would sound silly to say here is the one right way to use this hammer. I mean you can pound nails with one end, pull nails with the other, et cetera." She nodded.

"Another trick question," I said. "When did this happen? One word answer." "Well it was a couple minutes ago…but that's a bunch of words." I could tell her the answer but then she wouldn't learn to see for herself, to observe. "You were looking at the leaf shapes as they were…you were looking at the shades of green as they were….you were sensing the temperature in your mouth as it changed every microsecond but you were sensing the temperature as it is…" She looked at me blankly. "OK," I continued. "Multiple choice question. These things were all happening: a. in the past, b. in the future, c. now."

"Now!" she said. "Bingo," I said. "You got it. Now third trick question. You were looking at the shapes as they were now, the shades of green as they were now, the temperature as it was now. Were there any other thoughts in your head you were aware of?" "No." "Leaves and color and temperature are all part of nature," I explained. "So when you were meditating, what was your mind full of?" "Nature!" she replied. "Correct," I said. "Your mind was full of nature. Did that help you interrupt the all is lost negativity in your head?" "It sure did," she replied.

"You had more peace of mind in your human experience." I paused and challenged her. "Is that good or bad?" "Good," she replied. "But I thought the world was going to hell in a hand basket not so long ago," I said. "Well I didn't know this stuff," she replied.

"You were accepting yourself and what you were doing when you were meditating," I said. That was why you felt better. "It feels good to accept yourself, doesn't it?"

"Well I know my experience," she said. "Before meditating I was telling myself I'm screwed up. Then I got in what you call the present moment. I mean I've done some meditating before all this too, so I know some of the lingo. It felt peaceful and calm. Quite different from the nastiness of my thinking."

"You freed yourself from the nonstop cynical, critical thinking," I said. "You freed yourself from pessimism. You accepted the moment. You accepted yourself. You worked with the way things are. You let the thoughts flow in your mind. You let yourself process the information from your senses. It flowed. You were going with the flow of your experience."

"Ok," she said. "Now I guess I'm not trapped in an echo chamber in my head. Cool. I think I got it," she said.

Sammy had meanwhile walked over to a corner in the room and laid down on his bed. She was learning to care for herself. She was learning to treat herself with a friendly attitude. I didn't challenge her beliefs on climate change for a simple reason. She didn't challenge my beliefs on climate change either.

➤**LIFE SKILLS:** pet therapy, asking for help, stories with a metaphor, understanding processes, understanding values.

➤**ACTION STEP:** take a minute to meditate and then take a moment to appreciate how you have protected your life today from stress. Appreciate how you've acted in a life sustaining way and added value to your life. When you protect your life or someone else's life from stress and its harmful effects, you are adding value to people's lives.

Procrastinating creatively: happiness comes from saying "not now"

Many people are frustrated with how they procrastinate about doing things and don't get things done. Well, I say as long as it is a strength of yours, you might as well work with it. If you are good at putting things off, then put off doing one thing to get another thing done.

Procrastinate creatively. I call this the "power of not yet." I used that power to write this book. Once I put things off the right way, I had 20,000 words written in a couple months. What happened? I tapped into the power of Not Yet. I put off doing dishes and wrote a little in the book. Then laundry piled up. I put that off and wrote some more. The kitchen floor looked like a tornado hit it. Sweep it up? Nothing doing. I put that off and wrote even more in my book. For years I did just the opposite. I had ideas for writing. But when it came to doing the dishes or writing, I did the dishes. Writing always came second. Which means it came last. Which means I didn't get any good writing done. I was too busy doing dishes and laundry after work.

My secret? I don't give myself the option of doing nothing. I have the option of doing one of two things. Either sweep or write, either wash or write, etc. The choice I always make is write. You're reading the results. I've become a productive writer and this book is living proof that creative procrastination works and works very well indeed.

If I didn't put things off, I'd never get anything done.

Let me explain in more detail.

In the morning I put off breakfast until I feed my dog. I put off my morning walk until I have coffee. I put off dishes until I get my laundry started. I put off cleaning dirty mugs from my truck until I go to work. In the end everything gets done. You don't put things off and do nothing. You put off doing one thing on your to do list in order to complete another item.

I'm writing these lines while visiting Silverton, Colorado. I want to hike with friends—but Not Yet. I'll write first in the morning for an hour or two. All around me are 13,000 foot mountain peaks calling to me. The mountains are calling me but they can wait. My creativity is best when I'm putting off

THE POWER OF NOT YET:

PUT THINGS OFF TO GET THINGS DONE

FIGURE 1.3.2
The power of "not now." By Esther Phingmoo.

- 81 -

something I really enjoy. Once I finish my creative work, then I can have my outdoor adventure. I'm working with my creativity, with the ideal time to accomplish something—in the morning.

It's Time To Flip To "Not Yet"

It's time to flip from "Now" to "Not Yet." Pay attention to what kind of experience you are creating for yourself. Put things off that don't matter now. Live in the truth of what makes you happy. Put things off that are just busy work or things that will make other people happy. Indulge yourself. Do what makes you happy. The truth about what makes you happy doesn't live in books. Not even in this one. This truth lives in your experience. Go get it and love it. Put off everything else for now. Don't be in a rush about your happiness. "But I've got so much to do!" the emotional mind might say. My response? Not now. Chill. Tranquillo.

➢LIFE SKILL: use of irony and procrastination.

➢ACTION STEP: pick two small tasks you would like to do today. Then pick one to do, put off doing it, and do the second one instead. Then take time to appreciate how you've put things off to get other things done.

Feeling anxious

Jenny was in my office for her third session to treat her debilitating depression. She woke up as if she'd been in a dream. "So I'm not hopeless?" she said to herself. "I just have to let go."

Jenny had dropped out of college after one year. Her anxiety was too severe. She endlessly doubted herself. Doubting lead to depression. Depression lead to lower and lower energy and motivation to where it was hard to get out of bed and eat breakfast. She wondered where her life would go.

FIGURE 1.3.3
Young woman standing on an image of a circuit board.
By Esther Phingmoo.

In high school she was fascinated by math. Her aunt was an electrical engineer who designed circuit boards for computers. In a high school physics class, Jenny learned how to design circuit boards to control the volume on speakers using math. Jenny loved math; it made sense to her. She had a dream to become an electrical engineer. Now that dream was gone like a burned-out speaker.

Or was it? She wondered what it would be like to be hopeful. She imagined herself, thinking positively like she does when designing a circuit board, but this time asking a counselor and a doctor for help. She read online that counseling and medicine can help "re-engineer" someone's brain when they are stuck in depression. She imagined learning new ways to think. She imagined acting on the new thinking patterns and feeling better. She imagined taking medicine and feeling her brain respond more and more to positive thinking.

This daydreaming was very beneficial. It helped motivate Jenny to call a counsellor and a doctor and get started on the process of feeling better. After one month her depression was 50% better, after two months 80% improved, and after 3 months her mood was back to normal. Good sleep. Waking up well rested. Good focus. Good motivation. Excited about her future.

Her new thinking? Exposure and response prevention. She had been bothered by intense and automatic feelings of dread anytime she tried to leave her house or drive somewhere. She was flooded with terrifying feelings that she would be the victim of violence. She worried a car would hit her. She feared she would be trapped in a traffic jam and then her car would be hit and burst into flames, resulting in terrible injuries. She could see the blood, hear the crashing metal, smell the smoke.

It was all in her mind. It had become the "new normal" in her mind. The doctor informed her that biologically the brain can take as normal whatever it has been doing for the past month, whether it made sense or not. In her case, she had seen car accident pictures on the internet. They were bloody and awful. They made an impression that stuck with her. Her pessimism encouraged her to focus on what was dramatic and hopeless and so she did. More frequently the frightening images came to mind any time she got in a car or left her house. Her pessimism pushed her to think she wasn't capable of initiative and asking for help. Her pessimism created false feelings her problems were bigger than her. She couldn't learn from setbacks. She was a victim to her environment. She felt hopeless. She felt she had to latch onto what she couldn't control now—her anxiety, the frightening images, the way her heart beat in her throat when she tried to walk outside her house. She let her pessimism have a gorilla like grip on her emotions. She developed agoraphobia, an intense fearful reaction to being around people.

Jenny found it helpful to have a name for what was troubling her. She wasn't the problem. The problems were depression, anxiety, and agoraphobia. These problems were treatable. Medicine calmed down her racing heart and shaky hands. Then her nerves responded to what the counsellor called exposure and response prevention. She did just what she was afraid of but prevented the anxiety response.

She stepped just one step out the back door of her house and used deep breathing and the three step meditation method to prevent shortness of breath and anxious thinking. She only went back into the house when the anxiety calmed down. That was response prevention. She felt the anxiety and calmed it down. She escaped the anxiety by dealing with it, not running away from it—that would only make the agoraphobia worse. On a stress rating scale of 1 to 10, she was creating a stress level of 1. Later she would address higher levels of stress. After 50 repetitions of this exercise over an entire day, the anxiety calmed down from a 1 to a zero in reaction to taking one step outside of her apartment.

Now the brain associated calmness with going outside the house. What had been a stress level of 1 was now a zero. Medicine, meditation, and deep breathing all helped. In the past, the brain wasn't open to learning like this. It was paralyzed by anxiety. But now anxiety was calmed down with meditation and medication. The brain was also paralyzed by pessimism. But now Jenny neutralized pessimism with her new found positivity. That kept her fired up to do the long work of desensitizing.

Her next task was to stay outside longer. At first she just took one step out the back door and calmed down. Later it was two, then 10, then 20 steps, and once she calmed down she went back inside. Then she started stepping out the front door and got used to that. Then came driving. The same "gradual desensitizing" worked here again. It was daily work. She was relentless. Jenny saw how she could make a little progress every day. She saw that was exactly what she was accomplishing, and she privately gave herself credit. "Good job!" she told herself.

Sometimes Jenny felt like giving up. But she had learned the basics of a good attitude, one focused on personal success. She knew pessimism could cause her to give up on herself. She saw positivity encouraging her. She saw the two in conflict inside her—and she always was free to choose what attitude she wanted today. She saw that the light at the end of this tunnel of trouble wasn't a train—it was freedom to live her life the way she wanted to—not forever controlled by anxiety.

With 12 months of hard work, Jenny emerged from her agoraphobia. Life felt so good. She felt in control of herself. She felt in charge of her future. She looked online at a list of colleges in the Midwest. Kansas, North Dakota, South Dakota. She had so many choices now. The future looked wide open. She imagined what kind of lifestyle she would be living after college. She looked up the salary of electrical engineers and saw she could live a middle class lifestyle with that. If she worked 30 years at that salary she could own her own house. Not bad. She imagined driving an average car and living in a peaceful neighborhood. Going to church. Volunteering for a nonprofit company abroad. Giving back to others who had given so much to her. Now she had a chance to afford a house, health insurance and what she wanted most in her life. A family of her own. It felt so good to be putting her happiness first and then being relentless in pursuing it. This must be what America is all about, she thought to herself.

Jenny looked back at how scary life had once been. Her doom and gloom attitude seemed to fit with the scary news stories. It was like she had come under hypnosis. She was seeing what she wanted to see. Her counsellor had called her pessimistic beliefs a kind of "self-hypnosis." Those thoughts had felt as real as rain so she believed them totally. She came under the spell of pessimism. Over time with pessimism filtering out all the positive things in her experience, she lost contact with the real world that was full of opportunities. More and more she believed her distorted feelings. Gradually her pessimism lead to anxiety. Anxiety lead to agoraphobia. And agoraphobia lead to her becoming a "shut in" and stuck in her house. One more mental illness casualty caused by pessimism.

A practical, results oriented attitude helped Jenny wake up from this bad dream of pessimism. She focused on what works. Pessimism doesn't work. Counseling works. Medication works. Asking for help works. Prayer works. Thinking about your goals works. Meditation with a three step method worked. More and more she loved what worked in her experience. She developed a private contempt for pessimism after seeing how it ruined her life.

Jenny kept the agoraphobia out of the way and went on to enroll in college where she did well. She eventually phased off her medication. She had re-engineered those trillions of circuits in the circuit board of her brain. There was nothing wrong with medication. She just didn't need it anymore. Jenny still used her guides, her counselor and her doctor. They were her support team. Her brain was still deceptive and capable of tricking her into a cycle of irrational thinking. She understood the power of a support team. It was everything. She knew if she quit working with her doctor and counsellor she could get tripped up again by negative thinking. The tough guy "Lone Ranger" approach didn't work in engineering or in life. After several more years she had mastered meditation and dozens of thinking skills. She then phased off her counseling after carefully going over all the skills she had mastered. But she resolved to contact the counsellor right away should the anxiety come back. She always had her support team backing her up. And she always had her meditation and positive attitude to strengthen her mind every day.

➢**LIFE SKILLS:** attitude awareness, putting happiness first, visualizing success, use of medication, use of exposure and response prevention.

➢**ACTION STEP:** pick one thing you are anxious about doing—it is a 1 out of a possible 10 level of stress. Now do it anyway to desensitize to it. After finishing the task, re-evaluate the level of stress for that task. Has it dropped to less than 1.0, such as a .9?

If so, take time to appreciate you have desensitized to a task. You are growing in emotional self-control.

Feeling stuck in life

Cynthia is losing pessimism and weight with her positive attitude!

Positivity has a new face. Ordinary people are doing extraordinary things. Cynthia is an ordinary person who took one step forward on her goals, then refused to get distracted, but made excuses--and took a step back. This "one step forward, one step back" habit is a common form of self-sabotage that eats away at motivation. Your motivation suffers because you feel your efforts have been getting you nowhere. Because that is the case: you took one step forward and one step back.

After years of failure, Cynthia decided to take charge of her attitude in her weight loss efforts. She wouldn't tolerate taking a step back if it was avoidable. She would make choices informed by medical science. She was:
- avoiding pessimism
- recognizing accomplishments
- working with a counsellor

Positivity helped Cynthia lose 30 pounds and that gave her the motivation to reach her goal. She had been 60 pounds overweight and realized this extra weight would wipe out her back and joints, possibly leaving her with diabetes and chronic pain for the rest of her life. She saw that happen to so many of her aunts and uncles.

Cynthia had failed in the past because she constantly craved the unhealthy foods that were diminishing her life. When she dieted, she would lose five or 10 pounds, but then she would make excuses for bad behavior and gain the weight back.

Cynthia learned her "yo-yo dieting" was caused by **pessimism**. In the past, she would give up on dieting and

POSITIVITY HAS MANY BENEFITS

exercise (pessimism's lack of initiative) and feel personality wounded (took setbacks personally). She felt hopeless (another pessimism quality) because she felt she wasn't learning anything (pessimism again). If she lost weight in one week, she would forget about it because dwelling on that was selfish (another trait of pessimism). Instead of letting go of the past she latched onto it (her sixth trait of pessimism) and all her failures. She didn't realize she was practicing pessimism.

We all encounter setbacks in life, but Cynthia took them personally. We all have accomplishments in life, but Cynthia took them for granted and forgot about them. She focused on her failures and stopped learning about what worked for her.

Pessimism made Cynthia think that she wasn't worth the effort of planning her meals out, buying whole foods and cooking healthful recipes. Once she changed her attitude, she realized she was worth the effort.

Once Cynthia saw the stark contrast between positivity and pessimism, she saw she needed to quit pessimism. She didn't need to give up on herself. She wasn't the problem. Pessimism was the problem. She had all the intelligence to succeed in getting to a healthy weight like other women had done. As she looked back she saw how time and again she succeeded in losing five or 10 pounds—but it was pessimism that got her to take a setback personally and give up on herself—rather than give up on pessimism. This insight was revolutionary. No longer was she going to be in the gorilla grip of pessimism.

Positivity says you are worthy because you have intrinsic value. You are a meaningful person in and of yourself because God made you. You are amazing. Cynthia accepted that humanitarian attitude and gave herself extra time to shop for healthy items. She gave herself an extra half hour per meal to cook healthy things.

"I saw all my accomplishments!" she said, looking back at her efforts to live healthy. "I never saw this before because I was caught up in pessimism. Or I just wasn't paying attention. But it's an accomplishment when I follow a healthy routine. When I get to sleep early enough at night, I set myself up to be successful at getting up early enough to make a healthy breakfast and do my morning meditation. It feels so good to start the day grounded in

FIGURE 1.3.4
"I'm worth it." By Esther Phingmoo.

the present moment. I'm no longer tempted to eat junk. I mean how could I treat myself that way after I've been meditating in the morning. I have so much more self-respect now."

"It's an accomplishment to organize my day. It's an accomplishment to actually plan out my meals. It's an accomplishment to stay on schedule and not make excuses to eat processed food or junk food. It's an accomplishment to simply be aware of my attitude. It's an accomplishment to say no to temptations. It's an accomplishment to say no to laziness or being distracted. These are all accomplishments I didn't recognize in the past and that's why I regained the weight. This kind of knowledge and insight is really liberating! I've lost 30 pounds now and I feel so much better. I have more energy for everything I want to do."

She paused to gather her thoughts.

"I was so pessimistic before and I didn't even know it. I was afraid to walk in the neighborhood because I thought people would see me and I would look so fat. Now I could care less. My self-image doesn't depend on what I think other people are thinking of me. That's not very smart. I'm focused on being smart. It's not smart to make your happiness depend on what you imagine other people are thinking—like you are some kind of child and they are your Mommy or Daddy. So ridiculous."

Cynthia learned her positive attitude needed to be nurtured. A great outlook doesn't happen by accident. You get out of it what you put into it. Cynthia determined to invest in her attitude every day. That investment stopped her yo-yo dieting.

In her own way, working with her counselor, Cynthia used the I SHALL acronym of positivity for organizing her day to empower her positive attitude. Rather than looking at all these strategies as things she "has to do," Cynthia sees them as opportunities. She "gets to do them." Cynthia also developed a new relationship with food. Food is a source of nutrition but it is also psychoactive. It stimulates emotions in the psyche. Different foods stimulate different emotions. Some foods stimulate cravings for carbs and reduce the motivation for exercise. Those are on Cynthia's "dangerous foods" list. She mostly avoids those foods altogether because they are so toxic to her. These include alcoholic drinks and highly processed foods.

Cynthia also is using medication to take care of her brain. Her reasoning? If it works, don't knock it. Doing what works to take care of your brain is an act of personal responsibility. "I mean every day we use toothpaste to prevent cavities or under arm deodorant to prevent bad smells or sunscreen to prevent skin cancer," she explains. "We are using artificial things to prevent bad things from happening. This is the same thing when I use a medication to help my sleep or help my body lose weight. Why would I want to stop using a medicine and let a disease happen that I could prevent? I'm not into avoiding personal responsibility. Why would I want to make my life more difficult when I can make it easier?"

Making sense is what Cynthia is all about now. She has become an expert about herself. She has mastered the art of how to be successful in life. She follows a lifestyle that makes sense because she is thinking through everything she is doing and is relentlessly caring about what works. The results are amazing!

➤**LIFE SKILLS:** use medical science, meditation, goal setting, reject pessimism, obsess on accomplishments, healthy routines, use of a counsellor, self-image management, willingness to change.

Feeling broken

Cindy came to my office seeking help. "I feel so broken," she said to me. Her skin looked pale. Her voice was strained. This college sophomore had hit hard times. Her roommates were loud drunks. Recently, the police had been called on her roommates and their landlord had threatened eviction for everyone! For Cindy, insomnia had lead to depression that lead to diminished attention, memory and grades. I felt frail just listening to her.

She'd done nothing wrong. This was just life. She kept living with nasty roommates and now she was going to share in their consequences. Life was coming at her like a hurricane. "I feel so helpless," she said. For a moment, I felt helpless hearing her say that.

Positivity is focused on a plan

"We're not helpless," I said. "We just need a plan." By seeing me she was asking for help, I told her. That is a powerful move: to ask for help from a physician who uses the medical model to solve problems.

I explained the medical model is as old as Hippocrates who practiced medicine several thousand years ago. An expert is trained to teach a patient to break big problems down into smaller, solvable issues. "That's why they call me a 'shrink,'" I said. "I shrink big problems into smaller ones."

Cindy felt weak because she wasn't getting her needs met, I told her. Her landlord wasn't giving her a safe residence for her medical condition. I wrote the landlord a letter informing him that her renter had a medical condition—and a disability—made worse by her roommates' behavior. This would empower the landlord to evict the roommates, but not Cindy, because the landlord now understood the roommates were a threat to Cindy's health. I was just appealing to the landlord's good will.

Next I sent Cindy a copy of the letter describing her medical condition. She could show that to the police if they were called so hopefully they would protect her from her roommates—not lump her in with them. She breathed a sigh of relief. The university, the police and her doctor were on her side. The letter was her "ticket" to that protection. She felt like there was power in numbers here.

I wrote a third version of the letter asking the University to provide accommodations for her medical condition: a tutor, extra time for homework and tests, a note-taker, a quiet test taking room and the option to retake classes at no extra cost. I told her this letter was asking for services she deserved based on the Americans With Disabilities Act. "Do you know what that is?" I asked her.

"No," she replied timidly.

"It's a federal law," I said. "It says people with disabilities can't be discriminated against. They deserve an equal opportunity to benefit from a college class compared to someone without disabilities. From now on, nobody is going to mess with you. The university will help you. I'm going to help you. You can call me anytime day or night. You're going to be ok," I said.

For biological problems... biological answers

I explained the new medical model of the brain understands that with medical issues, there are three aspects to them: biological, psychological and social aspects. We decided to address Cindy's biological problems first. Her skin was pale from a poor diet. She ate fast food and processed food, no colored vegetables or fruits. A blood test showed she was low on Vitamins D. A diet rich in colored fruits and vegetables and lean meat would remedy that, along with milk. For her insomnia, we made a plan to try melatonin and, if that failed, trazodone. To improve Cindy's physical wellbeing, I told her she needed to log in 5,000 steps per day. That would boost levels of nerve growth factor in the brain which in turn would help boost levels of dopamine (for attention), serotonin (for mood), and acetylcholine (for memory). We would focus her counseling on meditation and self-awareness, something called dialectic behavior therapy. If that didn't help her mood we would add an antidepressant. If that wasn't successful, I would give her a medical withdrawl letter to drop out of college for a semester at no cost to her. "The university always supports me," I said. "It will always support you."

For psychological problems... psychological answers

To stop Cindy's self-defeating obsessions at night that were interfering with getting to sleep, I prescribed a meditation technique called meditation for sedation. To stop self-doubting obsessions in the day, I prescribed a technique called three step meditation. It crowds out problematic thoughts so she could focus on her schoolwork.

The three-step meditation is simple. Do three focused activities with your senses. That makes your brain so busy it can't use words during this exercise. Words are what stir up negative

THE NEW MEDICAL MODEL OF THE BRAIN

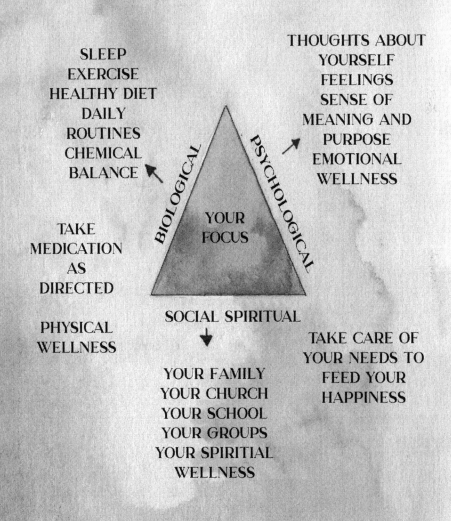

SLEEP
EXERCISE
HEALTHY DIET
DAILY
ROUTINES
CHEMICAL
BALANCE

THOUGHTS ABOUT
YOURSELF
FEELINGS
SENSE OF
MEANING AND
PURPOSE
EMOTIONAL
WELLNESS

BIOLOGICAL

PSYCHOLOGICAL

YOUR
FOCUS

TAKE
MEDICATION
AS
DIRECTED

PHYSICAL
WELLNESS

SOCIAL SPIRITUAL

YOUR FAMILY
YOUR CHURCH
YOUR SCHOOL
YOUR GROUPS
YOUR SPIRITIAL
WELLNESS

TAKE CARE OF
YOUR NEEDS TO
FEED YOUR
HAPPINESS

FIGURE 1.3.5

The new medical model of the brain. By Esther Phingmoo.

emotions. Your senses include what you: see, hear, taste, touch, smell. Three focused "streams" of sensory information could be: (1) study a repeating shape such as book covers or leaves, (2) study the many shades of a color in those shapes such as green, and (3) pay attention to the constantly changing temperature in the front part of your mouth as it cools when you breathe in and warms up when you breathe out. When you do these three things your brain will likely find it difficult to use words to get all worried unless you stop doing one of the three steps. If that happens, just remind yourself to do those three steps. Of course, do this in a safe place. Don't do this while riding bike or driving a car. I've taught this to over 400 people and they generally report feeling calmer within a minute. Almost everyone indicates that now they now have a tool to steer the mind away from unwanted negative obsessions—sometimes for the first time in their life.

For loneliness, she would attend interpersonal therapy to learn skills to make friends—respectful friends. For catastrophic, irrational thinking, I prescribed rational thinking skills, part of cognitive behavioral therapy. I could do the couseling to help her learn all these things, I told her, but in this case I preferred her to work with a female therapist in the community and I gave her several names.

Meditation for sedation

In meditation for sedation, a person lays down to bed and then does three conscious mental activities that put you in the present moment. This is a form of the "Three Step Meditation" described earlier. These are typically information processing actions involving some of your five senses but not involving words. Words open the door to stir up the emotions. An example of three actions done at the same time might include: Feeling temperature in your mouth go down and up as you breathe in and out, feeling muscle tension in your chest get tighter and more relaxed with breathing in and out, and counting to three with each breath in and out. Now the brain is too busy to use words. If it does, just redirect it gently to the three actions. Kindness matters here. You're treating yourself with respect as your mind perhaps is fighting you. Be firm, fair and consistent as you teach your mind a new trick—to calm down and fall asleep at night.

For social problems...social solutions

For legal issues Cindy might encounter, she would be equipped with letters from me, the landlord and the university. For rude roommate issues, the letters would trigger a response from the roommates' parents, I predicted. "You knew them beforehand and now they are just acting immature," I said. For social isolation, she could find new friends in the university's social clubs. She liked salsa dancing and hiking and there were groups for both on campus, I told her. She looked relieved. "But I think your roommates will come around. But if they don't then you have options."

She felt hopeless despite all this planning, she said. I noted that sometimes emotions are very slow to pick up on the reality that things are going to get better because you have a plan—so you can have hope even though you don't "feel hopeful." She found that somewhat helpful and agreed to think about it some more.

For psychological "attitude problems" ...positivity

We then went over the basics of pessimism. Pessimism is an irrational belief that problems are bigger than you when the evidence is to the contrary. "That's me—pessimism," she said. For that I prescribed positivity. I explained the six basic elements of positivity, or optimism. "I'd love to learn that!" she exclaimed. "I always thought of myself as an optimist, but I just didn't know what to do to be optimistic in this situation." I explained that was a very common thing for me to hear.

"Positivity is a life skill," I said, "that usually isn't taught anymore. I don't know why that is. It seems like the world has forgotten about it. It doesn't matter. I'm going to teach you all the elements of positivity that helped me get through medical school and practice medicine for 20 years."

"Cool," she said, smiling.

"Then you are going to know how to face problems down," I said, "and think like a doctor."

Her face brightened up. I saw a trace of a smile. She acted like she had some hope because she did have hope—in a realistic plan that someone was going to act on with her. She wasn't alone anymore. She had asked for help. That took courage. She was getting help. She accepted the help. At that point, all we needed to do was work like a team. That was the easy part.

Stay focused on results

At the next visit, Cindy's sleep was better. Melatonin failed but the sleep medicine desyrel worked great. Cindy wasn't thrilled about using Western medicine but she agreed to use it for a few months until her private nightmare was over. However, the sleep medicine didn't work unless she meditated at night, she noted. That was Eastern medicine's meditation helping Western medicine's medication work, I told her. She accepted the combination of Western and Eastern medical traditions coming to her rescue. "Life is full of sacrifice and compromise," I told her. "I'm glad you are doing whatever works for you and your future."

At a later visit, I learned the letter got a great response from the landlord and university. The roommates got a warning letter from the landlord. They shaped up. Apparently the landlord also sent letters to the parents of the roommates whose names were on the apartment lease.

In still later visits, she learned the basics of positivity and how to use them. She learned the basics of pessimism and how not to get used by it. She learned professional time management skills with to do lists and a day planner. Also she mastered empowering daily routines that are summarized in the RAMP acronym. More about that in a few pages later in this book. Good communication skills and interpersonal skills let her meet dozens of new people before Cindy really connected with several good friends.

We feel like we act

If you act weak you are going to feel weak. Sometimes, however, it is hard to know exactly what to do in a difficult situation to stay strong. Many situations are challenging. I know. I've been there. I learned the hard way. I'm passing on what I've learned to you. You can build on my experiences. You too can know how to act with strength—with positivity. In a world this full of pessimism we need more people with positivity. Gradually, Cindy became one of those people.

In later visits, Cindy continued to make progress. She withdrew from one class and took it at a later semester. She finished other classes over winter break. With good sleep, her mood brightened and gradually her depression faded away. Her usual good focus and memory returned. By this time she had developed excellent time management skills. Cindy had learned to organize her life like a doctor does.

"Not everyone learns these skills," I said. "But you had the courage to ask for help, so why shouldn't you get the good results?" She smiled. "Maybe that isn't fair for other people who never asked a doctor for help. But who said life is fair?"

Reaping hard-earned rewards

Several years later I saw Cindy again. "How did the job interview go?" I asked her. "I had to do a few interviews," she replied. "Employers were impressed with my poise and time management. And my preparation. And that I was so confident in my own abilities I was applying for a job months before I graduated."

"Did you show them your to do lists and planners?" I asked.

She made good, steady eye contact with good posture. "Of course!" she replied.

Her job was taking her to Boulder, Colorado to work at an engineering firm that was helping design the electrical circuits for lighting at Denver International Airport. So someday if you land there, looking for a connecting flight, take a moment to admire the excellent design of the lighting. The lighting is so consumer friendly and efficient. Someone I know helped make that happen. Like all good things, that design didn't happen by accident. It took action with an insistence on excellence. Cindy's unstoppable positive attitude didn't hurt either.

This story—based on many real people I've worked with—illustrates the use of positivity's six basic principles:

- Goal setting (get support for schoolwork) and initiative (seeking therapy)
- Taking setbacks as temporary (believe in the plan and act on it)
- Staying hopeful (reject pessimism that the plan won't work)
- Taking accomplishments personally (be proud of getting the job)
- Letting go of what you can't control (like roommates, landlords, rejected for the job, etc).
- Learning from everything (time management, become an asset for getting a good job)

Did Cindy still feel brittle five years later, when she and her husband bought a house and started planning for a family? Yes, to a degree. "But my anxieties are much weaker nowadays," she notes with a confident smile in my FaceTime call with her. "I'm moving on and it feels so, so good. They're like, normal, you know. Just usual life worries. They're not holding me back now like they used to."

She still felt brittle. I feel brittle too, from time to time. Look at all the people who have rejected me, for instance. I don't think brittleness ever totally goes away. We are all a little brittle. We all can be broken. For that reason we all need to take care of ourselves. We are all human. Let's keep it real and not pretend any of us are indestructible.

>**LIFE SKILLS:** goal setting, asking for help, using a doctor, use of medical support letters, working with systems, assertiveness,

respect for authorities, follow through, willingness to change, willingness to accept guidance.

Feeling limited

Brian was another student who came to me seeking help. "I feel like I just don't have anything left," Brian said. He had dropped out of college after two years. The stress was too much. Between working 30 hours per week and doing school 30 hours per week, he was going WHERE? 10 hours per day, seven days a week. It was too much. Brian felt pulled by obligations to parents and friends…and the list went on. He could manage his time decently. "But inside me I just felt drained, empty," he said. "I felt as much chaos inside me as in the world out there."

After several meetings, Brian decided he really liked working with his hands and he would like to go into a trade, such as construction. After several more meetings, he decided on plumbing. A few weeks later he was working as a journeyman plumber at a local plumbing company. But still self-doubts plagued him. "What is all this for?" "What is work good for?"

I explained that more than 4 billion lives have been saved by vaccines and other advances in Western Civilization. I did an internet search and showed him the list of vaccines and who made them. He said he hadn't heard that. I reeled off other accomplishments of the "civilization you are part of" such increased prosperity, declining levels of diseases and fewer children growing up in poverty. "If I told you that you had a chance to be part of a movement that has lifted billions of people out of poverty and disease in the last 50 years, would you join it?" He nodded.

"Well, when you work, pay taxes and buy things—you put people to work all over the world. Now billions of people live above the poverty line. Thanks to science, technology, engineering, art and mathematics. Your plumbing technology is part of that. It delivers clean water. I think that's awesome." He nodded but looked like he still had his doubts. "I'll give you some time for those facts to sink in," I said, smiling.

With positivity now counteracting Brian's existential dread, it was time to move on to building emotional toughness and self-control. "No better method exists for that," I said, "than the RAMP method for organizing your daily routines."

Boost your initiative every day by RAMPing it up

Life skills help you live your best life, I explained. Learn them by observing carefully. I'm going to teach you how to learn from your experience. We live in the present moment, looking forward. But to understand life we look backwards and piece things together. We can't help but live this way, said the philosopher Soren Kierkegaard. Such an irony! But let's work with that. Let's look back at how your day unfolds naturally in your experience.

Remember when you woke up this morning, you started by being drowsy then became more and more aware you are waking up? Then you used words to explain your experience, such as, "I'd like to go back to sleep." That was me this morning. Remember, we use words to organize our experience and to make sense of our experience by creating a story. This is our inner narrative. Words give us meaning and purpose in life. While we are at it then, why not be aware of what we are doing and do a better job for ourselves using words?

Remember then you acted on those words you thought about at the start of your day. Maybe you acted by packing for a vacation or procrastinating about that. Then you reflected on those actions while they were happening. It felt good to be getting packed. You reflected forward on what was coming up. It will be good to see those friends. Then the next moment you reflected back on how hard it was to get started packing.

Do you see a natural pattern here?
- We start our day thinking words
- We act for or against those words
- We reflect on our actions and learn something
- We look forward and backward in our life to apply what we've learned.

These are four things we do every day. Repeatedly. They are part of our human experience. It can't be helped really. I mean how can you live your day without words? Without thinking ahead or looking back and learning something? We use these four steps any time we ride a bike or drive a car.

So if you are doing these four things, you will notice everybody does them a little differently. That's ok. We are all different and unique and individuals. But some people seem to have more peace of mind and more motivation with how they do these four steps. The four steps are in sync with their personality and life passions.

I call these four steps your RAMP to live a better life. You are the expert about your RAMP. You can change each element so it works better for you. Let's look at these four elements in more detail.

R stands for read. It is about being aware of the words you use and then being deliberate and intentional about them. We use words when we wake up and then those words can wander into worry and pessimism. Observe what your experience is like when you guide the flow of those words by reading something positive or recalling something you read. This morning I recalled a passage from the Bible, "I can do all things through Him who strengthens me." And that inspired me to write more. The right words are like medication for the soul.

A stands for acting on the words you've wisely chosen. The right actions are also like medication for the soul. If you think positive thoughts but don't act on them, you will weaken the power of those words. You can make it a habit to be aware of what positive or pessimistic words you are using in the morning, and then choose to act on those optimistic thoughts and ignore the negativity in your mind.

Act with purpose. If you act in a random fashion, you can lose your momentum in the morning. Act on the positive words you use. The good life is a life of action. Act in ways that bring out the best in you and the people around you. Pessimism often leads people to not act but just ruminate in a self-defeating way. Avoid that. This morning I made up my mind I would act by opening my laptop and writing. You are reading the results.

M stands for meditate. Reflect on your current experience in some fashion. Be deliberate about that. It is important to start your day being aware of the present moment. Pessimism is always ready to tempt us to get lost outside the present moment. What a mental trap. You can waste your whole day lost in worries and dwelling on the past and future and the "woulda, coulda, shoulda's." Guard against that negative thinking by starting your day in the present moment and, as odd as it sounds, by being aware you are in the present moment. Awareness is everything. If you are aware of the present moment you can catch yourself when you stray from it.

The three-step walking meditation

Several minutes of walking meditation helps in this regard. I walked along a river this morning with my dog. I did a walking meditation. I got in the present moment by noticing three kinds of things with my senses in a focused fashion. That blocked out the use of words. I noticed the shapes of rocks along the river, the shades of gray in the rocks, and the sounds of rushing water. Boom, I was in the present moment. I was one with the river. I was one with nature. I was one with the present moment. Nature truly filled my mind.

A minute later at the river, I focused on three things. The shifting waves in the river, the shades of green in those waves and the sound of the river. I was one with the river. One with nature. One with the present moment. My mind was filled with hundreds of different shapes and hundreds of different shades of green and hundreds of different natural sounds. My mind was healing with the therapeutic sights and sounds of nature. It was an awesome thing to experience.

This is one kind of meditation. Another kind of meditation I do regularly in the RAMP method is meditate by planning and visualizing the day in front of me.

Planning. Visualizing what is coming up, what your goals are, what you are going to do. What might go sideways. How to be ready for anything that goes awry. You mentally prepare but also you are toughening yourself up. Things rarely go according to plan. But you won't be surprised by problems. You are prepared not only to solve them or deal with them but to learn from them and be the master over these problems. The more you visualize overwhelming a problem, then you are making it more and more difficult for that problem to be overwhelming.

Visualizing a plan A and a plan B is helpful as you plan for each activity. You can even visualize what to do in an entertaining way. That might even make you a funny person. It's never worked out that way for me but don't let that discourage you. When you visualize being ready, then you are ready for nearly any eventuality. Visualize not just what is good for you but what is good for "us" meaning your family, your friends, your pets, your work group, your community. That will help you be a more loving person today. Kindness is what counts. Be the person you'd like to have as a friend.

Preview and post view your day

P stands for previewing and post viewing your day. Previewing I reviewed above. Postviewing is looking back at how the day went by the end of the day. Compare that with your plans. How well did your plans work? Your attitude? You are the best source of understanding about yourself. You are the expert.

At the start of your day, plan out your day. You may use sayings you memorized from what you read to help you guide your experience. Today I used, "I can do all things through Him who strengthens me." At the end of your day, evaluate how well those sayings worked. Did they help you live passionately and purposefully? Did your visualizations help you plan out your day? Did you help others have a good day? Name one thing you improved about yourself today with the elements of RAMP you used.

The RAMP isn't a formula you are imposing on your experience. These are techniques you use anyway, every day, but now you are using them deliberately to create a better life for yourself. You are the one who is in the best position to know about your experience, so you are seizing the opportunity to evaluate how your day went and learning how you can make the next one better.

As for my morning, the Bible passage worked well. I let myself feel it's importance for me. I was emotionally engaged in the experience. Bible verses sometimes don't work for me if I am emotionally detached or distracted. But this morning I was emotionally engaged so I felt energized by it. It got me writing and taking a walk with my dog. The walk led to an invigorating walking meditation. I felt one with the turquoise waters of the mountain stream. I felt as they say in Spanish, "tranquillo." I planned the rest of my morning. Planning inspired me to write more. The elements of my RAMP method worked well for me and you are reading the results.

Your RAMP experience will be different. Your style of using it will reflect your unique personality. But the RAMP principles are still the same for everyone. Get the most out of four things that we do every day, anyway. We all read, act, meditate, and reflect—but now you are refining those actions and making them powerful. RAMP provides an awareness of how to organize your thoughts so they are in sync with your personality, your hopes and dreams, your life passions and your family. You are tapping into a storehouse of wisdom that comes from your own experience. This is another example of using those galaxies of connections in your brain that you probably didn't know you had—until now. Once you understand the basic technique, you can amplify the power of the RAMP in your day.

Pro tip: Some things you read are better at making you stronger

Pay attention to how strong you feel. What words were you thinking when you felt strong? What ideas were streaming into your mind? In the minutes around that time, what words were you taking in from your environment: music, videos, podcasts, social media or mainstream media?

Also pay attention to how weak you might feel at other times. The way some governments and businesses try to manipulate people is by creating doubts that the individual is "enough" to handle their problems—and that's why the individual needs to buy that product or support that government. "Is your house full of dirt?" an ad might say. "Time to buy our new product!"

Or a government might point to all the problems in another government, to get people to doubt that government. Doubt is a powerful tool in the hands of media people. If you feel dragged down by doubt, check the facts for that doubt. If you can't find facts to back up that doubt, then doubt that doubt!

"American is really not a democracy," said one politician. I thought about that. American elects representatives, so it is a representative democracy. I doubted what that politician said because America is a form of democracy: a representative democracy. But for a moment that politician had put some doubt in my mind. I doubted that doubt and then removed it. That is how you can "clean up your attitude" and not let it get ruined by irrational doubts—in other words pessimism.

I let victimhood take over my mind

In my 20's I felt weak because I thought of myself as a victim to my situations. Everything I read was about people being victims. I encountered this theme in newspapers and magazines, and heard it in songs and on talk radio. People were victims because of race, poverty, gender, sexual orientation or lack of employment. At times people were not victims but felt that way. I never asked who was and who wasn't a victim. If they said they were a victim it must have meant they were a victim. Why? Victimhood was my identity. I saw myself as a victim. I saw people around me as victims too. That was my way of showing I cared about others. The environment was a victim. When I thought about the environment as a victim, that was my way of caring for the environment. Anyone who challenged that was evil! The big reveal? This is pessimism, pure and simple. Pessimism sees problems as bigger than us. This is another version of that.

Everywhere I looked I saw either the powerless or the powerful. Big surprise I couldn't imagine there was anything else. What else would you expect from a pessimist who didn't even know he was a pessimist?

How the RAMP got me out of victimhood thinking

I felt a victim because that is all I read about: people who were victims. Then I changed the kinds of things I read. I challenged myself to read something new. I started reading self-help books. They taught me there were many, many ways to look at life. These books challenged me with a new idea: to become more "valuable" to myself and others—and the environment—by picking up life skills. This message was so hopeful and refreshing. I could quit obsessing that I was a victim! I could focus on self-improvement and make it work! It worked. I learned skills that promised to make me more valuable—and did. But that only happened because I stayed committed to only reading things that helped me with my self-improvement quest.

I found all words are not created equal. Some are weak and some are incredibly powerful for one's self-improvement work. Look at words the same way you look at your food and drink. You don't just see food and eat it. You read labels on food products. You smell some things like milk before you use them. You taste something like a sandwich before you eat it all. You double check someone else's information with your experience.

A friend of mine today tasted a bottle of "all natural" flavored water with pomegranate. It looked good. But she said it tasted like hair spray. She dumped it out. Likewise, you should "dump out" information from your mind that makes you feel weak or act flakey. Treat information like something you put into your body. Because you are doing just that.

Be choosey. Be picky. Be suspicious. Don't be quick to believe. You don't have to be dramatic about it. Look for the warning signs of pessimism in the information you take in. Double check what you think is true. Check out what other people think. Check out facts that might go against what you believe. Be brave enough to challenge your beliefs. Sometimes your beliefs can get you in trouble.

Limiting beliefs: they have real consequences!

Don't be gullible and believe the first thought that comes into your mind. And don't quickly get emotionally attached to that belief. Doing so can have real consequences. Which reminds me of a story.

The drinking water story

I once took a trip into the mountains in Wyoming. My friend Carey had invited me to stay at his cabin in the Snowy Range near Laramie, Wyoming. There was great weather for hiking in October. The scenery was gorgeous. Yellow aspens painted the mountain slopes. His cabin was perched on the side of a mountain below some beaver ponds. Of course beaver ponds are notorious for having water that can make you sick.

He met me on his porch. I had been hiking and said I was thirsty. He said he had good drinking water in the cabin and I could help myself. He motioned for me to go in the front door. I clomp, clomped inside with my hiking boots. I was so thirsty my lips were sticking together.

Maybe I was dehydrated and not thinking clearly, I don't know. I saw the kitchen faucet and I believed the first thing that came to my mind. The water from the kitchen faucet must be good drinking water. Did Carey say that? No. I just assumed it. I justified that belief with how thirsty I was. When you have some random feeling and then work to justify it with your thinking, you are headed for trouble.

I then saw there was also a water cooler perched on the counter next to the kitchen faucet. Two sources of water. But I was already focused on the kitchen faucet so I opened the faucet and poured myself some clear water and drank it. It tasted great.

A good question to ask yourself when you are in a new situation is this "What is one thing that could go wrong?" I looked at his kitchen sink and next to it stood a large water cooler with a spigot. What's that doing there, I could have asked myself. Was he just referring to the water cooler when he said he had good drinking water? Why did he even need a water cooler?

I asked these questions after I took a drink of water from the faucet. Let that be a lesson to you. If there is a reason to doubt something, better do your doubting first, before you believe and act on something. Once you act then you can start creating a whole bunch of new problems.

I felt a lump in my throat. Should I dare to ask if the faucet had clean water? Or ask was the cooler the only source of clean drinking water? Would I look stupid for asking? Would I look even more stupid for not asking? What would happen if I didn't ask? All these questions raced around in my mind like little ants in an anthill. I was feeling a little disturbed.

What got me in trouble was my emotional attachment to the idea that clean water was coming out of the faucet. Why did I believe that? That feeling now seemed very suspicious. I decided to not ask about the faucet. But my thoughts were now going in circles in the echo chambers of my mind.

I suddenly felt I had to ask Carey the question.

No I didn't.

Yes I did.

No I didn't.

My emotions echoed around like that for about 5 minutes as I stared at the faucet.

The suspense built up. I blurted out the first question that came to mind.

"Is the water from the faucet OK to drink?" I asked Carey. I felt stupid the moment I asked it. But relieved. Then I felt smart. Carey laughed. I looked at him as his lips moved in slow motion. "Ha! I'd never drink out of that faucet," he said pointing at the kitchen sink. "It comes out of the creek that's just pond water. I wouldn't even give that water to my dog. It's polluted."

"Oh good," I replied, faking a confident facial expression. "I'll use the water in that cooler then." Somehow, I felt lucky. I felt somehow the bad water wasn't going to affect me. Again I made an emotional attachment to a belief in my mind. A flakey belief.

The next morning I woke up and my stomach felt like it was on the losing side of a boxing match. I confessed my mistake to Carey. Carey helped me out as best he could. The day after I drove home. I was still feeling sick and weak but also much the wiser about how to think about what safe drinking water is. If somebody says they have some good water for drinking, don't be afraid to ask questions so you can just drink what safe drinking water is! Better yet, just drink bottled water! When it comes to drinking water, there is no such thing as a stupid question.

➢**MORAL OF THE STORY:** Clinging to an irrational belief can have real consequences!

Test what you are hearing or reading to see if it is true. Does it make sense? Does it fit with your experience? Does it fit with what other people are experiencing? Does it fit with facts you know? Could it be a mistake? Are there better explanations than the one you are listening to? These are some of the questions involved in what is called "critical thinking." Doctors use this kind of thinking all the time.

➢**LIFE SKILLS:** RAMP method, daily routines, observing effect of routines, adjusting routines, reading to increase your power, suspending your belief, not believing every emotion, letting ideas earn your belief, keeping track of consequences.

➢**ACTION STEP:** pick one action and track its consequences throughout your day.

Feeling like nothing matters

Kay had been referred to me to treat her depression. "I dropped out of college," said Kay. "But since then I just can't get anything going in my life." The 27-year-old talked about a string of failed relationships. "I never felt close to him so I moved on," she confessed. Then there was a string of failed jobs. "I came in late or didn't, like, follow some rule, so they would say they 'had to' let me go."

Kay grew up in a middleclass family in Ohio. Both her parents worked. She was bright and carried A and B grades in grade school through high school. Kay had no addictions or learning disabilities to hold her back. She had thrived. She felt loved by her parents and friends.

Then she went to college and majored in English. Classes on social inequality introduced her to empathy for the under privileged, which was good, and also to cynical theories about society. These theories did not have critical thinking: a weighing of facts for and against a certain theory. However, those theories were cynical, meaning they thought certain groups of society were cold and uncaring—motivated to make a profit at other people's expense. They didn't explain how private self interest (ie., the making of a cell phone for profit) can lead to the public good (people in developing countries starting businesses that sell items through that cell phone). The end result was she thought society was full of people taking advantage of other people—including her. No wonder she felt so bad! She was surrounded by victims and was one herself!

She increasingly saw her suffering as someone else's fault. She saw herself as a victim like the classes had shown was happening to other people. She never questioned the narrative that everyone is a victim. No other student questioned that narrative, nor did any teacher, so it just seemed to be true. We are all victims of one kind or another—to the actions of selfish people!

A pessimist looks for facts to confirm their pessimism

With that attitude, Kay looked for facts to confirm this pessimistic world view. That's natural enough. How many people look for the facts to disprove something that feels real? Yet what you feel can feel real but be really wrong. So she made a bad choice to not question her feelings.

In her defense, what else was she supposed to do? She found plenty of so-called facts to confirm her pessimism. Food was more expensive at the grocery store. That meant stores were exploiting people. The same was true for cars and gasoline, to say nothing about the cost of renting an apartment. People all around her were being "used." And the dirty, polluted air was evidence nature was being exploited as well. She couldn't find any other explanation. It was obvious. She didn't look for any other explanation of people's suffering, either, and the facts to support other points of view. Another big mistake. She was sliding down the path of pessimism without even knowing it ends in nihilism. Nihilism is the feeling that nothing matters and society is meaningless.

Post Modernism is bad for your mental health

No one in her college classes told her she was being taught Post Modernism. No one suggested that political enemies of democracy use Post Modernism to help young people doubt democracy. No one told her there are many alternative philosophies to Post Modernism—such as the idea of progress. That people can solve human problems using science and technology. No one told her Post Modernism has been found false by many intellectuals. Also, certainly no one told her that Post Modernism can make her mentally ill. Any mention of that would certainly rain on this academic parade of Post Modernism now wouldn't it?

But that's just what I did.

"Do you feel used all the time?" I asked.

"Pretty much," Kay said with a wry smile.

"OK, thank you," I replied. "You at least gave me the benefit of the doubt. You didn't have to do that, but I appreciate you sharing that with me."

"Well, I decided to come here," she explained with a shrug of her shoulders.

She reached down to pet my Labrador Sammy. He waved his tail.

"Life is stressful," I said. "'It comes with the office.' That was a quote from Abraham Lincoln when he was talking about his

PRESCRIPTION FOR POSITIVITY

stress being a president. And that was a saying that helped him to a degree just wave off that stress and accept it as natural but not overwhelming all the time."

"I wish I could deal with garbage like that, just shrug it off," she said.

Try to not take criticism personally— but take complements personally

"I don't shrug it off. Well, I try but it's easier said than done." I replied. "Criticism hurts. We all feel tempted to take what someone says personally. We might act like we don't care what someone else says. Or that we're taking it as someone else's take on a situation. But deep down most people are a little disappointed when people don't agree with everything they say—like they should be worshipped like some Queen or Pharoah in Egypt."

"Well you don't act like you are all beat up emotionally," she said.

"I try not to take it personally, for sure," I said. "I try to learn from them. And I'm a good actor! Ha ha!"

Kay rubbed Sammy's ears and he flopped on his side on the floor so his silky soft ear could get more therapy.

"I'm sorry college didn't work out," I told her. "And I'm sorry those jobs didn't work either. It sounds like they were not a good fit for you." She nodded. "What would you like me to help with?"

Kay explained that she felt she didn't fit anywhere. It was her fault. Jobs just seemed so fake and trivial. Companies seemed to be using people nonstop. Relationships never lasted. They lasted if they were convenient. Also, money was always seemed in short supply. Everything seemed to be costing more. She couldn't stop worrying about all these things at night. With no end in sight for all these troubles, "I feel like nothing matters," Kay confessed. "I don't matter. Nothing matters. And I've been having thoughts I wish I wasn't here at all."

Given her Post Modern attitudes, it wasn't surprising she was using all the elements of pessimism and then getting all the predictable consequences, even nihilism.

Post modernism leads to mental illness

I thanked her for sharing what was for her an incredibly painful experience. She said no, she didn't have any thoughts of "ending it all," no plan, no intent, but she wanted to feel like life mattered somehow. "I have friends who are happy," she said, her eyes welling up. "I just can't seem to get there." I asked if they had lost jobs and relationships like she had. She nodded. Did they have loving families? She nodded. Did they have some spirituality? She shrugged her shoulders. Did they learn from their losses? She said it seemed like they did. They changed careers or changed majors in college. They found different kinds of boyfriends who better fit their personalities.

"But all of that seems so fake," she said. "It just seems like people are using one another and that's all they do. It sucks. But that's life. And I don't want to be a part of that."

"You talk with such profound insights!" I replied. "You have a great command of language. I can see why you majored in English. You are also quite philosophical."

"I only took one class in philosophy," she said, smiling. "It was pretty boring."

"How so?"

"All they did was explain someone's philosophy and then show what was wrong with it."

"That must have been an Introduction to Philosophy course, or something similarly titled." She nodded. Kay reached down and scratched Sammy's ear some more. Sammy let out a sigh. "Oh my gosh," she said, "his ears are so soft!"

"I'll bet he has no idea about that!" I replied.

She was quiet a moment. "Could I sit on the floor next to Sammy?" she asked as she already was moving in that direction. I said sure. "I just want to know what's wrong with me," Kay said. "There's so much wrong with me. Some of my friends are happy. I'm not and it really, really sucks."

"I don't think I can help you there," I replied. She looked up. "I don't think there is anything wrong with you," I said. "You're obviously bright. Caring. Sincere. With a good memory. Good conversation skills. Affectionate. Good command of the language. These are quite valuable. You've really been working on yourself to develop these skills."

"Well, whatever," she replied. "I am also so sad and F'd up, excuse the language. But it's true."

"I hear you," I said. "I may not agree with you but I hear you. And how am I doing listening to you?"

"Fine."

"Ok, and it's always ok to give me feedback such as, 'I need you to understand more of this, or I don't think you understand enough of something else I'm going through.'" She nodded. "If you don't give me feedback on how well I am understanding you—or not—then quite possibly I could get the wrong idea and misunderstand you. And when that happens, I become useless for you. And I sure don't want that to happen!" Kay looked up at me and smiled. She looked down and nodded.

"This is called accountability," I said. "I am accountable to you. I am focused on helping you with your goals to... I don't think we formally went over them."

"I just want to feel like my life matters," she said. "Right now, I don't." I wrote that down in her chart.

We reviewed her strengths as noted above. "Do you give yourself credit for having these strengths?" I asked. She looked at me with a blank face. "You're bright, caring and sincere. I'll bet you've said something to someone that made them smile in the last couple days." She said she thanked her roommate for cleaning the dishes in the sink and her roommate smiled.

"There you go," I said. "You made a difference for someone. Give yourself credit!"

Kay frowned. "That would be a little selfish and petty. That's for grade school kids." That was her idea of the situation, I noted.

"If you asked your roommate if your complement was petty what would she say?"

"Oh she would say it was great but she's all overly happy all the time," Kay said, waving her hand in a circle and rolling her eyes.

FIGURE 1.3.6
"Support Life." By Esther Phingmoo.

"Well that's your idea that what she says is less than genuine, but I'll bet that's not her idea."

Kay thought a moment. "Ok, I guess I've been judgmental. People do appreciate me," she said.

I told her that now I noticed she wasn't imposing her ideas on other people's ideas. She was just taking life as it comes. Information first, then draw conclusions. Take things as they are, instead of imposing her pessimistic interpretations of people's behavior.

I gave her a chance to think about that. "Does it feel better to let information come into your mind first and then draw conclusions?" She nodded. "And sometimes people are fake or petty. OK. But you can weigh the evidence on both sides of a situation before you draw some sweeping conclusions about someone's actions or their character." She thought about that and acted like she didn't know what to think about that.

"I feel like you are lecturing me," she said, smiling.

I thought a moment. "I think you're right!" I said. "I am!" She smiled. I didn't apologize. I thought she needed a little lecture right now. I'd found her using pessimistic thinking to keep herself depressed. She doubted her friend's honesty and sincerity when they complemented her. That kept her believing she had no value for anyone—when the opposite was the case. Her roommate truly did value her and what she did.

"I had this idea you were just going to believe everything I said without thinking about it," I said in jest.

"That isn't happening today," Kay replied, smiling. "But I get your point. I think I've been putting up walls around me to keep people away. People are a lot more genuine and kind than I've been letting myself believe."

What supports life is good: a value system

"You are pretty good at thinking things through," I noted. She winced at the complement. "That is a good life skill. It cuts down on stress. A lot of times, if you think things through, something you are worried about seems either very unlikely or just of no consequence. So it cuts down on stress. And that supports life.

Emotional stress causes stress hormones to be released in the body and they have a damaging effect on serotonin nerves, the feel-good nerves in the brain. So anything that cuts down on stress is supporting life. And whatever supports life, I think, is valuable. Don't you agree?"

Kay looked annoyed. "Sorry for lecturing again," I confessed. She smiled.

"Supporting life, that sounds like a good idea. Something I could get behind, you know," she said. She paused. "My friends have been supporting me," she acknowledged. "I've been supporting them too in my little ways." She paused again.

She adjusted herself in her chair. "I thought the meaning of life would be a little more Earth shattering than this," she said.

"Supporting life is a good thing," I offered. "Anything that supports life is a good thing. That's my little personal philosophy. What do you think about that?"

"I hadn't really heard that before," she replied. "But I'll think about it." I didn't tell her what that insight might do to her Post Modernism that she was holding onto so feverishly. I didn't even tell her she had Post Modernism. Sometimes the best thing about therapy is about what is left unsaid. Then people are free to work out their own meaning in life. Their own salvation.

>**LIFE SKILLS:** insight into what is critical thinking and what is not, pet therapy, openness to new ideas, seeing the importance of an idea being open to be disproved, commitment to truth, working with your strengths, rejecting the victim attitude, seeing value in what supports life.

FIGURE 1.4.0
Meditation allows you to discover the galaxies
that live within you. By Toso Borkovic

4

Learn meditation easily with positivity!

Learning meditation—it's part of a positive attitude

What if there was a stress relief technique that would allow you to both see your mind in action and change it? What if it could be learned mostly by observation—and then it would support your independence and self-reliance? It would be even better if it could stop those pesky negative obsessions. Better still if it could help you sleep at night and start each day with peace of mind.

Meditation fits the bill. You can learn meditation in many ways: on your own, with a guide, from an app, in books, at workshops, through lectures, via YouTube videos, or by talking with others. There are many forms of meditation to explore. A great way to learn meditation is by observing and then putting your observations together to design techniques that work for you and your personality.

To learn guided meditation, focus on what you observe and build upon that knowledge of your immediate experience. You don't have to be systematic but it helps. It also helps to write down questions and keep a journal of what you are learning because you'll accelerate your learning curve. In each exercise, I invite you to read the exercise first, then close your eyes and do the exercise for a minute or two.

EXERCISE 1: **Discover the present moment**

(Read this first, then practice it for a minute). Discover the present moment. Right now you're reading this book, so in this exercise stay where you are and go through your five senses. What are you seeing as you look at this page? What are you hearing, tasting, smelling, touching and feeling? What is the temperature in the air and on the book? Take a few moments to reflect on these things then come back to the text.

Welcome back. Did you notice that when you tried to focus on what you were noticing, you perceived things more deeply? You were in the present moment. Some people will observe their attention wandering after several seconds and leave the present moment. Thoughts might go to the past, future, overthinking, overanalyzing, unfairly judging yourself or thinking about others. These are not in the present moment. They are adding to your experience of the present moment with unnecessary judgmental thinking—thinking that has bad judgment, such as being unkind. Or else they try to avoid the present moment entirely. Now you've learned your mind can experience the present moment. But also your mind can be deceptive and try to avoid the present moment and create drama without a need to do so.

EXERCISE 2: Discover a pattern in your thinking

(Read this first then do the exercise). Watch the flow of your thinking. I'd like you to take 30 seconds and try to observe your mind in action and how it works. When you're done, move on to the next paragraph. Here are some tips. Do your thoughts flow like traffic down a highway, mostly straight? Does it flow like water down a stream, meandering? Does it stay still like a rock? Does it make frantic movements like a lost puppy? Does it move back and forth like your eyes reading these sentences? Is it stubborn and refuses to change? Take 30 seconds to see if you can spot a pattern. For the sake of the exercise, you can focus on the shape of the leaf in the following illustration (the leaf of life goals), but let your mind wander to the use of words and then observe the words. If that doesn't work, you can close your eyes and just watch the flow of words and observe what you see (figuratively speaking). (OK, now do the exercise for roughly a minute).

Welcome back. What did you learn? Maybe you have new insights into how your mind works. What is the nature of the flow of your thinking? What pushes it? What pulls it? What draws it in? How do your thoughts affect your emotions? How do your sensory experiences affect your thoughts and feelings? Is there a repeating pattern to the thoughts? Examples might be feeling good about yourself for a reason, or feeling poorly about yourself for a reason that is related to other people and how you imagine they think about you. If this kind of thought keeps coming back, again and again, take note of that. This is a dynamic: a repeating pattern of behavior. Your thoughts might have a predictable pattern to them. Knowing that could be a valuable insight in your personality. Self knowledge is a good thing.

Notice how much (or how little) you can answer these questions. This is your starting point for being able to see your mind in action. Some people have little to say here, others can say a lot. There is no one right approach. No one is being graded here. You just want to establish what kind of self-knowledge you are starting with. Now you can gauge your progress since you know your starting point.

Your experience here teaches you where you're at with your own ability to observe and self-guide your own learning. It's the "Lone Ranger Method." How good is it? That's for you to decide. You of course can always share with others what you are learning here. That can ramp up your insight and learning, for sure. But, as to meditation's strengths or weaknesses, make sure you make some observations. Everything has its limitations including meditation.

EXERCISE 3: **Watch the wandering mind**

Now let's give your brain a task. Does your brain like to have a task? Let's test it and see. You can observe the results. Let's give it one task with one of your five senses, sight. Look at the book in your hands without reading. Or if you're looking at this book on a device, look at the screen for 30 seconds, and observe what happens with your thoughts, emotions, and actions—how they wander and where they wander to. When you're done move on to the next paragraph.

What did you observe? With one task, was your mind more focused or less focused on a certain thing? We're using one of your senses in an unfocused manner. It is unfocused because I just gave a general direction to look at the book or screen, not any certain part or aspect of the book or screen. This gave your mind more opportunity to wander, so to speak. Let's see what happens when we direct your senses to gather information in an organized and focused manner.

EXERCISE 4: **Focused use of the senses**

In this exercise, look at the outline of this shape.

FIGURE 1.4.1 Leaf of life goals. By Esther Phingmoo.

Study the outline in a focused manner. Notice how your mind might wander: is it more or less than when you used your vision in an unfocused manner?

EXERCISE 5: **Focused use of two streams of information**

With myriad connections, your brain is wired to process information. Now I'd like you to focus your sensory information processing in two ways: study a repeating shape in your visual field, and study the many shades of a color in that shape. Study the shape of the leaf in the following illustration and the shades of green in that leaf. Just study those two things: the shape and the shades of just the color green.

FIGURE 1.4.2 How positivity naturally grows. By Esther Phingmoo.

Notice if your mind wanders less or more than it did in exercise 4.

EXERCISE 6: **Focused information processing on three levels**

(Read this before doing the exercise). All these exercises might make you weary, I know! But you are now learning by observing. You are learning about your wonderful self! You are the source of information you are learning from these exercises. That is a game changer. It boosts your ability to be independent and self-reliant. Of course it is good to check with other people about your observations so you don't go "off the rails" with an unreasonable observation.

You have many senses. Pick another one you like and do that in a focused manner, in addition to studying shapes and shades of a color. For example, for temperature sense, notice the change of temperature in your nose or mouth as you breathe in and out. For sense of touch, notice how your back feels against a chair. For practical purposes, pick a stream of sensory information that has a lot of information because it is changing from one moment to the next. Avoid things if possible that have words. Words open the door for going off on tangents. You might put on some music but use instrumental music for the purposes of this exercise. (Now do the exercise for one minute).

Welcome back. Were you able to do three things at once? Some can; some can't. There is no "right answer." Did your mind wander less as you gave it more to do? With three tasks to do at once, is your mind more obedient? More peaceful? More self-controlled? You are learning to use descriptive words to paint a picture of the amazing flow of thoughts from your mind. Amazing!

EXERCISE 7: **Focused information processing on three levels without words**

(Read this first. Then do the exercise). You have been noticing how much your mind wanders. You have been noticing how much information you process. The more you notice, the more

powerful this tool can become. For this exercise, you want to avoid using words. If your mind wanders into using words, notice that, and don't reject it or get angry, just refocus your thinking onto the task at hand: focusing on three things at one time (that don't involve words).

If words came into your mind, did your mind give up on one of the three tasks you gave it? If that does happen, is that what you wanted? If it wasn't what you wanted, now you are observing "the wandering mind." That is the tendency of our mind to wander from an appointed task. It's neither right or wrong. It just is. But you can still train it. (Now do the exercise).

Welcome back. With three items of focus, did your mind wander less after you noticed you didn't want to use words? Do you see a trend with these exercises so far in what you can do to experience more self-control over your mind?

EXERCISE 8: **Focusing on the flow of words**

(Read this first, then do the exercise). For the next exercise, we'll focus on words. I want you to focus on the words that happen to flow in your mind. You might visualize them like leaves floating down a river, watching them as they come and go. Maybe they are like dust particles floating at random. Or perhaps they are like typed words flowing across a page. See what pattern best describes them. See what happens as you watch them. Watch your thoughts for 30 seconds. (Now do the exercise).

How did that go? What were you noticing about how much your mind moved with those thoughts and where they went? Left to their own sensibility, our thoughts might drift to the past or the future. They might drift to what you imagine other people are thinking. There might be a pattern of resentment and misgiving, or gratefulness and tranquility, or you might feel upset, anxious, nervous, worried. Whatever the pattern, these words are telling a tale about the flow of thoughts from your mind. You can work with them, cherish them, love them and adore them. You can be their best friend. How you respond to the flow of words will affect the flow of words.

Notice the emotions as they come up. What would be a metaphor in nature for how they act? Do they come out suddenly like the sun poking out from behind a cloud? Do they well up like a spring of water? Do they come crashing like water over a waterfall? Do they simply meander slowly like a stream? Are they stagnant like a swamp? You're learning to see the ebb and flow of your emotions and thoughts. You're learning about yourself. That is a wonderful and enriching thing to do.

EXERCISE 9: **Observing the deceptive mind**

Often people are stressed out because they are caught off guard by the mind's deceptiveness. They plan to eat healthy then buy processed food at the grocery store and blame themselves for eating junk (instead of blaming their shopping habits). This allows them to keep up their mistakes in shopping—which keeps them overweight. Self-deception.

Or they relapse with drinking. They drink after believing the thought that "it will just be one drink." And they know one drink for them leads to 10 drinks and lots of trouble, like blacking out. Or they say they love someone but ignore issues that basically make the person unattractive to them. (Like a person's temper tantrums when they don't get their way). They deceive themselves by saying to themselves, "we'll fix it later," even though they know this is a deal breaker in the relationship—and the other person doesn't want to be fixed. Self deception is such a big issue. It is a pattern of behavior of denying consequences of one's actions or refusing to take responsibility for one's actions (and perhaps blaming your actions on someone else).

In this exercise we will focus on doing two things with your senses and then see if your mind tries to deceive you by doing something else! Look at this book (or smart phone or tablet) in your hand and notice the shape. Notice the shape and the shades of a color in that shape. Do that for 30 seconds. (Now do the exercise).

How did that go? With two things to hold your attention did you have better concentration than with just one item to focus on? Did your mind wander from the task? If your mind was better focused, did it eventually wander? If so, were you able to bring it back to the focus of the exercise?

(Now repeat the exercise for one minute and two minutes)
Did your mind wander more with a longer exercise? When your mind wandered, did you notice a tendency of the mind to reject responsibility and blame it on "this is a longer exercise"? Or, "outside things are distracting me"?

➤**DISCUSSION:** With these exercises, you are learning how your mind behaves. Does it embrace responsibility for a period of time, then avoid it? This might be a subtle sign of a deceptive thinking pattern. Not to worry. It is just part of human nature. But now that you can observe it, you are less likely to be tricked by it. And we all get tricked by it! A great mark of maturity is to be able to catch our mind when it is fooling us and then reject the deception. Such as, "Oh! I was tempted to think smoking one cigarette wouldn't lead to more! What a deceptive story." Often sharing a story of this kind of self-deception with a good friend will deepen the friendship—and weaken the tendency of self-deception. It is almost like the mind doesn't try to get away with things if it knows it is being watched. And it is even less deceptive if it knows it is under the scrutiny of other people.

Self-deception in the dating world is dealt with in "The Evolution Of Desire," by David Buss. He says self-deception is a frequent cause of relationship problems. Time to deal with it! Support groups are a great way to deal with self-deception in dating and all kinds of other human endeavors. This is one reason support groups have become popular all over the world. They help you catch your own self-deception.

Support groups are also especially helpful in addictions. Witness the popularity of Alcoholics Anonymous and Weight Watchers. If you are struggling with an addiction, consider using a support group but also process what you learn with your therapist. Some support groups themselves get caught up in a deception so you have to stay on your toes. Always work with your therapist.

By now, you are also seeing how your thoughts respond to you observing them. You are seeing how your mind responds to certain tasks focused on perceiving information from your senses. This kind of knowledge of "knowing how my mind works" can help you better face stressful situations. Like asking difficult questions in a relationship or asking your boss difficult questions about what it will take to get that promotion or raise. Knowing your weaknesses, such as avoiding approaching people or fear of rejection, can help you strengthen those skills so you can have more success in life.

Congratulations on completing 9 exercises for deeper insight into the mind. You've learned to teach yourself by observing. Much more can be learned from teachers in meditation. I wish you the best on your journey of learning.

JOURNAL YOUR LEARNING HERE:

FIGURE 1.5.0
The world is high value. Realizing your high value involves seeing the great value of the world to sustain life. Pessimists can't see the value in the world because they are so self absorbed in neurotic obsessions about problems. By Toso Borkovic.

5

How to become "high value" for yourself

Feeling my value in the world

"Life is an event that occurs over a semi-permeable membrane," said my professor. I was in my first year of medical school and the lecture was on physiology, the study of the flow of chemical processes in the body. We were studying how surprising life is. Life involves the flow of electricity across the coverings of cells in the body. Electricity flows from inside a cell to the outside and vice versa. Electricity also flows in pulsating waves down nerves—dozens or hundreds of feet per second. That's how your brain works. Electricity also flows outward from a group of cells in the heart and then the heart beats. That is how the heart works. Every cell has a flow of electricity in it to sustain the life of that cell. That is how life works.

I was so amazed. We were looking at the microscopic building blocks of human life—and of all life. These facts were true of every living thing. Electricity was flowing across a membrane because there were very small gates with doors that let chemicals like sodium and potassium in and out of the cell in a very precise manner. When these chemicals shot through the gates they left an electrical charge on the outside of the cell.

It turns out the covering of our cells is an amazing machine unto itself.

Life is an electrochemical event

"What is life?" the professor asked rhetorically. "Life is actually an electrochemical event occurring over a semipermeable membrane." Semipermeable means the covering of the cell selectively allows only certain molecules to enter the cell but not others. Here I saw a principle of how life sustains itself. Living things are very selective about what it allows in them. Living things have to select out certain things to keep life going. In this I saw a metaphor for positivity. In a positive attitude you are quite choosey about what you believe and don't believe. You want to reject the false perceptions of pessimism, for instance, in order to preserve the life sustaining attitude of positivity.

When electrochemical events stop, the professor said, life stops. When these events are damaged you have a disease. Like multiple sclerosis or heart disease or strokes.

Suddenly the professor brought out a large jar with an object in it. He put a plastic glove on and pulled it out. It was half of a human brain. "Who knows where this came from?" Silence. "A human?" offered a medical student. "No," said the professor. "It came from an attorney!" And he motioned across the street towards the law school. The law school had recently beat us in a football game so we were still pretty sore about that. The room roared with laughter.

"Remember how you were tortured in your chemistry classes?" the professor said. "Remember all those different atoms in the Table of Periodic Elements? Well, properties in some of those elements are critical for sustaining life. The unique properties of sodium allow the electricity to flow down the nerve when sodium flows in and out of openings in the nerve membrane—hundreds of times per second."

Something clicked in my head.

Value.

The unique properties of sodium had value. Cells could use it to sustain life. Sodium, the same sodium in your table salt, has properties that allow cells to use it to sustain life.

Because of the value of sodium, cells could live. Too much or too little sodium and the fragile thread of life suffered. There was a happy middle range of sodium concentration that cells needed for life. One concentration was good inside the cells, another concentration was good outside. It was a delicate balance. Too much sodium outside cells spelled trouble for the body.

"As physicians," the professor continued, "you'll be checking blood tests to see if sodium is too low or too high—if blood levels are out of balance that means there might be a disease process at work in the body."

Later in the lecture, he elaborated on many other chemicals in the body, including potassium, magnesium and calcium. They all had properties that living things used to sustain life. They had value for life.

Life is so fragile and so precious. Life hangs in the balance of these atoms surging in and out of the cell hundreds of times per second. After seeing my dad battle back from a brain tumor and a heart attack I knew firsthand how fragile life is. Life is so easily lost. But the properties of these chemicals help sustain it.

I raised my hand. "How do these chemicals sustain life— what are they actually doing?"

"Sodium and potassium have charges on them," he replied. "It's all about electrons. These atoms accept or donate electrons."

"Where do they go?" I asked. He acted a little frustrated with my question. I was persistent. "It's a little off topic," he said. "But remember all those cycles that occur in the membranes?" he asked rhetorically. I nodded. "Like the Kreb's cycle," I replied. "Yes," he replied. "An electron is flowing in all those cycles from one step to the next. If there's no electron, the cycle doesn't work and life stops." I nodded again. He went on with his lecture.

After class, at lunch, I grabbed a sandwich out of a brown bag. All these chemicals I thought were just random things produced in a random universe—actually had meaning. They sustained life. And life was the most amazing production in the universe.

After class, I walked out on the steps outside the lecture hall and sat down. I remembered back to working in Southern California. I'd felt so useless. That was because I didn't have a value for others that I wanted to. Now with this knowledge from these lectures I had come to see there was so much value in the world. Soon enough I'd learn ways to apply this knowledge to help people and my own value would increase.

Feeling the value of myself

I walked several blocks towards my car, cutting under the large cottonwood trees that bordered the old brick lecture halls on campus. Ahead I saw a familiar figure. He was older. He had long gray hair that fell over an overcoat that draped down to his knees. He was overweight with a slightly shuffling gait. I walked closer and saw a familiar face. It was my old philosophy professor Ben King. I hadn't seen him in five years.

"What are you doing back here?" he asked with a smile. "Good to see you." I looked to him as the Socrates on campus. He was an advisor for us in the Honors Program and he always showed up if we were having a meeting to protest something. He was like a father figure.

"Well," I said, studying his face. "I applied to medical school and I got in!" He couldn't hide his disappointment. He studied me and then the ground I was standing on. "Well, whatever you do," he advised, "when an authority says this is the way it is, ask 'Is it so?'" I smiled. "Will do," I replied. "There's a lot of authority figures in medical school!" This was classic Professor King. I wished him a good day and continued my walk.

With that he strode down the sidewalk one way and I went the other. He taught us to be skeptics in his lectures in philosophy. Now I wondered how that would be used in medicine. I mean, doctors are notorious for being skeptical about things. But what would that look like? And how did doctors come to believe in something? Some skeptics doubted everything and ended up bitter and hopeless. Was that how doctors ended up? Was that where I was headed?

How doctors doubt and believe

I had to wait for a year until my private question about how doctors doubt and believe would get answered. In the first year of medical school you learn how life works in the body. You study body chemistry, anatomy, genetics and the list goes on (and so do the tests). Nearly every month there was a marathon day of tests—6 hours or more—then back for more lectures the next week. There is almost no catching up if you fall behind. There is a tremendous volume of information coming at you every day like a wide-open fire hose. You simply must throw away everything in your life and do whatever it takes to keep up.

In the second year you get to learn how life falls apart. How disease unravels the fragile thread of life. How those electrons don't quite flow how they are supposed to. Then you get diseases of every sort, high blood pressure, obesity, heart disease, depression, etc.

In this year we get a look for the first time at how physicians use all this information. Before, it was just lectures. We wanted some "hands on" demonstration of how one uses all this information—with a real, live patient.

Medical school training was like looking at the outside of a jar labelled "how to be a doctor." I wanted to get in the jar and look at the inside view of the label—and see how doctors do what they do. I wanted to know how they think. I was still dealing with the scorching of my emotions back in California with my career crisis. Then I understood the system in America was ruining the environment. I saw all kinds of facts to back that up. Would the medical system be no different?

I was in a life transition. I wanted to make myself valuable for others to fight diseases. My life once was consumed with environmental and social justice issues. Now my life was enlarging to include other things, like a deep appreciation for the awe-inspiring intricacies of life. All those tiny moving parts articulated together to sustain life. I was developing an ability to put that information together to help people.

"There will be a demonstration of a physical exam this afternoon with Dr. Jorgenson," we were told. (Dr. Jorgenson's name is fictitious). We shuffled into a clinical office and met a kindly old family doctor with a mop of gray hair and a white coat. "The patient I'll examine today," he began, "is not real. She is an actress, let's say, but she's very good and this will be representative of exams you will be doing later on."

The woman came into the room. She was a modestly dressed and looked about 35. In the interview she revealed she had a cough that wouldn't go away. She worked as a prostitute. She coughed up some clear phlegm from her throat but no color in the sputum.

In all, Dr. Jorgenson interviewed her for 15 minutes, then did an exam. Her listened with a stethoscope to her lungs and heart. He thumped on her back and watched her legs twitch when he tapped her knees with a reflex hammer. To us it all seemed so simple. Then he asked her to go.

He turned to us and started to ask us questions. "Ninety percent of the diagnosis has nothing to do with technology—it is by history," he said. I thought that was odd. Then he asked us if we recalled what she said at different points of the interview.

We mostly said no. Then he reminded us of exactly what she said, how she said it, and her body language.

In a moment it dawned on us he had a photographic memory. That was a little scary.

Then he asked us what we thought her diagnosis was based on the exam. We guessed at a cold or sinus infection. He asked us what labs we would order.

Now we were looking at those chemicals and molecules we got lectures on in the first year of medical school. That was interesting, I thought.

I still wanted to get a look at the inside of the mind of a doctor. How did it work?

A smart ass in the class then asked the professor a question. "What do you think is the diagnosis?" I was still thinking about how he had a photographic memory of the history and the exam.

"You don't start by picking one conclusion; you start by gathering information," he said. "You create a number of possible diagnoses—at least 2 or 3. Can you guess why?"

"So you don't miss something," came a reply from the students.

"Exactly right," he replied. "When you miss something you become a doctor who betrays the trust the patient puts in you. Not good."

"She came in complaining of a cough. She is a prostitute. The cough could be from..." he gestured to the crowd of 50 students. "Sexual activity," said the smartass in the back of the class. That got a few laughs.

"Yes," said Dr. Jorgenson. "And what else?"

Silence. "A sexually transmitted disease."

"Yes," Dr. Jorgenson said, "Chlamydia can cause that. So let's test for Chlamydia. We'll also check for HIV. Did you notice how pale her skin was? We'll order a complete blood test. She might have anemia. Did you see the fine tremor in her hands? We'll check her vitamin B12 level. She might have a poor diet. Did you notice the strained voice she talked with? She's under a lot of stress. Prostitutes can live a dangerous life and are often victims of assault and deal with periods of poverty and depression. Now let's look at the differential diagnosis, the list of possible causes of her cough." He wrote a dozen items on the list.

All this was overwhelming to me. It was a lot of information but I was finally learning how a doctor thinks.

"The blood tests come back," Dr. Jorgenson said. "Now you tell me what you'd do. The complete blood cell count comes back with mild anemia."

"Give her a multivitamin with iron," said one student.

"Another test showed high sodium but all the other blood chemistries were normal." Silence. "That means some of the red blood cells broke and you might have a false positive for high sodium. Now what would you do?"

"Redraw the blood sample," another student said.

"Yes," said the doctor.

"All the other tests were normal but the B12 was low. Now what?"

"Prescribe a B12 supplement," offered a student in the front.

"OK," said the doctor. "But why is she low on B12?" Silence. "She might not be eating well or she might have a stomach ulcer or she might be vegetarian and not eating enough beans. If you don't figure out what is going on, you haven't really helped her. On a followup visit you can remind her to deal with the potential cause of the B 12 deficiency by improving her diet."

He paused.

"Her strained voice might be from depression," he said. "If she's depressed then what do you do?" Silence. "That's where you refer her to a counsellor and maybe a psychiatrist." He paused again and studied our faces. "There are high rates of depression and suicide among prostitutes. If she has depression and you catch it, then she might actually take the pills you prescribe. If her mood gets better she might care about her life again. Care enough to quit being a prostitute. That might save her life."

Another pause.

"Don't latch onto the first thing that comes to mind, when a patient comes in," he said. "It's usually wrong or half wrong. Don't force your information to fit one diagnosis, one theory, one explanation. That kind of narrow-minded thinking isn't helpful. You are going to miss things. You are going to go down rabbit holes thinking there is just one diagnosis, one problem, and you are going to ignore information to the contrary. Does that happen to us as physicians? Yes. But we should have a broad differential diagnosis when we meet a patient. By that I mean a longer list of potential diagnosis that we can analyze, one by one. We should challenge each diagnoses and look for, seek out, information that proves it right or wrong."

Pause. "So you gather your information and then see what single diagnosis—or multiple diagnosis—fit with the facts. You have to keep all the information in mind from the history and physical and labs to see how it best supports a certain diagnosis." That sounded overwhelming.

"Now you are becoming a clinician that people can trust," he said. "This is rigorous thinking, critical thinking. You come up with one theory after another in your mind and test them. You look at the supporting information and the conflicting information. You are constantly checking and rechecking on what the one or more diagnoses might be. You are flexible. You are willing to change your diagnosis as the facts direct."

A student raised his hand. "Yes," said the doctor.

"How do you deal with what you're not sure about. There's maybe a lot of possible diagnoses with any patient."

"Good question," replied the doctor. "There's no such thing as a stupid question, by the way. We have a saying in medicine, when you hear hoofbeats, think horses, not zebras." The students laughed.

"With experience you will find what the most common diagnosis is for each kind of presenting complaint. With your experience and critical thinking skills, you will come up with alternative explanations and rule them out with every patient visit. You really want to be considering and then ruling out a couple diagnoses for each diagnosis you rule in. That keeps your thinking sharp." The student gave a "thumbs up" to show his understanding.

The doctor then answered several more questions. The workshop was now two hours long and my fellow students looked tired. The doctor then ended the lesson and we left the building.

The doctor was all about being positive. Focus on people's strengths. Lift them up. But also be skeptical in your thinking process. It wasn't so much pessimism, which doubts people's abilities to overcome, as skepticism. Question the alleged truth of some knowledge. Don't take anything at face value. This gave him his clinical sharpness. He had what he called an "index of suspicion" about everything. Because everything could be wrong: blood tests might get mixed up with other patient's tests. Patients might lie or forget things. A technical error with a machine might lead an X-ray to miss something. It didn't matter. The doctor was ultimately responsible for the process working. He had to be alert to all the potential errors or mistakes in the process. No excuses for the doctor. I liked the "take charge and no excuses" attitude the doctor had. He also had an easy-going confidence about him that I admired.

Feeling my critical thinking working

"Hospital day is today," said my classmate Barry, smiling. "Should be good." Who gets excited to get into a hospital? A third-year medical student, that's who. The hospital is the inner sanctum, the place where big decisions are made in a moment. Lives are saved or lost. It is the incubator where medical students turn into more of the doctor they want to be, a place of metamorphosis. We were in a cocoon our first two years of medical school, mostly getting a lot of book learning. In the hospital, we would put that knowledge into practice. We would start to fight diseases. The hard shell holding us back would start to crack.

I saw the bigger picture. It was all about value. We were becoming more valuable to people in their greatest hours of need. Like when my Dad had a heart attack, and earlier when he had a brain tumor operation. And when I was in grade school and my Mom overdosed on something. My brother and I lived with neighbors. Then Mom came home. She was OK. We had a mom again. It felt so good to have Mom and a home. But behind it all were the doctors and nurses that raised my parents back to health. Here in the hospital I would get a glimpse of that high-power decision making that heals people. Of course, all these thoughts of mine were private.

The big question in my mind was how do doctors think? That was where their value comes in. They somehow know how to diagnose and treat. Say the right thing or at least do the right thing. Use all this artillery of medication and technology to peer into the working parts of our bodies to ferret out what is wrong and fix it.

A high value world

Barry and I strolled down a hallway in our short white coats. A name badge identified me as "Medical Student/UND School of Medicine." Our supervisor motioned us into a back room. "We're meeting," he said. "Shhh." Barry and I sat down behind four doctors in white coats.

"I have a 55-year-old male, two days post MI, stent, but not recovering," said one white coat. He mentioned some numbers, then "suggestions?"

"Maybe angiography," said one white coat.

"His kidneys are not good."

"Then cardiac echo, look for any change."

"Right."

"I have a 78-year-old female, 2 days post appendectomy. Sharp pain in lower right quadrant, " spoke another white coat. "One centimeter mass in the abdomen on CT today. It wasn't there before surgery. Scope or surgery?"

"I'd wait, recheck ultrasound in a day."

"Then what?"

"Scope it if it's growing; watch her if it's shrinking."

"OK."

Another white coat spoke. "Got an 82-year-old admitted on a fall, concussion, now not eating, depressed, nobody visiting him, not getting out of bed." Silence.

"Exam?"

"Normal."

"Psych?"

"Depressed. Prozac didn't help for three weeks."

"Heart?"

"Fine."

"Addictions?"

"None."

"Labs?"

"Fine."

"Try Ritalin and have physical therapist show up an hour later. Push fluids and protein shakes."

"Prozac upset his stomach."

"Oh, then desipramine 25 mg in the am, just watch his blood pressure and make sure his gait is steady all morning." Silence.

"Recheck his EKG in one day and desipramine blood level in four days."

"OK."

"Is he a Veteran?"

"Yes."

"Have someone visit him from a Veteran's support group."

It was all about the facts and what works. So impressive, I thought. They were pushing for change, but pessimistic about potential side effects. Positive all the time; pessimistic all the time—to guard against bad outcomes. Factual all the time. Reciting just the pertinent lab results. Careful. Plotting routes of treatment. Confident about what they knew and what they didn't know. Confident to ask for help. Confident they'd get it. Confident they'd act on it. How did they learn all this? I guessed that one day I'd find out.

It was all about calculating chances to help someone get better and prevent them from getting worse.

A white coat glanced at our supervisor. "Ok." We were motioned to leave.

I thought back to the rapid-fire discussion in the "morning rounds." It was so high value. It was about six doctors— resident doctors in training—putting their heads together to find the best plan for the best outcome for the patient. There was an open look at labs, history and physical exams. There was an open examination of the diagnosis and treatment plan. Did everything line up and make sense? Did the treatment need to be adjusted for a better outcome? Was a diagnosis missed? All these ducks were put in a row for the best treatment possible.

I found this method so refreshing. Unlike many of my college classes, there was an open investigation here. The commitment was to the truth. What are the facts in the exam? How is the patient doing? What are the facts with labs that back up the assessment? There was an objective reality here and the doctors were dealing with it. They were accountable to the patient and to each other. They didn't seem to get emotionally attached to anything. They were willing to change their beliefs in light of any new facts. They were willing to change their perception in light of another's perception—based on that person's expertise. They were, in every sense of the phrase, "high value."

High value thinking skills

I especially liked what I didn't see. No doctor was "grinding an axe" favoring his pet diagnosis. The diagnosis had to fit the facts. Doctors were willing to change the diagnosis if a different one fit better with the facts. This attitude was so refreshing. All these components had to "fit" the facts and make sense to the doctors:

- History
- "Pertinent positives" in physical exam
- "Pertinent positives" in labs
- Differential diagnosis (the several most likely problems to explain the presenting problem)
- Diagnosis
- Treatment plan
- Discharge plan

"It all seems so overwhelming to figure out!" I told Mark, a fellow student.

"One step ahead of you," he replied. "Remember my friend, Reggie?" I shook my head. "Yeah," he said, "we visited him at his little apartment where he was studying for his national board finals." A vague image came to mind. I nodded. "He passed his national boards! Isn't that great?" "Awesome," I replied. Reggie was a Native American fellow, tall, athletic and brimming with confidence. I remembered him sitting at his little desk in his one room apartment next to a stack of notes three feet high. They seemed so out of place leaning against the corner of the wall next to his desk. They were in a corner, Reggie said, so they didn't fall over.

"Why are you keeping all those notes?" I had asked.

"I have them memorized," Reggie had said with a wry smile. "I'm just taking practice exams to lock in what I know I know. If I get something wrong I look up the right answer in the notes." The stack of notes was three feet high. Memorize them? That didn't sound humanly possible. But he passed his boards. The rascal had those notes memorized after all. I felt like I was a spectator in the company of academic Olympians.

"Reggie gave me tips on how to memorize the information in those presentations we saw today," Mark blurted out. "You write out the 6 or 8 basic parts on a recipe card and read them out loud, then try to remember them without looking at the card."

"And then what?" I asked.

"Well, then you know the formula for the presentation. You basically memorize the lecture so you can give it. This is how we will talk to other doctors the rest of our lives so it's good to know," Mark said. "Reggie said on hospital rounds we are supposed to read the doctors like a book, see how they do what they do. Our task is to talk like they talk, act like they act, think like they think."

"I'm not much into copycat stuff," I replied.

"This isn't that," Mark replied. "We are learning how to practice medicine. It's a way of thinking." Something clicked in my mind. This was at the heart of the value of what doctors had to offer: their critical thinking. They criticized everything they were thinking and doing and what others were thinking and doing, in a relentless effort to get at the truth of what was going on with a patient. It was fast and furious.

High value conversations in a high value world

I wrote some words on a recipe card that night and got to memorizing them. The next day, recipe card in my pocket, I shadowed a doctor in the hospital. Sure enough, she talked in that formula to quickly get at whatever she was asking another doctor.

"I have an 83-year-old with a urinary tract infection, mild renal failure, hallucinating. Normal liver labs. What do you recommend?"

"I have a 78-year-old with an MI recovering but chest pain persisting. Normal chest X-ray, CT, EKG no change. Has Afib. Recommendations?"

On a lunch break, I flopped down on an old sofa. Opened up my brown bag lunch. Fished out a turkey sandwich. Opened up a medical textbook. Looked up some concepts the doctors had referred to. I still had no idea of how to think like a doctor or talk like a doctor, as Mark had talked about. I was lost. Oh well. I would get found some day, I decided. But I thought back to my past. In just a few years I'd changed so much from that cocksure journalist I'd been. And then there was that day that changed my life.

Recalling the pivotal moment that changed my life

I was so different then. First, when I was called to the scene of a story, I already had my idea of what was going on. Someone was being exploited or there was a tragedy that would pull on people's heart strings. Maybe there was a wrong that needed to be corrected. Whatever the case I would get the story. I would interview someone just long enough to get the facts that fit my story. Write a short story about 10 column inches, about a two-minute read. Then stop. A good hook in the first line. Then a good wrap up line at the end. And I was done.

I could go anywhere and write a story with that formula. Also I knew with freedom of the press I had my rights. It practically made us quite protected so we could say the most dramatic things. As long as you stayed on public property—you were not trespassing on private property—you could write whatever you wanted. The world was a tiger and you had it by the tail.

Then came that pivotal day. I was working in the office in south Orange County, California and got a call from the main office. "There's been a shooting," said a voice, "here's the address. Check it out. Get a story to us by noon." It was 8:00 am. I hustled over to the address. It was in a sleepy residential neighborhood. I saw a house wrapped in yellow tape.

Knowing my rights, I got my camera, stuffed some paper and a pen in my pocket. I walked back and forth on the sidewalk in front of the house waiting for something to happen. A few minutes later the front door at the house opened. An officer emerged. Then an elderly man walked out. I took a picture. The man locked eyes with mine and came at me like a junkyard dog.

"What are you doing?" he hissed at me. His face was red. His eyes looked bloodshot. "I'm from the paper," I replied calmly. "I have a right to be here. I'm on the sidewalk." "I suppose you are going to put that picture you took in the paper too," he barked at me. "I don't know," I replied. "What is going on here? Was there a robbery?"

"That's my wife in there," he said, pointing back at the house and the policeman who was keeping an eye on me. "She had cancer. She just shot herself. Now are you happy? Are you going to put that in the paper for all my neighbors to see?"

The guy looked like my dad. Tall, lanky, with bushy expressive eyebrows and a square jaw. I was in shock. I said the first thing that came to mind.

"Sir, if you don't want it in, it won't go in," I replied. He looked me in the eyes and stalked back to the cop. I walked back to my car. My job was done. I drove back to the office. I called the main office and told them what I learned. They said skip the story. They don't write about suicides. It's against the newspaper's policy. "Come on by the main office about 5. The boss would just like to chat with you. You did good," a voice told me.

At the end of the day, I pulled my car up to a sleek office building with steel and glass shimmering in the California sun. I walked in and a secretary showed me to the office where I had been hired a few months before. My boss smiled and shook my hand. He showed me a chair. I sat down.

"Rough day?" he asked. I shrugged. He empathized with me. It was my first time at the scene of a shooting death. He was trying to show his support for me, he emphasized. I said I appreciated that. But next time, he said, don't tell people what will or won't get printed in the newspaper. That is the editor's call, he emphasized. That's how things work. That made sense to me, I said. He repeated I did a good job, just no story for today which is ok. I nodded. I stood up. I shook his hand. I walked back to my car.

Driving home in bumper-to-bumper traffic, it hit me. This career made me an enemy to some people. Like the man who lost his wife today. Something deep inside me wanted to help him. In the past I hadn't wanted to get involved in people's difficulties like this. I'd changed. Now I wanted to get involved. I'd matured. I'd also failed. Here, after six years of college and two years in a new career—eight years in all of hard work—I once again failed to find a career fit. I'd failed again.

Hot tears ran down my face as I drove down Interstate 5. Failure again! Then and there I vowed to take all that energy from anger at myself and direct it in a useful way in a career search. This would be my new life mission.

Confirming moments

Looking back at that history, I understood I could have gone into journalism focused on medicine or health sciences. But I wanted to be directly involved in people's care. Or so I thought. Sometimes a career looks one way from the outside, and another when you are "inside the jar" and looking at the "inside of the labels." I was doing that now. Learning to walk and talk like a doctor felt so good, so exciting and I embraced all the challenges. These doctors were really dealing with the facts of the real world, fighting diseases and human suffering, making the call about what the treatment team should do.

I loved that it was facts first, then make a treatment plan. In my former life in the media, I had to pick the facts that made the story interesting and leave out the rest. Facts came second. The interesting story came first. It felt so good to be in a facts-first career where critical thinking was highly valued.

Feeling emotionally stronger

There are many limiting beliefs that are part of our culture. They are a given. They keep some people "marginalized," stuck on the sidelines of life, with lower incomes and unable to pursue their dreams because of poverty or discrimination. I felt myself sinking into that after I realized a career as a news writer was not for me. What else could I do? I discovered a passion for medical science but felt hopeless to pursue it—because of my limiting beliefs:

- I lacked intelligence
- I lacked finances
- I lacked will power

Wonder sentences

A great way to challenge limiting beliefs is to use wonder in a sentence. "I wonder what it would be like if I expanded my intelligence." I imagined reading all kinds of medical science articles as a doctor and somehow putting them into practice. It felt good. After a while it felt possible. I imagined being surrounded by medical students who had the willpower of lions. I imagined what that would like to have that willpower. Soon I felt my willpower growing.

I understood I could improve my IQ as an adult. The same with finances, willpower and anything else I needed to become a doctor. I had a sense that rigorous exercise and mental hygiene habits could transform me.

More confirming moments

One thing I knew for sure: the Lone Ranger approach didn't work. There was power in a team approach. I first needed more information about what a career in medicine was like and if it was even possible for me to get into it. I spoke with a Dr. William Sears whom I'd interviewed for an article. He invited me to his home! I met him there with his wife and ten children. I only had a few minutes. I asked if a career in medicine was possible for me. He said yes, with my 3.6 GPA in high school and college, I had the academic skill. I just needed to work very hard. I said I could do that and thanked him for his time. He and his wife had authored many books on parenting and childcare. I was amazed by his life's work.

Then I talked to a physician friend in North Dakota, and he said the same thing about my potential. A high school friend now in medical school, Brian, confirmed what the others had said: it was possible. I read several books on what a medical career was like, and they confirmed my beliefs: a career change into medicine was possible for me. The question now was, did I want to take the risk?

Pivotal moments

What I needed was a new brain. One that wasn't afraid of change but embraced it every day. One that charged hard in the direction of my dreams. One that was sharper, with a better memory, better focus. One that had more mental toughness.

I looked hard at my daily experience. I could feel my memory improve after I was jogging regularly, say half an hour three or four times per week. I would up that.

I turned in my resignation to the main office of the newspaper and moved back to North Dakota There I had the best chance of getting into a medical school—I was still a resident of North Dakota. I planned to live paycheck-to-paycheck in a basement room, doing whatever it took to reach my goal of getting into medical school. I decided to make everything in my life focused on what it would take for this new career.

I moved to Grand Forks, North Dakota, which is where the medical school was. I believed I would make friends there somehow. I believed I could learn what it took to get in. I got a menial job as a baker in a pastry shop. I made friends wherever I went. An old friend, Rob, told me of a friend of his who worked in a microbiology lab before he got into medical school. I called him and he said Dr. John Andrews had been great to work with.

I met Dr. Andrews twice and both times he didn't have a job for me. The country was in a recession and jobs were hard to come by. But he was fun to talk to. We both enjoyed camping and fishing. We traded stories. He said I should come back in a few months and see if there was an opening. That seemed like an eternity.

I read some documents he had written. I read everything I could find about medical schools. I believed I needed a higher IQ so I started jogging hard. I felt that wasn't enough. I recalled seeing a picture of someone jogging with weights in their hands. I read that meditation also increased intelligence.

I started jogging with weights. I found some steel bolts intended to bolt down street lamps and I jogged with them—on bike paths where I wouldn't be seen by as many people. I wanted to save every penny I had so I used those instead of buying weights. When I jogged, I counted 3 steps and then lifted a weight with one hand, then after three more steps I repeated it with the other hand. It was exhilarating. I got an hour's worth of exercise in half the time. When I jogged without weights it felt effortless. I felt I could clearly experience my memory improving with more intense exercise. Project accomplished.

As a baker, I had to get up at 3 am to be at work by 4 am. Then the frozen baguettes and croissants needed to go in the warmer so they could be baked and in the display rack by 9 am. I finished at 1 pm. I took advantage of that time and visited Dr. Andrews again one afternoon.

He was interested in my love of writing. He needed someone to edit a paper for a microbiology journal. I heard myself say, "Yeah, I could help you with that." I hadn't even had a course in microbiology. But my confidence was overflowing. Then he said he had a job for me! It was washing test tubes. I jumped on it. I was in. I was now involved in medical science work of some sort. I could get closer to learning how doctors think.

The commitment

It was fun working for Dr. Andrews. Every day he challenged me to do a little more in the lab. I soon was adding cells to petri dishes where they could grow. After work I read a number of self-help books. The take home message for me was every day do something to increase your value. The world was high value. It gave me opportunities to learn those skills in the lab. However my attitude was still to just get the job done. A low value attitude. I didn't want to be challenged too much to learn all the details of what went into an experiment. I just wanted to get my job done.

However, I needed to improve every day to become high value or I'd never get into medical school. So I made up my mind that every day was a self-improvement project. It would start with washing test tubes with a brush but I'd push myself to learn new things every day.

Dr. Andrews hired me as a part time employee. I still kept working at the bakery. Each day I was proving myself. I came to work on time, got things done by deadlines and showed great attention to detail. He gave me more responsibilities and paid me for more time. Eventually he hired me to work full time. He was having me run experiments. I used a dropper to put human leukemia cells into a Petri dish full of calf serum, the clear liquid that is in calf's blood. In a week, the cells multiplied and filled the dish. He added different chemicals to the Petri dishes to change the DNA of the cells. Cells were spun in a centrifuge and then radioactive tracers on the DNA were counted in a machine. Eventually I did all the work.

But all was not well. I was over my head. I'd never even taken a course in microbiology. One day I was working with a dropper, putting cells into a dish in what was called a "hood." A hood is a glass-enclosed cube with a sterilized interior. My gloved up arms reached into the hood through a narrow opening. Absentmindedly, I used my shoulder to scratch an itch on my face and my hand with the dropper came out of the hood for a second. It was contaminated by fungus spores that normally fill room air. But I thought a second wouldn't matter. I said nothing. It was embarrassing. But I thought my hand being outside the hood for a second wouldn't matter. This was on a Friday.

Monday morning I walked into the lab and I could tell Dr. Andrews was upset about something. "Well let's look at the dishes," he said, tension filling his voice. He opened a door in the warmer cabinet and pulled out a petri dish. He looked in the dish with a microscope and saw small white islands floating on the surface. All the other cells were dead.

"Fungus!" Dr. Andrews hissed. "You contaminated the whole experiment! It's all ruined! Hundreds of dollars of supplies and time! What do you have to say for yourself?" His red face was in my face. I felt some of his spit land on my face.

I was shocked. My first reaction was fear—and to run. I could quit. But I had done that so many times already. Now I was staying put. I knew my value here. This was a setback. I would learn from it. I was new at this science thing. I would make the setback temporary—a learning experience. Dr. Andrews was acting like he wanted to put me in one of those plastic Petri dishes and shove me in the warmer with the rest of the dead leukemia cells.

People mirror the emotions around them. But instead of mirroring his anger by getting angry at myself, I gave him half a smile and took a learning attitude like I imagined a doctor would do. I let him mirror the confidence I had in myself. He didn't. He was still furious.

"I'm sorry," I said. "I obviously did it. But I'm still committed to being the best lab assistant you've ever had. So if you want, I'd love to see every painstaking detail in just exactly how to do this experiment perfectly. I will be 100% committed to getting it done perfectly. If I fail, then ok, you can let me go. But I would like a chance to prove myself."

He backed off. Thought a moment. Nodded his head. "Follow me," he said, and I followed his white coat over to a hard cover notebook. He opened it. "Here are the 60 steps to doing the experiment, from growing the cells, to treating them, to analysis of results." I looked at the notes. I asked if he could explain in detail what each step entailed—for me to do it perfectly. I had no background in college classes showing me these things. He nodded. He showed me how he did the steps. I took my own notes, so there was no room for me to misunderstand what he said.

"We need to be able to run the experiment several times and get the same results," he said. "Repeatable results are what science is all about." I said I understood that meant no "operator error." He nodded. I got busy.

Over the next several months my work improved. I never contaminated an experiment again. There was no more yelling. I helped the doctor get the repeatable results he wanted. "You've learned these procedures as well as anyone," he said finally.

My value extended to helping him write as well. We sat next to a stack of journals he referenced in his article, hammering away at paragraph after paragraph. I edited for grammar and punctuation. I made sure the footnotes were correctly styled. I made sure one paragraph flowed to the next. When he finally sent it off he listed my name as a co-author. Months later he told me the article was accepted in an international microbiology journal. My smile lit up the laboratory. It was, as they say, one of those affirming moments. I was on the right track after all. The next step was to apply to medical school.

Feeling devastated

"Have you seen this letter from Dr. Andrews?" the white-haired woman asked me gravely. She held up an envelope. On each side of her sat half a dozen men and women dressed in suits and dresses. They were the admissions committee for the medical school. They were doctors and nurses who now controlled my destiny: if I would be accepted into medical school or be rejected. It would happen in the next few hours.

"No, I haven't seen it," I replied confidently, adjusting my suit. "I didn't need to." "Did you ask to see it?" she asked intently, studying my face. "Didn't need to," I replied, smiling and looking her in the eyes. I glanced at the others.

She opened the envelope and pulled out a letter so everyone could see it. "I'll read it," she said. "It is from Dr. John Andrews," she began, "Here is Harris Jensen. What you see is what you get." I waited for something else to be read. She looked up from the letter and gave me a second to register what she had read. "What do you think he meant?" she asked.

I was devastated. I gave him two years of my life to work in his lab. In return he gave me two sentences. But part of my new philosophy of positivity was to have a healthy dose of skepticism.

Anticipate setbacks so you are ready for them because they are common. And here was one. I was ready.

"You can look at my resume," I said. "I think it is quite clear what he meant. 'What you see' on the resume is that I worked for him for two years. After graduating with a degree in communications with honors several years earlier, he hired me to wash test tubes. After two years he said I ran experiments in his lab as well as anyone had in ten years." I paused to take a breath. "You can see my university transcript shows no course in microbiology or biochemistry. You can also see on my resume I am listed as a co-author of an article published in the journal 'Biochemistry and Cell Biology' which we wrote together." I paused. I purposely didn't elaborate on the facts. I didn't want to come across needy.

My face was calm. My voice was measured. Here was a chance to demonstrate my character. I felt I'd been insulted. I acted like it didn't happen. I rose above the pettiness of the insult and showed them I had a sharp mind and a thick skin, two qualities they were looking for.

I showed my character. I was confident without neediness or self-importance. I showed I was a man of integrity, the kind of a man you would want as your doctor. The committee asked a few more questions about my background. "I see you were a journalist," one gray haired man said. "You worked two years and now you're here. Why is that?"

I made steady eye contact with him. "I wanted to help people and found I couldn't do that very much as a journalist," I replied. I looked around at the other committee members. "I met a pediatrician and author, Dr. William Sears, and he inspired me. I read several of his books on parenting and childcare." I glanced around at the committee again and paused. "Then I repented of my sins," I announced, lifting my eyebrows. "And here I am." The room burst into laughter.

They asked their last question and excused me. I looked at each committee member's face and smiled half a smile and said, "Thank you for this opportunity." I stepped out the door and walked down the empty hallway. I looked down at my hands and they were shaking.

Several months later I was visiting my sister, Cristy, in Denver, Colorado for Christmas. There was a knock at her door and a man delivered a letter. I opened it. It was from the University of North Dakota School of Medicine. It said I was accepted!

Feeling value in nature

Life is so precious, so rare, so hard to find the right words to describe. Contemplating these things as a medical stuident, lead me to learn endless details about the fragile fabric of life— and the brutal disease processes that take it away. Meditating on these things brought me to the conclusion it is amazing that anything stays alive at all.

Contemplating these things one night in a library, it occurred to me that any kind of orderliness that sustains life must be a good thing. From the orderliness of scientific knowledge to the efficiency of dish soap cleaning dishes, if it sustains life and guards against disease, it must be a good thing.

Anything that supports nature keeps the miracle going. Life support systems[48] are all around us. Let me share my walking meditation on nature.[49]

I took a walk this morning and breathed in the fresh air. Oxygen filled my lungs and was distributed to the blood in my veins. Where would we be without oxygen? I exhaled carbon dioxide. The plants around me will use it to grow. Plants and animals support one another in many ways. We can't live without each other. I like to take time to appreciate that symbiosis.

I walked along and studied the textures of tree trunks and shades of brown in them. I felt the ground pressing under my feet. My mind was filled with nature. The very ground I walked on supported life. The atoms there are just right so they can be used to spin the fragile threads of proteins in every living thing. If they were not this way we wouldn't be here. How awesome! The gravity that pulls me down to this ground is just right. Any less and we would lose our atmosphere; any more and the atmosphere would collapse. There is a natural order for these things.

I take time to appreciate the orderliness of nature in my neighborhood. This orderliness sustains life.

When I walk, I study the shapes of rocks. I take in their shades of gray. I enjoy feeling the warmth of the sun on my skin. My mind fills with appreciation for nature. The warmth of the sun is just right. I appreciate this warmth. It's part of how nature nurtures life. It feels so good.

I turned to walk down a block lined with lush trees and well-kept houses. I focused on the shapes of leaves. I noticed the shades of green. I felt the warmth of the breath in my mouth. When I breathed in, my mouth cooled. I breathed out, my mouth warmed. My mind in this way was filled with nature.

Keeping these thoughts in mind, I turned and walked down another block.

I studied the shapes of the blades of grass and the shades of green in them. I felt the earth beneath my feet as I walked along. My mind was full of the present moment.

When I looked at houses, I studied the shades of blue in them. I feel my breath warm and then cool my sinuses. People sustain life as well. They are working hard, serving others, keeping us safe and making progress. I feel safe. I take time to appreciate their work. I feel part of humanity's progress. These houses sustain people and people sustain our culture. There is a goodness in houses. They shelter us. There is a goodness in fences. They let us have yards for our pets and privacy. There is a goodness to streets and sidewalks. They keep it safe to drive and walk here. There is a goodness to the cars that come and go. They give us a freedom of movement.

There is a goodness to the internet cables under the streets. They connect us to the world. There is a goodness in the people all over the world who make these things, maintain them and improve them. They are part of this global, common good. They sustain life. Take away any one of these things and the fragile thread of life will begin to unravel. I take some time to appreciate all the working people in the world. They are making the world a better place. I feel safe. I take time to appreciate their work. I feel a part of humanity and humanity's progress. I take time to appreciate the work of students in the neighborhood. They are our future.

JOURNAL YOUR LEARNING HERE:

FIGURE 1.6.0
"Reject false shame to have more chances for love."
This principle and many other principles of positivity work
together so you can bring more love and passion into your life.
By Toso Borkovic.

6

How positivity principles work together

Overview of positivity

Positivity is so powerful, it still amazes me. It can help you boost your IQ and reinvent yourself, which is what I did with it. I combined vigorous exercise with vigorous use of goals, affirmations, life skills and a positive attitude—and got wonderful results.

You will feel better if you take accomplishments personally and use your failures to improve yourself. We all have plenty of both; don't worry about that. Also, learning from bad experiences feels good.

This chapter will go into each of the six qualities of positivity in great detail. Most people wouldn't have much to say if asked, "What is a positive attitude?" Soon you will know the answer in "great depth." With rating scales you will also know how you measure up. Most people have no idea how optimistic or pessimistic they are at any given time or in any given situation. Then they wonder why they can't make things happen. You will know where your attitude is at from one moment to the next. That's a game changer.

Job hunting offers a great opportunity to use positivity. It also applies to job improvement or starting your own business. I go into detail on how a positive attitude gives you the edge whether you are trying to get hired or you are the one hiring. I have been on both ends of the deal with a pessimistic attitude and I can tell you they were crummy experiences. You will feel better if you stay positive.

Three fundamental qualities

The three fundamental qualities of positivity give you control. These are three great life skills. They are fundamental because positivity dies without them:
- Take accomplishments personally
- Don't take setbacks personally but learn from them
- Learn from everything you experience—and remember you can control this learning

How can you apply this information? If you are feeling "down in the dumps" one day, do a quick reality check on your attitude. Have you taken time to appreciate your accomplishments today? Have you taken your setbacks with detachment? Don't do this lightly. Sit down and take five minutes to appreciate those accomplishments. People often find if they do this, they have made twice as many accomplishments than they thought they had. Take time to appreciate the difference your initiative made. Appreciate the sweep of many accomplishments made in the past week and month.

Have you really detached from your setbacks? Have you let go emotionally 100%? Now again take five minutes to learn from your setbacks. What did you learn to do differently. Resolve to take action in the next day or two on what you've learned. When you act, it energizes your attitude ten times more than all the thinking you've done. The power of positive thinking is quite weak compared to positive action, so take advantage of that. Swing into action!

These first three qualities, the "ALL" in the "ISHALL" acronym, are now qualities of you and your character.

On the other hand, what if you rarely showed initiative? What if you never looked forward to growing in your relationships or accomplishments? What if you stayed fixated on the past and all the things you can't change like other people's opinions? That would truly be a thorn in your side now, wouldn't it?

Six basic working parts

As time went by, I found three other features were needed for positivity to be powerful in a person's life:

- Take initiative, because positivity requires action
- Stay hopeful, because positivity always looks forward to growth
- Let go of what you can't control. Because if you try to control what you can't control then you are acting hopeless and soon you are going to feel hopeless—and pessimistic.

These are beneficial life skills to use.

Realizing these six life skills were needed for positivity to work, I called them the six working parts of positivity and invented an acronym to help people remember them. What good is knowing something if you can't remember it, right? The acronym is "I SHALL" and suggests that intention to assert yourself in a positive, constructive manner:

I   Initiative is yours to use.

S   Setbacks are temporary and a source of learning.

H   Hopefulness is a choice.

A   Accomplishments are yours to take personally.

L   Let go of what you can't control.

L   Learn from everything.

The results of this kind of positivity: amazing life changes! People making their dreams come true! Is this too much to hope for with you? What I learned along the way is people can build these life skills. All of us already have these qualities—but they can be focused, made to work together, and built up in strength to a very large degree. You might live in a situation that seems full of poverty and no opportunity for progress. Then just work on yourself for now. Nobody can stop you from doing that. Later you can improve your situation. Now just how do these life skills work together?

How "I SHALL" Works

Here are some quick examples with hypothetical stories from three heroes who are applying positivity to overcome big setbacks:

Wendy felt hopeless after getting rejected by her boyfriend. She got smart about relationship skills and found an even better boyfriend. How did she do that? She took initiative and was willing to change everything about how she communicated her personality. She got a new hair style that reflected her sassy personality. She got her nails done to reflect her classiness. She upgraded her clothes to a little more sexy and stylish. Then she posted a new profile picture for herself on social media. She upgraded her attitude. Really great guys just were not calling her back because her conversation was boring, she guessed. So she studied videos on how to start conversations and keep them interesting. She got better at smiling instead of being so reserved. She worked on making better eye contact. Instead of focusing on her fear of rejection, she focused on the threads of conversations and really tried to understand who she was talking with. In the past she was just focused on making a good impression. She watched standup comedians to improve her sense of humor—she found herself often too serious and judgmental about herself and others. Out with the old! In with the new! She soon found a young man with great qualities she admired—and soon they were dating. Looking back, her efforts seemed so obvious: make yourself more interesting and people will notice. *Also remember this:* reject false shame about being rejected!

Sam got demoted at work. He channeled his anger into finding ways to be more valuable and got a new job that paid more. How did he pull that off? He took a sober look at his performance. How well could people count on him? He was often a few minutes late for meetings. He made up his mind to always be on time. He didn't say much in meetings because he didn't like them. That was a bad attitude. He decided to act like he was in a position he wanted to get promoted to. That person would be leading the meetings and would be very well prepared for the items in the meetings—so he didn't waste people's time. Soon he brought new ideas to meetings and even asked to lead part of the meetings he was most interested in. They gave him a chance. He did well. It was no big surprise he got promoted six months later to team lead at his company that provided technical support for a software that helped customers market their business on social media. He was on a roll!

Julie got low grades on a test. She focused her frustration. She studied the material she got wrong and improved her study skills. The next test grades were much better and crushed the next test.

What exactly did she do? To improve her attitude, she saw she often didn't even know she was passive or pessimistic. Big issue. She put up a sticky note on her refrigerator that said, "What attitude do you want today?" That helped her take action. And be more self aware of her attitude and correcting it as need be. After all this was her life she was improving!

Then she put a big upgrade on her study habits. She was studying in the morning but she just wasn't a morning person. So she pencilled in times to study in the evening in her schedule. But that was when her friends liked to go out and have fun! She decided her career was more important and that life is full of sacrifice and compromise. She would eat from 5 to 6 pm. Then she'd study from 6 to 8 pm when she seemed to be the most alert and motivated. Fun time would be something she would "earn" by studying—and she'd join her friends from 9 to 10 every night. In the past, she'd stay out some nights to midnight and then be tired in the morning. Her grades suffered. She wanted to get into nursing school now, and low grades would ruin those career chances. So she made up her mind to be in bed by 10:30 pm, "like a grownup," and get to sleep by 11 pm, even if she needed to take some herbal supplement and meditate to get to sleep. She used the "meditation for sedation" technique along with some chamomile tea and it really helped her stay on her new "adult" schedule. She loved the feeling of taking charge of her life and showing initiative to do what works for her future. Now she was much more alert for her 9 am class and she even had 15 minutes to skim the material that would be in the class's lecture—a great technique that helped her "master the material" in the lecture at the time of the lecture. She was so happy when she saw her test grades come back. Before she was always stuck with C's. Now she was getting A's and B's! Before she used to joke to her friends that she needed a "brain transplant" to get better grades. Now she saw all she needed was an "attitude transplant" with the life skills of positivity.

The stories are hypothetical to protect the privacy of the people in the story. I've changed the names and details to protect privacy, but kept the essence of the story so you can learn from it. Stories change lives when they help people learn new skills to practice their positivity!

Insight into the "I SHALL" acronym!

First let's look more deeply at the positive thinking skills. The I SHALL acronym summarizes them succinctly.

- **I** is for initiative. Thinking and planning take initiative. Acting on a goal you set take initiative. Sometimes your plans will not work out and that's called a setback. Setbacks in a weird way are good.
- **S** is for setbacks which are temporary and can be used to fuel progress. Remember how frustrated you get when things don't work out your way? Let that frustration drive you forward! You can also learn from setbacks. Setbacks are great teachers.
- **H** is for hope. Because you are learning from setbacks and accomplishments, you can keep making progress even in the toughest of times. You create hopefulness by learning. No one can control the learning that goes on in your own mind except you! Here in the freedom and privacy of your own mind you are free to chart your own course in life and learn whatever you want to learn.
- **A** is for accomplishments. Because you showed initiative in good times and bad, you created accomplishments through your sheer willpower. Good for you! Give yourself credit for your accomplishments and take time to feel good about them. Congratulate yourself often!
- **L** is for letting go of what you can't control. Naturally, you create accomplishments by changing what you can

control and not getting hung up trying to change what you can't. This is a game changer!

- **L** is for learning. Positive people see learning as the wind that fills their sails. Life is for learning and when you learn something every day you are fulfilling one of your ultimate purposes in life.

I SHALL summarizes the six basic principles of positivity. All the other elements of positivity build on these principles. The more you practice these principles, the more positive you will feel.

How did our three heroes use positivity?

Wendy lived these principles. She felt in charge in her life! She took initiative and learned from her setback. Her ex-boyfriend was afraid of commitment. She stayed hopeful, learned communication skills, took that accomplishment personally and let go of the past. She pushed herself to learn new hobbies and be more outgoing. That allowed her to meet a lot more people. She learned how to follow threads of a conversation. When she found a good guy, she turned on the charm and was in a new relationship.

Sam practiced these principles. He felt empowered! He showed initiative and asked his boss what did people do who got demoted. He learned he needed people management skills. He learned those in an online course, put them into practice and talked about his success to his boss—who didn't promote him. Sam used that setback as motivation to look for a new job. Sam got hired on at another company that valued his skills. He later got promoted.

Julie acted on these principles. It changed her life! She took initiative and analyzed why she got questions wrong on a test. She got things wrong when she studied while pessimistic, tired, passive, disorganized, hungry from skipped meals and moody from lack of exercise. She corrected those problems with new study skills and new routines—and crushed the next test.

Powerful skills

How do some people make such big changes? All people are created equal. But all skills are not created equal: some are stronger than others. There are three levels of life skills.

Grade school level skills: do what the teacher says and get to class on time, work with respect for others, follow directions. Do that and you'll pass grade school.

High school level skills are more complex: it's up to you to understand and follow the daily schedule and get to class on time. Use to do lists to keep up with assignments. Write in a daytimer when you are going to do assignments so you don't get "overbooked."

College level skills put it more on the individual to take charge of their learning. You are now learning things you will use the rest of your life to support yourself. Use to do lists but prioritize items so you don't waste time doing lower priority items. Use a planner to write in when you are going to do assignments, but plan ahead so you never turn an assignment in late! Being on time is of the highest importance! Coordinate your classes so you get a degree that fits with your personality and life goals. Ask for help in all these areas when you don't know what to do (very important).

To apply all these skills you need to have a positive attitude! With these skills, you are creating an orderliness in how you do things that will help you get things done on time and be the person other people can count on. Half the stress I see people have who are in their 20's is from them lacking skills in these areas.

Do you know when you are being positive? Most people don't. Do you know when you are thinking pessimistically? Most people don't know that either. Some people ruin their good attitude with pessimism. That is why it's worth it to know when you're being positive or pessimistic.

When you put together the six thinking skills of positivity, you organize them like gears chained together in a bicycle.

How positivity skills work together!

Why should you organize your thinking skills, you might ask.

I SHALL components all work together. What good is taking INITIATIVE if you take a SETBACK personally and feel defeated as a result? What good is staying HOPEFUL if you ignore your ACCOMPLISHMENTS and as a result feel like you're getting nowhere? What good will LETTING GO do, if you feel no sense of direction because you can't remember all that you are LEARNING from your experiences this week? All these skills matter! They need to be used together.

Making these changes may be easier than you think: positivity is just about getting organized and making little improvements here and there. Keep it simple! Notice what works and what doesn't work.

How positivity works

Positivity helped me write this book. I set aside time to write in the mornings but sometimes I put off writing. I had a habit of procrastinating. Then I decided to work with it instead of being a victim of it. I got up and put off doing dishes and other chores so I could write. I put writing first. "First things first," as the saying goes. But now I translated it into action. I wrote for several hours each morning. Then I took care of other chores. I found the best time for writing was in the morning—so I worked with that reality instead of fighting it. At the time I am writing these lines my word count is 97,188 words for this book. Putting first things first is working. Here are stories from other people who thought positively and put first things first.

Jason, a high school student, got a low grade on a test and used his frustration to ask the teacher for help. Because he took intiative, he learned better ways to study and got a much better grade on the next test!

Angie, a college student, was rejected by her boyfriend. She was upset and used that energy to learn better confidence and

FIGURE 1.6.1 Four college students smiling. By Esther Phingmoo.

communication skills and met people dancing—so it was easier to find a boyfriend she had a lot in common with. She found love with her positivity!

Francie was upset by how people talked behind her back at work. She learned skills to make new friends and ignored the gossip, thanks to her positivity. She enjoyed socializing at work more after dealing with the gossip than before.

All these people suffered setbacks. They bounced back by learning new skills to power them forward, making progress in their life.

Life skill: rate your positivity

Rate yourself

These quizzes to chart your growth are optional. The quiz just takes a couple minutes. Take the quiz if you want to know how positive you are.

FIGURE 1.6.2 Positivity qualities. By Esther Phingmoo.

The healthy positivity rating scale

Rate the following on a 1-5 scale: 1 is strongly disagree, 2 is disagree, 3 is neutral, 4 is agree, 5 is strongly agree. These questions assume you are focused on constructive activities.

1. I am taking initiative today. _____
2. I am taking setbacks as temporary. _____
3. I am staying hopeful. _____
4. I am taking my accomplishments personally. _____
5. I am letting go of what I can't control. _____
6. I learn from life. _____
7. I can't control everything but I can improve my outcomes. _____

Total positivity score: _____

Way to go! You are taking action to see how positive you are. You are taking an **active** role in learning about your attitude. That's a game changer! This adds to your independence and self-reliance.

Life skill: rate your negativity

What are the qualities of pessimism? They are the opposite dualities of I SHALL.

- **I** is for initiative, which pessimists lack. Pessimists think they are victims of their situation. If you are a victim, how can initiative make any kind of a difference?
- **S** is for setbacks. Pessimists take setbacks personally. They feel setbacks will last forever and that there is nothing that they can do about them. Setbacks are like nails in the coffin of their future!
- **H** is for hope. Pessimists think hopefulness is silly, stupid, juvenile or ridiculous. They roll their eyes in contempt for the idea that things could ever get better. Hopelessness is the flag they wave as they try to get attention for themselves.

- **A** is for accomplishments. Pessimists feel they have no ability to improve outcomes, so they don't take the time do feel good about and learn from their accomplishments.
- **L** is for letting go. Pessimists latch onto what they can't control. This might be society, the economy, money or other people's behavior. Pessimists can't control external forces but they want to complain about them as if complaining could change something.
- **L** is for learning. Pessimists don't think they can learn anything useful and so repeat the same actions and get the same results, feeling stuck.

No matter how positive you are, you can undo it with negativity. Rate your unhealthy pessimism here with the unhealthy pessimism rating scale.

The unhealthy pessimism rating scale

Rate the following on a 1-5 scale: 1 is strongly disagree, 2 is disagree, 3 is neutral, 4 is agree, 5 is strongly agree. These questions assume you are trying to focus on constructive activities.
1. I am **not** taking initiative today. _____
2. I am **not** taking setbacks as temporary. _____
3. I am **not** staying hopeful. _____
4. I am **not** taking my accomplishments personally. _____
5. I am **not** letting go of what I can't control. _____
6. I **don't** take life as for learning. _____
7. I **can't** improve outcomes. _____
Total pessimism score: _____

Pro tip: Use a heads-up attitude (healthy pessimism)

Have you ever gotten surprised by a problem you didn't anticipate? There is a simple fix for that. It is just as important to focus on your goals as it is to notice what might come up to ruin

FIGURE 1.6.3 Comparison of the qualities of positivity and pessimism. By Esther Phingmoo.

your goals. This is called a heads-up attitude. How much is this attitude adding to your positivity? Take the heads-up attitude survey to find out!

FIGURE 1.6.4
The good professor also had a great level of healthy pessimism so he was ready to deal with situations--I give him a score of 27. I get just a 12! By Esther Phingmoo.

Life skill: rate your heads-up or healthy pessimism attitude

John Curtis, my old camp director, loved adventures and seeing something new. This might happen through hiking a mountain range like the Bear Tooth Wilderness Area in Montana or canoeing a lake in the Boundary Waters Canoe Area in Minnesota. Because he was going after new things, he liked to stay alert and anticipate problems that might happen. He taught me to have a heads-up attitude.

The healthy pessimism (heads up) attitude rating scale

Rate the following on a 1-5 scale: 1 is strongly disagree, 2 is disagree, 3 is neutral, 4 is agree, 5 is strongly agree. These questions assume you are focused on **anticipating** what might cause a problem so you can avoid it.

1. I will take **initiative** to avoid things that are not healthy. _____
2. I understand some **setbacks** can have longer-lasting consequences. _____
3. I understand **hopefulness** can be damaged by bad or weak behavior. _____
4. I can see how **accomplishments** can be undone by bad behavior. _____
5. I can envision problems caused by not **letting go** of what I can't control. _____
6. I understand I can create problems by not **learning** from my mistakes. _____
7. I know that if I think I can control everything, I will be disappointed. _____

Total heads-up attitude score: _____
Add your positivity and heads-up scores together: _____
This is your total positive attitude score!

Rate the Good Professor's Positivity!

FIGURE 1.6.5
Positivity works and here's proof. Here I am with The Good Professor at my medical school graduation. He didn't want his picture taken!

The Good Professor's positivity rating, as mentioned earlier, was 35/35. He was a towering giant of optimism to me. My positivity was much less. My scores were: I-2,S-0,H-0,A-1,L-0, L-2, C-1=6. No wonder I looked up to him! His positivity was more than 400% bigger than my attitude!

Application: job hunting

Job hunting is a great place to test your attitude. Here you will be working hard and often get no feedback on how you are doing. Also you'll get paid nothing. How's that for a cool job? And yet it is one we all will have periodically in life. Of course, from the positive point of view, job hunting is an excellent situation to work on:

- Your work ethic
- Assessing your value in the workplace
- Feeling your value
- Improving your value
- Communicating your value

When you work on those qualities, you are making a big investment in your most valuable possession: yourself. Many people report to me that when they worked on their job hunting skills they made dramatic improvements in the quality of their life that lasted for years afterwards. They discovered they had far more valuable work skills than they previously understood. Furthermore, they found they could combine those skills in a variety of different ways—and they often found ways that lead to a better paying job and a higher quality of life for themselves and their family. Take Brenda's example.

"I got a college degree in social studies. When I started job hunting I was shocked at how I couldn't even afford apartment rent in my home town with my degree. I brainstormed for ideas. A friend got a degree as a project manager. I took two classes at a community college to get a certificate as a project manager. There were lots of job openings that paid more than $50,000 per year. I got one of them. I am so thankful I can stay in my wonderful hometown with this job!"

If you are intimidated by the prospect of job hunting, and find yourself slipping into feeling pessimistic, consider checking on your point of view. There are two sides to everything. Coins have heads and tails. Books have the author's point of view and the reader's perspective.

Job hunting is like this. There are two points of view here: the hiring company and the job seeker. The interviewer has a job to fill and is looking for the right fit in an interviewee. The interviewer could lose money in lost revenue if they select the wrong employee—perhaps $40,000 or more. The interviewee is looking for a job and hopes for a good fit between the job and their personality. Meanwhile the interviewee might be losing hundreds of dollars each week they go without a job. What point of view should you take? How about both?

Develop multi-dimensional thinking

Close one eye and you get monocular vision. You can see height and width and somewhat for depth: limited three dimensional perspective. Now open both eyes and read this line with both eyes. You have binocular vision. You can see in three dimensions: height, width and an expanded depth—and a wider field of view.

When you look at job hunting from your point of view and the employer's, you get that expanded point of view. Here's are examples of limited perspective and expanded perspective thinking, with stories ripped from real life experiences.

Terry got "rejected" for a job. He took a limited perspective approach. He spent hours obsessing on how unfair this was and how well qualified he was. He sent out a couple resumes per week after his obsessing so drained him. He had one dimensional thinking because he just looked at the situation from one perspective: his. In three months he sent out 24 resumes, got two interviews and no job offers. His attitude was entitled, dejected, pessimistic. "Society is screwing me," he said. He found many facts to support his (pessimistic) point of view.

Now look at Robin. She lost her job but took an expanded perspective in job hunting. She looks at things from her perspective and imagines the employer's perspective too. She has depth of perspective on the whole process. "I'll send out resumes and it's either going to work out or not work out," she said. Conserving more of her mental energy, she lets go of the employers who don't even reply to her resume. "Can't control them, oh well," she said. "It's a process."

See how she is emotionally detaching from trying to control the employer and the outcome by the words she uses? Very artful. But now she can send out 7 resumes per week. In three months she got just 3 interviews. But she got a job offer! Her response? "Until I start the new job, I'm going to keep sending out resumes," she said. "What if the new workplace has a bad vibe? Or bad office politics? If that happens, I'm ready to move on. It just didn't work out!" She is saying "it just didn't work out." If she rejects her prospective employer or if the employer rejects her. Nice work.

It's an art to detach emotionally and yet be excited for the outcome you want (but can't control). That's positivity in action. She's got it going. See the importance of applying a positive attitude?

This is a metaphor for life. Positivity is about seeing things with different attitudes and different points of view to:

- Lower stress
- Bring people together
- Boost life skills that aid success

Understanding your own attitude and using optimism is a game changer.

The unique style of positive thinking I learned from Professor Curtis[50] at my first job didn't come from books but from his life experience in the American Midwest.

How Professor Curtis taught me a deeper perspective in positivity

I had been stunned when I was 15 and my boss, a camp director, told me I could do anything I worked at! Previously, I was convinced I was going nowhere. I was hopeless. Everything changed when he took me on a bird identification walk. He shared insight about birds and about me. If you know one or two key things to look for, he said, then it is easy to identify something in nature. A small slender bird that is bright yellow all over is a yellow warbler. That easy to apply insight amazed me.

Professor Curtis was a sharp observer of human nature. He picked up on me acting hesitant about learning. He rightly concluded I was pessimistic about myself. He demonstrated positivity by explaining he watched me learn to identify three species of plants and birds I never knew before—all in 30 minutes. This provided a foundation for being optimistic about my ability to succeed in life.

"I think," he mused, "you can do anything you put your mind to!"

While I was busy looking at the facts to confirm my pessimistic attitude, Professor Curtis looked for facts to confirm a positive attitude was the way to live. He had the insight to know if you believe whatever random attitude comes to mind, you will have trouble succeeding. You first must pick your attitude. His attitude was all positive.

Since an attitude is what steers your life, it makes sense to first focus on what kind of attitude is justified—optimistic or pessimistic. First look at the facts and the situation and then pick the attitude that makes sense. Stay optimistic that you can succeed. Professor Curtis taught English composition to students at Minot State University[51] where he used this "attitude talk" to encourage students to learn to write more effectively.

Three key insights about positivity

Professor Curtis had three key insights about attitude:
- Sometimes it makes sense to be optimistic and hope for the best in a situation.
- Sometimes it makes sense to anticipate the worst and be pessimistic about the situation. The choice is yours.
- Your attitude about yourself should always be positive.

I first learned this positivity from Professor Curtis at summer camp in 1974. Later we became best friends and travelled all over the American West together. On these trips, I learned to view life as an adventure.

In a quirky way, Professor Curtis refined his attitude at antique shows he attended as an antique seller. He had a hobby of buying and selling antiques from the Old West—the western United States from about 1800 to 1885. He was always hopeful of finding a rare, pristine antique—but skeptical that someone might try to pull a fast one and sell him a fake.

He took me on a dozen of these antique road trips where I saw him at the top of his game. Con artists were everywhere. He outfoxed them and came home with great prizes. At home in his den he stored the treasures from his trips: bows and arrows, a peace pipe, old Army belt buckles and several trophies for having the best antique collection at a show. One wall was lined with shelves of books including one he co-wrote but never published.

All the time at antique shows people tried to sell him fakes. They would walk up to his table and say, "I got something," and show him an item such as a leather saddle bag. He would slide his reading glasses down on his nose, pinching his lips for a moment as he did a close inspection. Then he'd lift his bushy eyebrows with authority and make a dramatic response. "Well, I think it's worth $50 and I wish I could pay more, I really do, but I saw something just like this in a magazine for $50 so that's all I can do. Sorry. But it sure looks great." Every now and then he found what he called "a winner." He paid a higher price and shook hands with the seller.

Professor Curtis had a photographic memory for prices on things. Still, he occasionally got swindled. He said that "just came with the territory" and laughed off the setback. He was ever the optimist.

FIGURE 1.6.6
John and I in his famous "den" dreaming up adventures.

He passed this positivity on to me and now I'm sharing it with you like he did, with stories. His attitude helped him become a distinguished professor and helped me become a doctor. Professor Curtis encouraged me in difficult moments in medical school. Years later it was my turn. When he wanted to quit dialysis for his diabetes, I hatched a plan. I had the book he wrote about Dodge City, Kansas published with a custom-made cover with photos from the Old West Town. I mailed it to him as a surprise. He was overjoyed. He told his friends and kept on with his dialysis. We made plans for another camping trip.

Positive people lift one another up. We did that for each other for 30 years until we tragically lost John to a heart attack in 2008.[52] That day a light went out in the world. Now I am trying to pass on his rare legacy along with a few things I've learned.

Professor Curtis taught me to bring out my potential and create more rewarding relationships. My ability to change my attitude allowed me to find a better career. That attitude helped me through medical school where John and his wife Em saw me graduate. He and I were best friends for more than 30 years. Positivity leads to great and lasting friendships.

The lessons I learned from Professor Curtis will be with me forever. If John had to discipline a staff member at camp, he always did it in private and said he was sorry as often as he could. He bent over backwards to be as clear as possible about people's job expectations. He celebrated people's accomplishments with emotions written all over his face. He also sympathized with their failures. He looked disappointed with me one night when I had hauled a dead fish up a flagpole at camp. A family of raccoons invaded the campsite including one that shimmied up the flagpole. I caught some hell for that one.

You can act like Professor Curtis. Be private with your negative feedback and public with your positive feedback. Celebrate your little accomplishments. They build up to big accomplishments.

Typical job accomplishments, according to Professor Curtis, include many things about one's character that are fun to learn. Job hunting accomplishments are cut from the same cloth.

- **Self-discipline**: Use good posture. Dress well. Be physically fit. Be mentally fit. Know your mission and be fearless about getting it done. Laugh at your faults.

Be demanding of yourself for great results. Be quick to forgive yourself. Great things come from great effort.

- **Good communication**: Write well. Make eye contact when speaking and listening. Say what you mean and clear up misunderstandings. Don't be self-important. Think before you talk. People will notice you do that.
- **Good time management**: Use to do lists and a daily planner. Be on time. Be someone people can count on. Love the act of planning and preparing for adventures. That's life.
- **Great value**: Do things with a high standard. Double check your work. Make your work your business card. Work hard but don't brag or complain about your efforts.
- **Accountability**: Be a team player. Celebrate others' successes. Help others succeed. Always follow through on your promises. Be the one person everyone knows they can count on. Guard that reputation.

I asked John's wife Em where John learned to do all this himself—and teach it. She said John had joined the Army reserves to help pay for college. They found he liked to swim down rivers at night and blow things up. So that's what he did. He was so good at it he taught classes on it in France. "Do you know what they call military people who do that brave stuff nowadays?" she asked me. I said no. She said, "Navy Seals."

Well then, it looks like I got taught about life by a military commando. Lucky me. Back to the job-hunting topic. Let's look at how to think positively about job hunting.

Interviewee with negativity: I'm so stressed out about job hunting! I send out applications and don't hear anything back!

Interviewee with positivity: I send out applications and don't hear anything back! I know everybody is busy and has their priorities. We all need to adapt to find a good job fit.

It's natural to focus on your immediate experience, but leave a lot of facts out to confirm the view that things are going bad. Just like newspapers do! Nice trick but the interviewee with positivity caught his mind doing it and got on track with positivity. The key to identifying pessimism is to recognize that hopeless feeling. It's ok if things aren't going perfectly. Life doesn't revolve around you. Turn a bad situation into a self-improvement exercise. Then everything you do is something you can talk about in a job interview. Everything you do is an investment in the most important thing in your life: you.

The employer's point of view

When an employer advertises a position, dozens or perhaps more than a hundred applications flood in. It's a problem. How does an employer narrow down the potential candidates when there are so many? This is a complicated task. There are many things to consider from both the employer and interviewee point of view.

The employer can lose a lot of money by hiring the wrong person. I have run a private medical practice for 20 years, so I know. I get feedback from my patients to learn if an employee is "not working out." I could find the employee doesn't really like the job and just took it for the money or because they desperately needed health insurance. Maybe the employee lacks self-discipline and comes to work late. Maybe the employee lacks empathy and greets patients with a careless attitude. There are dozens of things that could chase away customers or clients. Some employees just have a bad attitude and are upset when things don't go their way. Then they take out their anger on bosses or customers. THIS HAPPENS ALL THE TIME.

Some employees are not open to leadership. They are not team players. They don't like to be told what to do. They don't accept that there is a natural hierarchy in the world of business—and in the world in general. Naturally, people with the most experience will have knowledge of how things work. This is the inner logic of why there are hierarchies in groups of people. This is why people need leadership. EMPLOYEES IGNORE THIS ALL THE TIME.

The job hunter's point of view

It is stressful to be job hunting. You can put in a lot of effort with nothing to show for it. Sometimes you think, "Hey world: just give me a job! I'm not lazy. Give me a chance. Give me something useful to do with a decent wage." This is a dependent point of view. If you make your happiness depend on other people, you won't have it. This is so true and so common in job hunting. Here are the six qualities of positivity in action in the mind of a job hunter:

➤INITIATIVE. "When I'm job hunting it's really that I'm self-employed to hunt and find a job. I am going to either be dependent or independent about it. I am going to choose to be independent and create a routine for my day. That is building up the quality of being a self-starter. Also, I will work on being self-organized. I'll keep track of the things I am learning; these are skills I can share in a job interview. I will use my job hunting experience to make me a better job candidate. I will improve the value I have for myself and for others. I will make promises I can keep and then follow through to show myself I am reliable. If I am over my head, I will get ask for help. To emotionally connect with others, I will get better at identifying my feelings and talking about them, something called "emotional intelligence." I will build my social intelligence by getting better at anticipating and responding to other's emotional needs. It feels good learning these things." THESE QUALITIES WILL HELP YOU ALL THE TIME.

➤SETBACKS. "Getting no job offers from my applications is a setback! It would be nice if I was just given everything I want but that's not how the world works. I will use my disappointment to energize myself to think of creative ways to succeed in my job search." THIS WILL WORK FOR YOU YOUR WHOLE LIFE.

➤HOPEFULNESS. "I've got my goal. I've got my ideal job in mind. I can see myself growing professionally as the years go by. I'm going to hang onto this hope and work toward it. I don't need results to inspire me. My job is to choose to be hopeful. Hopefulness is a choice. I inspire me." THIS ATTITUDE WILL PROPEL YOU TO LEVELS OF EXCELLENCE YOU NEVER DREAMED OF.

➤**ACCOMPLISHMENTS.** "Getting out of bed is an accomplishment. Eating breakfast. Writing in my to do list. Taking action in the direction of my dreams. I'm going to take credit for my accomplishments. I'm making my life more orderly. I'm getting more self-control. It all feels so good. I'm not relying on others to do for me, for things that I can do for myself. I love this feeling of independence. Taking charge of my life. Taking responsibility for my life. I love the freedom it gives me to pursue my dreams. Job hunting is a challenge like anything else. It's just one day at a time and stay positive." THIS ATTITUDE WILL GIVE YOU MORE FEELINGS OF FREEDOM THAT YOU EVER IMAGINED POSSIBLE.

➤**LETTING GO.** "I can't care about what I can't change right now. I'm letting go of that. If I don't get a response back from an employer, I don't care. I'm moving on. If I don't hear back after a video interview, I don't care. But I might check my spam box for an employer's response too! If I don't hear back from an in-person interview, same thing. I don't care. I just don't care. I can't care about what I can't control. Do I want to care? Certainly. But will I spend a lot of time caring about what I can't control? I hope not. Lord knows, I value my vibe, my energy, my enthusiasm—so why would I go and do something that makes me lose my competitive edge? That's not what winners do." THIS ATTITUDE WILL HELP YOU WIN THROUGHOUT YOUR LIFE.

➤**LEARNING.** "I've learned so much from job hunting. I've upgraded my attitude. I took a lack of response as a challenge. I got better at customizing resumes. I improved my ability to dress for success. I challenged myself to learn more technical skills and pass certifying exams to prove it. I'm learning so much." THIS ATTITUDE WILL LITERALLY RAISE YOUR INTELLIGENCE QUOTIENT (IQ).

Getting a job and a lifestyle, from your job hunting

"I'm in my senior year in college and I'm a little scared about finding a job," Rosey confessed to me. She looked visibly stressed out. I raised my eyebrows. "Well, I'm a little confused about what to do and like, when to do it," she said. Pause. "My thoughts are going here and there and I'm in a mess about all this."

Pause.

Her parents had reassured her everything would be OK. Just get your degree, then hunt for jobs like everyone else. But she is talking with girlfriends who did that and graduated last year, and they are working as nannies and they have a college degree. They just couldn't find a good job. Employers said they lacked experience.

This was a big problem no one in her college was talking about. "My college said we have career fairs, it will be ok," she said. "My friends who are nannying went to those career fairs. So fairs are not very reassuring."

She talked to friends who got good jobs but they just sent out resumes. A shotgun approach, like her college said. The nannies did that and no job. Now they are nannying instead of pursuing the careers they wanted.

She talked to pastors and they prayed for her, which was helpful, but the elephant in the room remained. And no one talked about it. It's name? "How to get the job and live the life I want."

Her parents met and fell in love in college. They got jobs in a nearby town, Houston. It was natural. They both worked, so of course they could afford a home and daycare. Of course, the town was safe for raising a family. Of course, if you lived a life of faith God would care for you.

It worked. They raised three happy children who marched off to college. The problem?

The world had changed.

1. Jobs are not "everywhere." You have to go find them. They often don't pay well and require experience you only get from an internship—when you work for free to get college credit.

Students who look for that after graduation can't get it: they have graduated and they need money now. Student loans have to get repaid after you graduate or else the bill collectors come running. The answer: read the world like a book. Look for people with jobs you want and ask them how to get into it. Interview them. They are people in the know. They know what works in their community, in their profession. My case? I was interested in medicine. My friend Brian said the University of North Dakota School of Medicine was great, he was a student there. My other friend, Richard, also said the school was great. And he should know; he was a doctor. I was gathering information. They had it. I got it. I acted on it. I drove to North Dakota and applied to medical school. The information to succeed doesn't live in books. Life changes too fast for that. It takes at least 2 years to get information into a book and into the public eye. I know. I WROTE THIS BOOK.

2. Happy communities are not "everywhere." Many towns trumpet what a wonderful place they are to live and raise a family. But there are heroin needles in the parks. I know. I saw one a foot from my son in a city park in Denver. We moved to another side of the park. We still had a good time and danced on a stage lined with Greek columns. But we went home to a safe community where I raise my family. Research the happy communities in your area. One friend of mine said her family left one community because children were being kidnapped by drug lords for ransom! Others left towns because they were low value: full of homes that were messy, yards messy, schools with low test scores and high crime rates. But to look at social media you'd think all these communities are wonderful. The upshot: do your research.

3. Taxes and empty promises are everywhere. You might think you're getting a good job and it makes $30,000 per year. You can do well. But the government takes 25% and sales tax takes 5% and that's 30% so you've got about 20,000 per month or $1,666 per month. But rent takes $800 per month and food takes $200 and health insurance another $200 and gas and oil another $100 and car insurance $100 and suddenly you have $66 dollars left for the month for food and this is NO FUN. Sorry for the run on sentence, but people today are feeling betrayed by everyone else not preparing them for the realities of the working world. It's HARSH. But if you do your research well ahead of time, you are prepared. The problem: parents, professors, teachers, scoutmasters, coaches, friends, relatives— never faced these realities, so they don't know how to deal with them. My book is coming to your rescue! This book is a "capital" investment in your future.

4. Experts are often no help. What worked yesterday does not help today. Parents are great, but how do you keep on a financial budget so you can make $200 per month student loan payments? College is great, but some degrees don't pay for themselves, instead saddling you with debt that could be a nail in your financial coffin? Doctors are great, but where are the thinking skills that cut down on your need for medication? Therapists are great, but where are the thinking skills that give you emotional self-control? Teachers in high school are great, but why don't they get you ready for life? Pastors are so kind, but what don't they get you ready for in life? Political parties are great, but they don't teach you how to make wise choices for your success; they are more interested in the party's success. Friends care about you—but they just don't know what is good for succeeding in job hunting. To know that, you'd need to be at different times an employer and a job hunter. (That's me, by the way.)

I work in a private doctor's office so maybe because of that, students feel more comfortable to tell me what they are really thinking. When I ask students why they are not being taught these life skills for job hunting and "getting their life organized," they often don't know. But later I hear from those who want to teach them those skills:

- Teachers tell me a few parents have yelled at them because their kids are not being taught things that would help kids do well on college entrance exams. A few bad apples spoil the batch. Also there just isn't a curriculum for these things as such: a textbook. I think many teachers want to teach life skills and many parents want the life skills taught but they are not talking to each other about the topic. So I'm bringing it up!
- Parents tell me their kids don't listen to them. Their teenage kids think they are stupid.

- Employers say they are lucky if I can get someone to show up for work on time. Employees are often not "approachable" with any kind of constructive feedback except "good job."
- Pastors say they do but it's up to each person to practice their faith. It's unusual for people to seek out the pastor when their life skills are "weak."
- College instructors say they would but students would complain it doesn't help them do well on tests. It is hard enough to get students to learn the basic material, much less "life skills" that go beyond that. I HEAR THIS ALOT FROM COLLEGE PROFESSORS FOR THE LAST 25 YEARS.

Students say it feels like no one is helping them. Parents, teachers, friends, pastors just aren't helping. And they don't even know what to ask for to get their life together. It feels like the system is messed up and that's why they feel messed up.

Everyone is at cross purposes. I've talked to people from different countries and they say generally the same thing. It is hard to make progress on your personal dreams when the world doesn't support you. But it can't support you because it doesn't know you. And it doesn't know you because you haven't opened up to it.

The answer: let the world know what your dreams are. Ask people for help as part of "the village" that is helping you rise to a higher level of success. But don't depend on them. That will make you weak. Besides, you are the only one who can make decisions for yourself. You are the best person who can understand you. So ask people for help—to understand yourself and the world—then you start making choices and studying the results. Learn from your successes and setbacks. See who supports you and who is just giving lip service. Ask them and test them. I did.

Then fearlessly focus on your priorities and, like my Dad told me, "put first things first."

This involves "life organization skills." When I ask the hundreds of people I've taught this to, have they ever been taught this by someone else, 19 out of 20 say no.

Angie was approaching her sophmore year in college, ready to get her degree in business specializing in inventory

FIGURE 1.6.7
Use good advisers. They lessen the time it takes to solve life's big problems. By Toshow Borkovic

management. But she was anxious about the future. In the past, she wouldn't talk to anybody but now she talked to anyone and everyone she could find, from her parents to friends to the pastor of her church.

She even talked to her therapist.

She came up with an action plan:

1. Decide on a life mission and write it down. Angie wrote down "get married have kids in a safe community within half an hour of the mountains."

2. Decide where you want to live. With daycare about $15,000 a year, and knowing she wanted a few kids, Angie picked a place within an hour of her parents.

3. Decide on the lifestyle you want. Angie wanted to live in a middle-class lifestyle and a safe community with good schools and places that met her needs nearby. She didn't like small towns or big towns so she picked communities between 50,000 and 200,000 and circled them on a map.

4. Job search—big picture. Angie went on indeed.com and found the names of the big employers in the communities she wanted to settle in. She eliminated companies that might outsource a lot of their jobs to India or China. Then she went to company websites where more jobs were listed than she could find elsewhere. She kept a list of communities that had good numbers of jobs.

5. Real estate research. Angie researched what kinds of homes she could afford with her income and eliminated communities that were too expensive.

6. Church search. Angie did an Internet search just to see what churches were like in the qualifying communities.

7. Job experience. Angie saw the best jobs required work experience with certain software and certain kinds of projects. She made up her mind to do an independent study that would include experiences that would qualify her for more jobs.

Angie researched companies that might be interested in this kind of independent study and emailed 10 of them. She thought companies might jump at the idea of her working for a low or no wage job to get work experience that would be the ticket for a good paying job that "requires experience." She saw that if a company had to train someone it might cost $10-$20,000 compared to just hiring someone who already knows how to do those projects and work with those software programs. Angie wrote down what kinds of projects and software she needed in her résumé to get jobs in communities where she could afford a house.

8. Angie laid down in her bed and dreamed. She dreamed of getting a good job and coming home to her little house with her little family. She dreamed of fun parties with her friends from church and seeing their kids play with her kids. That was her dream. Then she gave it to God and decided she wasn't going to worry about her future since it was in better hands.

9. Angie emailed 20 companies and got responses from 10 and then had video lunch with them and picked five for follow up lunches in person, but only two said they had time. She liked both people and she shared her dream for an independent study. Both were receptive. She contacted her academic advisor and he agreed to read a paper she would produce from the independent study, though she would not receive any college credit.

10. Angie was grateful she had read "Prescription For Positivity" so she knew this whole process took one year—she needed to do it in her sophmore year so she could apply for an internship early in her junior year of college. Most people applied at Christmas time but she knew "the race goes to the swift" so she started months before anyone else. She used to do lists and day timers and filed important papers in folders. She was so grateful for her excellent time managment skills. And she used them with intensity. But her job wasn't over just yet.

11. In her work-study jobs, Angie learned the software and the business procedures for getting inventory jobs done.

12. Angie wrote down on a piece of paper 10 work skills she had that she could re-organize in different ways for different positions advertised. These included working with Excel, Access, Microsoft Word, email marketing software, image editing software and several software programs that were advertised in job positions. She focused on the kinds of software knowledge required for job listings and noticed there was often a difference between that and what her college classes offered.

13. Angie cleaned up her time management. She started making her to-do lists and planner notes neat and orderly, because she learned that bosses wanted to see what she had done and what was left to do so they could give her appropriate feedback. The lists and planner pages needed to be neatly written so they could quickly read it. Time is money. She wanted to be able to show an employer her to-do list and planner in a job interview and make a good impression that she could get tasks done and didn't need to be trained in using software, which would also cost the company money. The to do lists all followed a systematic format from left to write on lined paper: check box, number, line for due date, item to be done (5-10 words). When completed she'd only check the box not the rest of the writing, so the boss could see what was done. Also she would efficiently just scan down the vertical column of boxes and just read the items with an empty box when she was seeing what to do next. Efficient. Likewise her planner had a line for every 15 minutes from 8 am to 6 pm. When she opened it up, the left page and right page had a column for every day of the week, from Monday through Sunday. Now she could see the whole week at one look. And so could her employer.

14. Angie improved her interview skills. She read up on how to do well in a job interview and she practiced following threads of conversation, and other communication skills reviewed in this book. Her confidence rose.

15. To do well in a job interview, Angie practiced having good posture, dressing like a professional, using professional time management strategies, and making good eye contact while talking in a professional manner. She practiced these while interacting with people in class. She Googled topics on interviewing and watched YouTube videos.

16. Angie searched for the qualities that get people hired. She saw they were good communication and having an optimistic attitude. She worked on her attitude every day. Also employers were looking for people who looked like successful fellow employees. Angie made up her mind to redo her wardrobe to "dress for success." She researched women's magazines for how to dress for success topics. Then she hit the thrift stores and consignment stores and bought new clothes with money from a second job she picked up.

17. Angie started this process in September of her sophmore year in college. By December of her junior year, a full year ahead of her fellow students, she was starting her informal internship or work-study. By February of her senior year, with the experience and skills that mattered, she had a job offer—once she demonstrated proficiency in the software they used and at working with the team on projects. The company saw she was quick and a team player. Her friends started looking for work after graduation in May of their senior year—2 years and 8 months after Angie had quietly started practicing her "positivity for job hunting." They told her they were so frustrated that many employers asked for their work experience with certain software and certain projects. Angie's friends asked how they could get experience if nobody was willing to hire them and give them work experience in the first place? Angie recommended they read *Prescription for Positivity: Life Skills to Live Your Best Life.* She didn't tell them they were starting two years too late. That would not have been a very friendly thing to say. Better leave that for a book to do.

>**LIFE SKILLS:** initiative, learned from setbacks, stayed hopeful, focused on accomplishments, let go of what she couldn't control, saw life as for learning.

>**ACTION STEP:** write a to do list that is neat and tidy, using check circles. Check off the items this week to finish it. Then put it in a folder labeled "to do lists" so they are ready for you to show at your next job interview. Game changer!

FIGURE 1.7.0
Even the biggest wave of problems can be solved by
teamwork. But everyone has to show initiative.
By Toso Borkovic.

7

How "Initiative" skills solve big problems!

Combine habits with a positive and "heads-up" attitude

There is an awesome power when you combine good habits with a heads-up attitude and a positive, goal-focused attitude. In the following hypothetical story, the moral is little changes lead to big changes if you have a good attitude.

The First Responder story

One day you might be in a fire, flood or traffic accident. You will get assistance from a First Responder. First Responders are people responding to the scene of an accident or tragedy. They include policemen, firemen, paramedics and common citizens.

This man is now a First Responder. He learned courage and decisiveness, and not by accident. Positivity got him there. How? He gave his attitude a little jumpstart every day. Three years later he was ready to save lives. Let him tell you how he did it (to protect his privacy we fictionalized some parts).

FIGURE 1.7.1
First Responder.
By Esther Phingmoo.

He got sick of his (unhealthy) pessimism

"My attitude used to be down, focused on me and what went wrong. Very selfish and full of pain. All the time. I got sick of it. I signed up for a First Responder training course and got serious about improving myself. I started finding a little something that stressed me. Just a little. I'd tell myself this: that's not right. I'm going to fix it now. Maybe I forgot to look at my to-do list. Maybe I didn't plan a week ahead. Maybe I lapsed into people pleaser mode. Whatever. It was going to be no more."

He started with positive to-do lists focused on his life goals

"I'd figure a plan to fix it right there. I decided to look at my to-do list every day. I decided to always plan a week ahead. No more people pleasing. And then I got really serious. I mean I held myself accountable. No excuses. No BS. No whining. I hate whining now—from me. It makes you weaker. I just observed that in myself," he said.

He got excited about making little changes

"I needed to focus on making weaknesses into strengths. So when I'd get even the least bit stressed about something, I'd pounce on it. I'd say, here's one. Fix it. Here's another one. Change it. Right away. No hesitation. Now. Why wait? It's not a 'I have to,' it is an 'I want to' moment. A little urgent. Not rushed."

"Really positive self-talk helped me to keep improving. As a man. As a father. As a professional. I saw I had to constantly remind myself to stay up. Up in attitude. Up in results. Now you're not always going to be up. I get that. There will always be ups and downs. I think this is normal. You're going to have good days and bad days. I'm talking about my performance and how I reacted to it."

He learned from good days and bad days

"But my new attitude is this. You got to learn from the down days to have more good days. My attitude now is usually up. It's from all this mental preparation. I am part of a team. I don't want to badly affect the team by my attitude. No, I can't drag others down. I need to be a positive part of the team. I need to teach myself. When I get a little stressed, I stop and fix it. I move on."

The important thing: keep driving forward

"It's been quite a journey. First came a bad breakup. I needed to go through some bad circumstances. I needed to grow through some immaturity. I saw there were always going to be ups and downs. Always, always. The important thing is to keep driving forward. Now I'm a better man, a better dad and a better professional. It feels good."

The take home message: a little change every day goes a long way.

Interpretation

How did he use positivity? He focused on his goals every day! He used lists of what he liked and didn't like to find a new career. Then he used lists every day to succeed as a First Responder. He used positive thinking strategies such as goal-setting to make steady daily progress. He was focused on his mission on life: to become best man he can be. He encountered setbacks and just shrugged them off. In classic positivity fashion, he focused on little accomplishments he could make every day and then reveled in them. He got it: big accomplishments are only made from little accomplishments. When I asked him where he would be without this organization and attitude, gave me a one word answer with a blank look on his face.

"NOWHERE."

Discussion

Good things don't happen by accident. Every good thing requires work. The First Responder did a great job focusing on his goals, but he didn't do it alone. He frequently talked to close friends when he had tough times, like we all do. It takes a village to raise a child and another village to raise a professional and keep them at a high level of performance. The First Responder is what we would call a "high value" person because he has skills that are challenging to learn and that is why he can command a good salary. It's all about knowing your mission in life and staying focused.

The First Responder initially tried the Lone Ranger approach and it didn't work, even with lots of positivity. Finding great friends passionate about the same things you love can make all the difference. He did a great job reaching out, asking for help from others and creating a strong circle of friends who encouraged him and challenged him in his professional education. Do you feel your initiative rising after reading this inspiring story?

"Do you actually go into burning buildings?" I asked him. "With my training yes. I wear a suit and a breathing tank. Often the fumes alone are enough to kill you if the heat doesn't. Then we have to find the bodies—living or dead. We have to go into every corner of every room and make sure we are not leaving anybody in there—or animals. Yes we at times have to crawl. There might be a big fire underneath us or above us and vision may be very limited, so sometimes we are crawling and trying to find someone by touch, by reaching out our hand. Of course if the floor is about to collapse from underneath us we have to get out. Otherwise, we go through the whole house before we leave."

"That sounds scary," I replied, laughing at my own lack of courage for such situations. He gave me half a smile. "It's our training," he said.

>**LIFE SKILLS:** positivity, ramp method, asking for help, using a support system.

>**ACTION STEP:** find one small thing you've been pessimistic about and do one small thing today to make progress on it. Then take some time to appreciate your accomplishment.

What initiative is good for

Initiative is the first quality of positivity because it asserts choice. You can make the first move. You have free will. You can be a leader in your life, not just a follower. But if you don't believe it then you won't have that quality.

You have the ability to show initiative in your life. There are trillions of connections in your brain just waiting for you to use them. Set a small, five-minute goal and do one thing to make progress on it. I did that just now writing this sentence. It's not hard. But you can make it so hard it feels impossible. Limiting beliefs are the most common way we ruin our initiative. A limiting belief is like a leash for a dog that's already in your house. There's no need for it. It is an unnecessary restraint on your most precious possession: your freedom. Are you listening to me? Are you understanding me? Since this is just a book, it is only you who will see to the answer to that question. May God help you.

Limiting beliefs

One common limiting belief is the belief that you need to feel motivated to be motivated. "I wish I could get motivated to do this thing," is an example of this limiting belief. We do things all the time whether we feel motivated or not, like get out of bed and eat breakfast.

When I hear someone describe their lack of motivation, I can tell that person has gone down a rabbit hole of what I call an emotional illusion. An optical illusion is the experience of seeing something that seems real but is not, such as when heat waves on a highway look like there is water. That is an optical illusion.

An emotional illusion is an emotion that feels real—but it is really wrong. For example, if you feel like you lack confidence and you tell yourself, "I'll ask this girl out when I feel confident." The idea here is you have to feel motivated in order to be motivated. The emotions are wrong. You can ask her out without feeling confident. We do things all the time because of our thinking. We focus on a goal and act on it while our feelings change for the better or for the worse. But we stay motivated as long as we don't let our feelings be our guide. Our thinking is our guide.

In general, limiting beliefs are notions that we can't do something or be something because of outside forces. In the Middle Ages, people believed it wasn't possible to combat plagues and famines. Those are limiting beliefs. People thought calamities were curses on humanity from God. Now we know such curses can be fought with vaccines, modern farming methods and dams, all invented by the belief that we can use science to solve problems. All this science and technology was made by hard working people like you, tackling their goals one day at a time. How do I know? I worked in a microbiology lab for two years studying leukemia cells. Every day we set goals for the day and achieved them.

Dump your limiting beliefs that you can't do something or be something and start living your dreams, one day at a time. Make your dreams practical and fun. Initiative can be cultivated this way, like a garden. Learn what you find fun while making progress on your dreams. Let initiative make a little progress every day for you.

Don't wait for motivation. Get into the game of your life and your motivation will follow. Get used to the idea of taking action whether you feel like it or not. Spend time around others who share your passions. Feel their energy. Cultivate your creativity. Feel its energy. Cultivate energizing daily routines. Feel their energy. Open yourself up to nature and feel its energy. Get involved in helping people fight their troubles. Feel their energy as their lives improve.

Let yourself feel the energy of life. Let yourself feel the rhythm of life. The creatures of the earth and sky live in your neighborhood, wherever you live. They are moving every day. Let me tell you a story about that.

The rabbits and foxes

Every day when the sun rises in your neighborhood, the rabbit wakes up and the fox wakes up. The fox knows it must run faster than the slowest rabbit or it will go hungry. The rabbit knows it must run faster than the fastest fox or it will die. Either way, the rabbit and the fox know one thing. When the sun rises they are going to be running.

Do you feel your initiative growing after reading this story?

➢**LIFE SKILLS:** psychological insight, identifying limiting beliefs, spotting emotional illusions, replacing limiting beliefs with empowering beliefs, interpersonal skills.

➢**ACTION STEP:** identify one thing that feels real, but isn't true, such as it is going to be hard to brush your teeth. Then do just what you think is difficult to prove it isn't difficult. Rate your belief in the limiting belief (on a 1-10 scale) before and after your action to see how you can change how much you feel a limiting belief is true. Share your results with someone else and notice if your feeling of self-control rises. In the space below, circle what you feel:

- Belief in the limiting belief before the exercise:
  0 1 2 3 4 5 6 7 8 9 10
- Belief in the limiting belief after the exercise:
  0 1 2 3 4 5 6 7 8 9 10

Now draw an arrow from the top circled number to the lower circled number to show your progress. You're not trapped! Limiting beliefs can be changed!

Life skill: to-do lists speed up initiative

Since cave man days, we've been making marks, sometimes on cave walls. What works for you and your dreams? There are many ways to write things down. Pick a method that you feel good about, that feels a part of you, in sync with you. Use an app or create a bullet journal. The main problem with a to-do list is it gets forgotten. So let's customize a method that works for you. A to-do list involves:

- Paper or screen
- Check boxes
- Due dates or priority notes
- Items

The bonus of writing something down is you don't have to think things through again. The to-do list is like a second brain for you. Nice! It reminds you of your accomplishments so it is like a success coach. Very nice! It also taps into your wealth of experience, your inner genius. Bonus!

Four tips for better to-do lists

Here are a few tips to creating better lists.

1. Make personal, school and work to-do lists. Have a sheet of paper for each. That way you're organized. You can even have lists for certain projects. I once had a to-do list for "Writing a book," and look where that got me. You could have a to-do list for a party.

2. Keep the lists where you'll use them. I keep my book-writing to-do list in a backpack on a clipboard. Keep them where you'll see them. I keep my work and personal to-do lists on my desk or on my whiteboard. You'll find you get more things done just by having your to-do list open on the desk where you're working. If the list is on your phone, open it up and put your phone on your desk. Cultivate little habits like this.

3. Write down items in a way that is fun. Items should be 5-10 minutes to get done so if you have a bigger task, break it into smaller tasks. Alternate items that take energy with those that boost your energy. Read five pages in a book. Then call a friend for a party this coming weekend. You get the idea. Doodle. Write in smiley faces. Draw arrows. For check boxes, feel free to express your individuality by using circles, triangles, hearts, you name it. When you finish an item, you can draw a line through the circle or color it in. But make it so you can just skim the list and see the open checkboxes of things you still have to do. As you look down the list, for each item, there will be a checkbox, a number, a period, a due date, then the item itself. Now you can quickly skim down the list and just read the items with an empty circle or box. Time saver!

4. Visualize success constantly. Visualize doing well on a quiz or test every time you finish a little study item. Imagine how good it will feel to get the thing done—before you even start doing it. It's going to feel so good! Cultivate warm, loving feelings for your to-do list and it will reward you more. You are really just loving your life and its opportunities. You are using the positivity nerve network reviewed earlier, with the amygdala and RACC (rostral anterior cingulate cortex).

Does all this seem cold and mechanical? Then customize it! Use different colors or stickers...you get the idea. Personalize it. Does all this seem like it's taking away your freedom? Then reward yourself for your work. On your personal to-do list, write down something you are going to do to reward yourself for your effort. Set yourself up for success. I needed to get writing done for my editor, so I wrote down, "sip some caramel latte and do a walking meditation." You are self-organized, self-motivated and self-directed. Taking the time to make lists is an awesome way to transform your life! Now let's crank things up a bit.

How to tap into your inner genius

You and I both know you have a lot more potential, a lot more experience, than people give you credit for. Let's tap into that. But how?

Tap into your experience with the BEST WIN acronym. If you are tackling a project with excellence, don't just do the first thing that comes to mind. That's what everyone else is doing. You are going for a "WIN" or a good grade on a test (or, in my case, to write a good book), so use 7 questions that prompt you to think outside the box. Let's look at what those might be.

The BEST WIN acronym:
your magic wand for problem solving

B is for better. Think of one way to do something that would be a little better than what you are currently doing. THINK.

E is for easier. Is there a quicker way to get this done? Often the first thing we think of is the most complicated. Spending time thinking of a more efficient way will save time overall. BE INVENTIVE.

S is for simpler. If you don't ask, you won't find something simpler. I asked if there is a better way to organize sections of writing so I can swap them around like pieces in a jig saw puzzle. I found the software I'm using right now, Scrivener, and it's saved me 20 hours. That means I'm going to meet my deadline. Simpler is important. CHALLENGE YOURSELF TO SIMPLIFY.

T is for time-tested. Talk to people who are doing what you want to do. What has worked for them? That's how I found Scrivener. What will you find? BE OPEN TO A NEW DISCOVERY.

W is for the Web. Ask on the internet and see what people say on Quorum and other venues that seek to pool people's collected opinions or intelligence. If you don't ask, you won't find anything. TEAMWORK.

I is for important. This is for rating how high a priority you have for an item. Time to be skeptical. Ask, "How important is this really?" "Can I just leave this out?" "Is this a time waster?" "How will this really move me ahead for my goals today?" Value your time. Be a little impatient for big results today. Rate the importance of what you want: a gut feeling, a number from 1-5, a letter from A-C. Everything isn't equally important. And all important things don't need to get done today. BE AN EFFICIENCY FANATIC.

N is for necessary. How necessary is it to get a certain item done today? For every 10 items that feel necessary, two will do nothing for you and two you won't even remember tomorrow.

Look at your old to-do lists and you'll see what I mean. HATE WASTE.

Try using the acronym today. After using it, do you feel your initiative getting better?

I dug out of my career crisis by valuing my time in this manner. I blamed my job for being a dead-end job. But I wasn't valuing my time in terms of my life goals. When I used the BEST WIN method and other methods, I got back in the driver's seat in my life. I focused on discovering my passions, discovering a good career fit for my passions. After work I went to the Orange County library in Southern California, and pulled out my to-do lists and got to work on my life goals. It was so exciting.

On the other hand, all the to do lists in the world are not going to do you any good if you don't write down when you are actually going to do the items in your to-do list. For that, you are going to need an administrative assistant called your planner.

➤**LIFE SKILLS:** to do lists, thinking things through, creative problem solving, tapping into your experience.

➤**ACTION STEP:** pick one five-minute task you plan to do today. Run it through the BEST WIN acronym. Adjust your plan to make it better. Act on it.

Life skill: use planners to pounce on problems

Value is real. This book is about helping you become high value. You like high value things. You want a cell phone that is fast with many apps and that doesn't break. High value. You want a pair of shoes that are stylish yet comfortable to dance in. You want a laptop that is fast, has lots of storage and keeps on working. You get the picture. High value things are made by high value people.

Using a planner boosts your value. Anytime you need to do something, make a habit of writing it down twice: once on a to-do list and once in a planner. Then make a habit of looking at them every day or every hour. Planners are daily and monthly schedules that record when you are going to get things done. They usually have lines for every 15 or 30 minutes from about 8 am to 8 pm. They are for fun things as much as for work. You can bet that laptop and watch you like were made by people who planned out their work using a planner or organizational software. They got their work done then they went out and had fun. It's the "work hard, play hard" lifestyle and planners make it possible.

Planners boost your initiative because they help you make a commitment to do something at a certain time.

As you might imagine, all planners are not created equal. Some just work better. They get written in. They get looked at. As with to-do lists, I recommend you sync your life with your planner. Here are a few tips on picking a planner that fits your personality:

1. Make it small enough that you will be comfortable carrying it with you. If you don't have it handy, you won't use it. Do you carry things in a purse or book bag? Make sure it will fit there. Don't make it so small you won't use it. Many people carrying a schedule on their phone find they don't use it. The entries are too small to see.

2. Planners are your way to be reliable and dependable like that phone and laptop you admire. Get one with enough details to write in all the things you need to record. I like planners with a line every 15 minutes from 8 am to 6 pm. That is what is on the electronic medical record software I use. I used one like that in medical school as well. A line every 30 minutes gives you the option to slow down on a project and take 30 minutes to do what should only take **15.** Oops. You just dropped the value of your time by 50%.

Keep your planner open on your desk

3. Shop for a good one. Go to an office supply store and look at all the planners in a section. There might be a hundred. Open one up and ask yourself, would this work for me? Some show all seven days of a week on two pages. Others show one page per day. Only you can decide what would be best for you. Get one that is custom fit for all the things you are going to juggle: work, school and a fun social life. Ask people doing what you want to do what kind of planner they are using and why. Walk in the footsteps of the successful. Don't argue with success; imitate it.

Is all this a prescription to be another workaholic, another person giving their life so some corporation makes a profit? It could be. That was me. That was what got me in trouble.

"Don't argue with success, imitate it."

I just looked at what I had to do to get a job and keep a job. I was desperate. I just wanted a way to pay my bills and pay off my school loans. What's wrong with that? It is low value. I was acting like my only function was to work for someone else. I want you to keep in mind your hopes, your dreams and your expanding range of interests and passions. Your potential is expanding like the universe is expanding. Your personal to-do list should have one item every day to expand your life so you don't become a workaholic.

Brain imaging studies show there is tremendous growth of millions of new neurons and billions of new connections in your brain, EVERY DAY. Tap into your potential by exploring new things with your to-do lists. Explore new hobbies. Discover new passions. Learn skills with new side jobs. Be curious about life. Challenge yourself with a fun and playful attitude.

Do you feel a change in your initiative after using a planner? I sure did.

Q and A with Dr. J

Q: I feel like I'm a failure because some classes, like math, are super tough for me. I want to go to college or a trade school but numbers freak me out. How can to-do lists help me?

A: Numbers freak me out too. I got a low grade in pre-calculus in high school. I didn't ask for help. I got pessimistic. To-do lists are tools, like a hammer. But sometimes you need more help, like someone to tell you when to use a hammer or a screwdriver or a drill. A human being who will teach you. I spent 14 years in college so I often had to ask for a tutor or help from a teaching assistant. A friend acted as a tutor and spent several hours every week teaching me what I didn't get from the book or lecture for my chemistry class. His name was Kabuika and he saved me. He was an answer to prayer. So I think prayer helps too. My first grade in college physics 101 was 58/**100.** I got the courage to ask for help (positivity). The professor for this summer class spent an hour twice a week for about four weeks, answering my many questions. Then we talked about sailing and other adventures we'd had. Lectures often leave you with only part of what you need to learn. You get additional learning from reading and doing the homework assignments that apply what was in the lecture, so do them the night after the lecture, religiously. There is such power in such routines!

Tutors boost your initiative—and IQ— here's how:

1. Attend the lecture. Use advanced study skills. Skim the lecture material beforehand for about 5 minutes to understand the three main ideas in the lecture. During the lecture, put a "?" next to anything that doesn't make sense. This is a to-do list on the fly. After the lecture, if things still aren't clear, approach the instructor with your questions. You are paying to learn. If the instructor seems unwilling to answer your questions, see if you can take the class from someone else. In medical school I saw that the people who asked the most questions got some of the best grades on tests. There was cutthroat competition. Asking questions makes you more competative. Before you even apply to a school, ask what kind of support they provide for learning such as tutors, office hours with teaching assistants, after hours labs where tutors can answer questions. If a school doesn't offer that, seek out a different school and thank your lucky stars you read this book and did your research. In life, you mostly make your own luck. I am told a psychologist once created a curriculum for learning to be more lucky. You just made yourself more lucky. Many expensive schools with famous teachers do a bad job teaching but a great job marketing so they look desirable. Colleges rarely offer a refund if you are not satisfied. Buyer beware. You should be as quick to drop a class or a program or a degree, as a car that is a lemon and always breaking down. JEALOUSLY FIGHT FOR YOUR FUTURE OR YOU WON'T HAVE ONE.

2. Work with a tutor. To-do lists and a planner can help. And this goes for any learning task, in or out of school. I used this method to learn the software I'm using right now, as well as the electronic medical record software I practice medicine with. Read the text. Watch the video. Keep notes. For software learning, keep a recipe book with step-by-step instructions of what to do to solve certain tasks. Then keep a to-do list of questions just for your tutor. Keep a record of your step-by-step work to solve a certain problem and note where you got stuck with a star, so the tutor can hone right in on what you didn't understand. Ask the tutor what you could do to be better at learning the material. Is there a pattern in what you're missing? Is there a different study method you could be using? Often there is a common thread, such as when a person is trying to memorize facts when concepts need to be learned.

3. Recruit your team. Be patient. Be persistent. Slow and steady wins this race. If your tutor doesn't seem to be helping and can't say why, get a different tutor. Believe in your method. There are also other helpers. I was very stressed by giving up on my career and living in poverty. I probably needed to see a counsellor for better stress management. I think I also have a learning disability in learning math. Learning disability testing would have found that out and qualified me for special help, such as tutoring, in that field. Schools want you to succeed. They just don't know what you need. It is up to you to advocate for yourself. It is scary to have to speak up and say you need help. I know. I was there. I still am there. I have had to ask all kinds of people to help me to get this book written. Their names are in the acknowledgments. Don't think your education is all on you. It is a team effort. But you have to recruit your team and lead your team. That's what I did. My dream was to be a doctor and a writer. Here I am. BUT NO PERSON TAUGHT ME THIS. I HAD TO FIGURE IT OUT MYSELF.

This is positivity "turbo charged"

I have explained the items in this Q and A to about 100 college students and about 10 said they had heard it before but only two knew how to apply all these elements to working with a tutor. This is special insider knowledge. It applies to learning any new challenging task, such as writing a book or repairing a car. This is positivity turbo charged. What good would it be without a planner? Worthless.

Do you feel your initiative growing with the use of advanced study skills, a support team and a planner? I sure do.

➢**LIFE SKILLS:** using to do lists, planners, building a support team.

➢**ACTION STEP:** write down on your to do list the name of one person you are going to ask a question this week in order to get something done in a more sophisticated manner. Then ask that person the question. You are working smarter. His or her IQ is boosting your IQ.

Life skill: shopping lists add eco-friendliness

It is a trick to juggle all these life skills. It also costs money. Here is a quick and easy way to use a shopping list to get the things you need but save money and help the planet while you are at it. I've saved $500 per year for 10 years using this list. That's $5,000 in savings! Here's how you do it.

On your phone you have an app for making reminders or check off lists. Title one list "Hardware" for things you'd get at a hardware store. Title another," Retail" for clothes and other retail items. A third can get the title "Sporting goods." Lastly, title one "Freebies." On Facebook marketplace, Craigslist and elsewhere on the internet, there are people who want to give you things for free—or a low cost. If this is a priority to you, join your local "Buy For Nothing" group.

The environment has been taking a beating. Landfills are filling up. Air pollution is persisting. Gas prices are going up. Enter the positivity shopping list. Make up your mind you'll go to a grocery store just once per week and other kinds of stores just twice per month. This will force you to plan ahead and be okay with delaying the gratification of getting the things you feel you need. In reality, 10% of the things we feel we need are just comfort shopping items. So ask yourself, "Do I need this or is this just a comfort shopping item?"

Score a success for positivity and nature. Instead of those once per week trips to stores—that cost $10 per trip just in gas—you'll do it twice per month. That's 20 fewer trips per year. Twenty times 10 is a saving of $200 per year in travel expenses—and less air pollution adding to climate change. That's $2,000 in 10 years. Meanwhile, 10% of those "must have" items will drop off the list. You just won't need them. Maybe you'll find some style-upgrade items at a thrift store. Maybe a friend will give you some things you were thinking of buying. Maybe your life situation will change and you won't need what you thought you needed yesterday.

Isn't it great to know you can make a difference today for the planet? Just by planning ahead you are making decisions that are more compassionate for the planet. You are improving your relationship with nature. Plus you can cut your food bill by up to 30% with this technique. Realize most of us throw away 1/3 of all the food we buy. It is an awful, quiet, ongoing catastrophe nobody wants to talk about. Well I am. So show a little healthy pessimism next time you go shopping. Ask if you really will eat all that food you are buying. Ask how quickly certain things (like strawberries) get moldy or rotten (like avacadoes), and make up your mind to eat them quickly. Better yet: make a meal plan for the week and stick to it. Then see how much food you are throwing away after being a much more careful shopper. This kind of positivity can help save the planet for sure.

Do you feel your initiative is getting a boost from how you can use shopping lists?

>**LIFE SKILLS:** shopping list, applying values, delaying gratification, valuing nature.

>**ACTION STEP:** pick one thing you wanted to buy but then don't because you'd be "comfort shopping." Then comfort yourself another way—call a friend, meditate, spend some time with an inspiring pet.

Pro tip: Jump-starts boost initiative

If your initiative hits a wall, know that happens to all of us. Not to worry. A jump-start can save you. We can all use a jump-start in the morning and periodically through the day. Many of these techniques I first learned from Professor Curtis at summer camp. Jump-starts made his positivity very effective.

Here are the jump-starts you'll find in this book:
- Stories with a message (like the grizzly bear story in "Setbacks")
- Sayings (like "Make happiness up to you")
- Signs (like a setback is a sign you have something to learn)
- Symbols (like the symbol of balance)
- Asking for help from a friend (as I did with John Curtis)
- Getting a guide (as I did with John Curtis)
- Fact checking (like how you are making progress)
- Journaling (to see your accomplishments)
- Pet therapy (like having a dog companion you so you aren't lonely)
- Daily routines (like getting up with the birds)
- Brain science facts (like we have trillions of connections)
- To-do lists (once you work on one item, motivation increases)
- Diet (like minimize processed food and use caffeine in moderation)
- Exercise (it boosts nerve growth factor)

- Spirituality (like reading the Bible or spending time in a place that feels sacred)
- Creative procrastination (put one thing off to finish another)
- Music (find the kind you like and turn the volume up)
- Visualizing (if we imagine doing it, it becomes easier to do)
- Perspective (if you notice pessimism, you can let it go)
- Goal setting (keeping goals visible on a white board improves motivation)
- Setbacks (take risks because they are a source of energy and learning)
- Let go of emotional illusions (like believing you're bad if you feel bad)
- Retrospective view (look back at your accomplishments at the end of your day)
- Let go (of pessimism, of toxic people and of toxic media)
- Self-improvement (see life as a project to be a better you)
- Meditation (for self-understanding and self-control)
- Nature (it can be a wonderful source of inner peace)

Life skill: write your life mission

Does your life lack focus? That can cripple your initiative. Create focus by defining a life mission. It can be most anything, including "I want to improve myself" or "I want a life mission." This saying now is part of your inner narrative. As we grow and change, it is normal to adjust your life mission accordingly. In the preface I explained how I changed my life mission once I discovered how passionate I was about medical science.

Do you find you have more initiative once you have defined your life mission? It sure helps me! It sure helped Ginger too.

Ginger's story: from coffee shop to college

Ginger had a passion for anthropology and wanted to go to college, but she had no money for a degree. She needed a job. She connected the dots of her life goals: job to pay for college, college degree, work as an anthropologist. She kept those in mind and kept looking for a way to achieve her goals. She learned of a certain national coffee shop chain that offers scholarships for college degrees for qualified employees. She applied to work at that national coffee shop chain—and was hired! Later she applied for a scholarship and was accepted. Now she has her degree and is so happy about it. "This place has changed my life!" she says. That change only happened because she held on to her life mission: to work as an anthropologist. She organized her life so everything worked toward her goals.

➢**LIFE SKILLS:** define a life mission, creative problem solving, research, life organization.

➢**ACTION STEP:** write one sentence about your life mission. It doesn't have to totally describe it. Just describe part of it. Now let yourself emotionally connect with it. Let it inspire you.

Recap

You have learned that initiative is totally changeable. You can "amp it up" by using rating scales, myth busters, inspiring stories, to-do lists, planners, shopping lists, jump-starts and writing your life mission. Your awareness of these components alone is so valuable. Now it's time to re-rate your initiative. **Go back to the start of this chapter and circle the number that reflects your new sense of your initiative.** Did it grow? I hope so! My video training series also gives you more instruction on how to use these techniques so they become an automatic part of your life.

FIGURE 1.8.0
Unhealthy pessimism is a gorilla in your mind. The fist of unhealthy pessimism can grab you. Setbacks are a temptation to lapse into this kind of unhealthy skepticism. But positivity shows you the way to victory. By Toso Borkovic.

8

How "Setbacks" can make your life more meaningful

Setback rating scale: measure your progress

Setbacks—we've all had them. They sneak up on you like a sneeze, then they are gone. They seem like they are a reaction to when things go bad or not according to plan. We may obsess on how to avoid them. But here they come again, seemingly like the wind, for no rhyme or reason. Yet like the wind, could they be used to generate energy? Motivation? Inspiration?

Here is a chance to measure what you are learning from setbacks. Fill out the rating scales below to see where you are at with those questions at the start of this chapter. Repeat the test at the end. Put me to the test. How well did I do teaching you something? (If a teacher can never fail and never wants to be graded like the rest of us are—that would make you doubt their value now, wouldn't it? Circle one number for each of the questions below.

Before reading this chapter, rate how well you can use setbacks to:
1. Boost your energy 0123456789 10
2. Boost your ambition to improve your life 0123456789 10
3. Boost your learning about life 0123456789 10

After reading this chapter, rate how well you can use setbacks to:
1. Boost your energy 0123456789 10
2. Boost your ambition to improve your life 0123456789 10
3. Boost your learning about life 0123456789 10

How well did I do? No change? Read the chapter again! Did you then see a change in how well you can use setbacks to improve your life? I hope so! Don't forget to come back here and rate your progress when you get to the end of the chapter! And yes, sadly, one option is that I failed you. If that happened, I am sorry.

Turn setbacks into...

The bottom line: setbacks can be great! While initiative helps set things in motion every day, setbacks keep you going. Everything depends on how you work with setbacks. Fortunately, there are a lot of setbacks waiting in store for you. Remember me on the "walk with the Good Professor"? There were all kinds of setbacks on that walk and he waved them off like mosquitoes. Bird after bird flew away before we could identify one. We had dozens of setbacks in dozens of minutes. All the elements of positivity were there on that walk—including learning from setbacks. That's why it had such a powerful effect on me. If we had identified birds with every step it would have been easy and boring. But we had setback after setback. It was maddening! That gave me energy to be open to new ideas and **really listen** to what the Good Professor had to say.

And that morning my life changed forever. Let's take a closer look at those all-important setbacks that come loaded with such treasure.

Setbacks are what happens when things don't go the way you want them to go. You plan for "A" and you get "B." First off you have a negative emotion, such as anger, anxiety or stress. But it is an emotion and that energizes your brain. (Anxiety actually activates the amygdala which is also one of the two positivity centers in the brain.) You are free to steer it however you want. You can learn from it. You can learn endlessly about yourself and the world with this energy.

If things always went according to plan, life would be boring and uneventful. It would be unchallenging. The world would be revolving around you, which it certainly doesn't. If you are in that frame of mind, snap out of it! Look out for setbacks and react to them.

Setbacks are something you can look forward to today. They help you RISE in your value. RISE is an acronym of the four main values you get from setbacks:
- Reminders to get your mind off yourself
- Inspiration to think outside the box
- Self-challenge to do more in a new way
- Energy for your inner wildness
- "Inner wildness?"

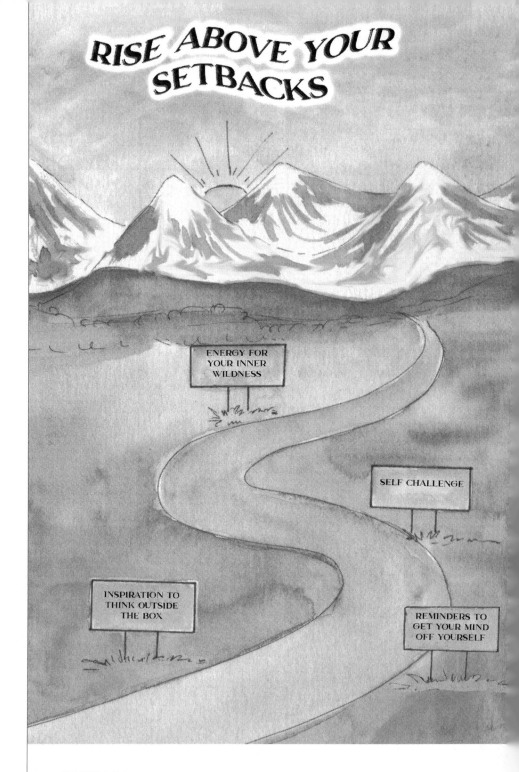

FIGURE 1.8.1

The RISE you get from setbacks. By Esther Phingmoo.

Yes. You have a free spirit that loves the adventure life puts in front of you every day. Which reminds me of a story that illustrates the RISE you get from setbacks.

The grizzly story: more spontaneity

FIGURE 1.8.2
Teddy Roosevelt on horseback in North Dakota's Badlands. By Esther Phingmoo.

It was winter and 20° below Fahrenheit. In North Dakota that means it's time to plan summer trips. John Curtis invited me over to his house. I glanced in the living room at a photograph of Teddy Roosevelt on some horseback adventure. John said, "Hey come on down into my den." We walked down the stairs, took a right, walking past a pile of camping gear to our left which included buffalo rugs and Dutch ovens, then we faced a wall of books. From floor to ceiling and 12 feet wide left to right, John had a wall of great literature including books about the art and literature of the American West. That was the title of a course he taught at the university in town. I was looking at a literary treasure.

We took another right into a 10 by 10 foot room lined with antiques from the Wild West days. (See Figure 1.6.6, a photo of

John and I in his den.) A painted buffalo skull hung on the wall along with a primitive bow and several arrows. Leaning against one corner was a flint lock rifle, a relic of the mountain man days. Beside his chair was a pile of maps.

Anywhere wild

He sat down and grabbed a map. "Where would you like to go this summer?" he asked. "Anywhere wild," I replied. "How about Montana?" he asked. "Except no bears!" I noted. "I'm afraid of bears. I just want to camp, fish and get away."

A smirk snuck across his face and he chuckled through his nose. Oh no, I thought. A story is coming.

He shook his head at something funny he couldn't stop thinking about.

"Well, I have an ungodly number of papers to grade for Freshman English every spring. I mean they never end!" he said with a laugh.

"Oh," I replied. I was in high school at the time. I had no idea what he was talking about.

"So when that's all done at the end of May, I just have to get out of here! One year I decided to go to a good camping spot I knew of. We'll have to go there sometime. It's in Glacier National Park. Anyway, I was hell bent to get out of Dodge, so after work, about 3 pm, I jumped in my car and drove to Glacier. It's maybe a 12 hour drive. So I got there at 3 am."

"3 am!" I repeated.

"3 am," John said nodding. "I knew where to go so I parked my car at a trailhead."

"What's a trailhead?" I asked.

"Where the trail starts," he said.

"So I threw on my boots and backpack and headed on down the trail in the dark."

The Glacier Park grizzly

FIGURE 1.8.3

The Glacier Park grizzly.
By Esther Phingmoo.

"The dark?" I asked. I was afraid of the dark as well.

"Yeah," he said, waving his hand and lifting his bushy eyebrows. "I'd been on that trail a million times. I knew where to go. I hiked up an hour and pitched my tent and went to sleep."

"Wow," I said. "Cool."

"Thoreau said 'In wildness is the preservation of the world.' And it was going to get a little wild all right!" he said with a snicker. "Ha!" He shook his head and hurried back to the story.

"So I got up at daybreak and had to take a pee so I wandered up the hillside. I was camped right by the trail so I had to get away from that. Anyway, I wandered up into the bushes and did my business. I turned around and looked at my tent just in time to see a bear go right into it!"

"Oh my gosh!" I blurted out. I felt like I was in the tent with the grizzly.

"Yeah," he said. "Well, I waited there on the hillside, shivering, while Old Griz shredded my tent and sleeping bag and everything in my backpack looking for my food. And she got that too. Then she walked away."

"Holy smoke!" I exclaimed.

"I gathered up my things, stuffed them in my backpack, threw on my jeans that were all shredded to hell, and walked down the trail back to my car."

"At least you were ok," I said. "Don't jump to any conclusions like that!" he exclaimed. "I still had to deal with civilization!"

"I don't need signs."

"Yes," he replied, "Civilization can be worse than a bear! I got to the parking lot and there was a park ranger inspecting my car." My eyes widened. "Yeah," John said, "and this ranger was looking really upset."

"Why?" I asked.

"He saw my shredded gear and shook his head. Pointing to the front of my car, he asked me, 'Didn't you see the sign?' He was really angry."

"Why?" I asked.

"I told him, 'I don't need any signs. I come up here to get away. I know what I'm doing. I've been here a million times.'" "He said, 'Read the sign.' He was writing me out a ticket and ordering me around. He pointed and I couldn't see anything so I walked around to the other side of my car and there is a white sign on a fence alright. There was a bear symbol on it and in red letters it says, 'Area closed. Bear danger.'"

"That was a tough trip," I said. "First the bear got you..."

"Then the ranger did!" John said, laughing loudly and shaking his head.

FIGURE 1.8.4

Wildness is good for us.
By Esther Phingmoo.

In wildness is our preservation

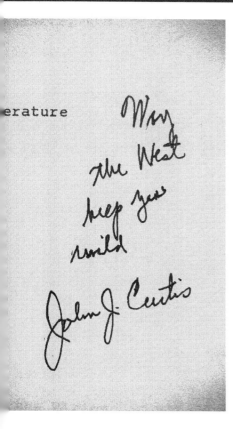

erature

May
the West
keep you
wild

John J. Curtis

FIGURE 1.8.5
How The Good Professor
signed his book to me.
"May the west keep you
wild."

Just telling the story brought a smile to his face and all the worries of the world vanished like so many vapors in the air. Just like Thoreau said they would.

This story is a metaphor for life. Some people impose their ideas on how life should be. Then funny things happen. They don't ask "What bad things might happen?" "How can I be ready for them?" "How do I keep myself safe?" "What are my weaknesses?" "How can that get me in trouble?" Because they don't ask the right questions, they don't get the right answers.

John learned to avoid trails with bear warnings on them. John looked forward to setbacks. They added to his swagger. They offered chances to make fun stories out of bad times. Adventures are made all the better by those bad times. And if you have a bunch of fun stories about a bunch of bad times, then you'll be the life of the party. John had that figured out.

➤**LIFE SKILLS:** storytelling using setbacks.

➤**ACTION STEP:** try to find the humorous side of the story in one setback you experienced. Then share that story with someone else. Now you're walking in the steps of the Good Professor!

More self-control

In the following stories you will see how people use setbacks for the four RISE principles that John Curtis first taught me.

"Why can't I make anything happen in my life?"

Jaimie felt stuck. She quit after one year in college. Everything seemed so tough. It was setback after setback. But then she dug a little deeper. What were those setbacks "in detail?" She couldn't tell as she looked back. But she was trying hard all by herself. She decided to open up to the idea she had all kinds of potential in life, she just needed other people's input, that was all.

A friend observed Jaimie spent hours on the internet. Jaimie told herself, "I'll fix that." Another friend suggested she talk to one of her college teachers. She did that. The teacher noticed Jaimie was often distracted in class and suggested she see a counselor for free. Jaimie said to herself, "I'll get on it." A friend showed her how to use to-do lists and a calendar with a "no excuses" attitude. Jaimie started doing that too. She was determined to transform herself.

Gradually, as the days went by, Jaimie felt herself becoming more and more confident about her future. It felt good to be organized. It felt good to be moving forward toward a goal. She felt so much more pride in herself. She went to a consignment store and got a new outfit for her new attitude. She felt confident over time she would find a career direction that made sense to her, like her new fashion sense made sense to her. A friend of Jaimie's had a similar experience.

"Why are other people dragging me down all the time?" Andy complained to himself.

Andy felt dragged down by the people around him. He felt like that dog that always howls when it hears a police siren. He was always complaining—about others and himself. Everyone seemed to drag him down. He felt like there was a "ring of fire" around him (to quote a Johnny Cash song) if the people around him didn't totally support him all the time with everything they did. He had fallen into this "dependency habit" without really questioning it. Big problem.

Andy talked to a friend. "I'm sick and tired of being sick and tired," he confessed. His friend wanted to be more positive as well. They made up their mind to check out podcasts and websites about thinking in an optimistic way. They heard you can use a saying to boost your independence and self-reliance. That was the tip Andy needed! If you don't cultivate a feeling of being independent, you are going to feel dependent on other people for your happiness. THIS WAS A LIFE CHANGING INSIGHT.

One simple way to do something to improve yourself, and quit being whiney and dependant, is to repeat a saying to yourself all day. Just one saying. Andy repeated the saying, "I can do it." He heard it on a song on the radio and liked it. When he said it to himself all day he found he not only got his homework done quicker but he felt more in the driver's seat in his life. Sayings really work, he concluded, so you don't have to feel like other people are dragging you down all the time. Nice!

"Why can't I advocate for myself?" Andy asked himself. Geogia was asking herself the same question.

Georgia felt like she was a magnet on a refrigerator door, stuck by invisible forces and going nowhere. She was afraid to speak up, to assert herself, to talk about anything if there was even the least bit of a chance for a disagreement. She was afraid of even the chance of setbacks. But at least she recognized that, she told herself. She confessed that to a friend, who said she felt the same thing about herself. They were afraid of anything going "wrong" in their life.

They listened to an interview with the singer Pink and felt inspired to check out other women's podcasts and websites on learning to believe in yourself. It all started from Georgia seeing that one setback: that she was afraid of setbacks. But now she was learning from them. Georgia was discovering new music, new podcasts and a newfound sense of her own specialness. Setbacks energized her, like to reach out to a friend, who helped her get out of the echo chamber of her own self-doubting thinking. Georgia is so grateful for setbacks and friends!

More insight into potential trouble: use a metaphor story for a truth about life

Why am I telling so many stories? Stories carry so much information and meaning in them. Just by reading a story you can understand new information and feel what it will be like to put it into action—or not.

Life doesn't revolve around you. Bad things happen to good people all the time. Be ready for setbacks with a "heads-up attitude." That means you are anticipating a setback with every goal you pursue, preparing for it with an alternative plan you've put some thought into.

Think before you act—or people will think you don't know what you are doing. Think before your talk—or people will think you don't know what you are talking about. I made both mistakes in this story when I was ten years old. This story is a metaphor. It symbolizes the trouble caused by not taking a heads-up attitude.

"Look before you leap!"

One day I was at the local river with a few friends and no fish were biting. We sat for an hour on the bank waiting for a tug on the line. Nothing. Our fishing bobbers sat there on the surface of the water like hot air balloons on a windless day. I glanced down the river and a movement caught my eye. A large, moss-covered snapping turtle crawled up on the riverbank to sun himself. "This is my chance!" I thought. "What a catch it might be!"

➤MISTAKE 1. I leapt up and didn't think about any bad things that might happen. My friends were caught off guard. I dashed down the shore as fast as I could. When I got to the turtle, it had just scrambled into the river. I jumped in and foolishly grabbed the monster's tail and hauled it up on shore. Its shell was covered with green weeds. Its mouth hissed and its sharp claws grabbed at the dirt and scratched my legs until they were bleeding. My friends were cheering back at the fishing hole. I was a hero!

>**MISTAKE 2.** I held onto what might hurt me. I grabbed the turtle, which was more than two feet long and I lifted it up not imagining what kind of problem might happen! This caused a big problem. The turtle wiggled back and forth and its sharp claws scratched me. My friends still cheered and clapped. For the turtle.

>**MISTAKE 3.** Sensing danger, I acted slowly. Feeling the turtle's weight, I lowered it but didn't put it on the ground. I just lowered it and looked at my friends. Suddenly I felt a sharp pain above my right knee. I looked down to see the turtle's head biting my knee! I screamed "Ahhhh!" And dropped the turtle. It let go of my knee–but oval bite marks remained.

My friends laughed and cheered even more. I was overly optimistic and made three reckless choices in a row! I went from "hero to zero" in a moment. That is what can happen when you don't use a heads-up attitude and don't ask what bad things might happen from your choices. I was lucky I didn't get a finger bitten off by that big snapping turtle. A short time later I lowered my tackle box of fishing lures to sit next to the turtle in a wagon I intended to pull. My three friends were looking as I lowered the box next to the turtle's head.

We saw no movement by the turtle's head but there was a loud "BANG!" under the box next to the turtle's head. All the lures in the box jumped and my hand felt the impact. The turtle had obviously struck so viciously and so fast the human eye couldn't see it. I thought if my finger was near the turtle's head, my finger would be gone in a fraction of a second and sliding down the throat of this moss covered monster from the dinosaur era. I shiver ran down my neck. I did for the turtle what everyone should do with things you can't control.

I let it go.

More self confidence: visualize acting on a "Plan B"

One way to "look before you leap" is to consider bad situations 10 or more times per day. Visualize your response to plan A, when things go according to plan, and plan B, when things don't go according to plan. Nobody does this enough. But I can tell you doctors do this. ALL DAY LONG. And so do high technology administrators I've talked to. It is a fundamental thinking strategy for success in Western Civilization, where success is dependant on individual initiative. Savvy? You will desensitize to setbacks.

The main stress from setbacks is the surprise when they happen. Visualizing responses gets rid of the surprise element automatically. That's a game changer. This makes you much more likely to become a manager at whatever job you have right now. Managers get paid to anticipate problems and deal with them quickly. On average, managers get paid $10,000 more per year. If you have 30 years ahead of you to work, then this heads-up attitude could be worth $300,000. Good job!

This isn't just more work. There is no coasting in life. You are either growing or fading away. Ironically, positivity teaches us to learn from tough times and be energized by them. Affirmations and visualizations are two additional ways to get energized by challenges.

Affirmations Empower Us

When we tell ourselves what we believe in the present tense it sends a message. "I speak up today." "I love others today." "I'm asserting myself today." "I am entitled to only what I can make happen today." These are the kinds of affirmations I tell myself every day. "I love nature." "I want to lessen global warming."

What I am writing now came about because I told myself, "I'm writing in my book today." Affirm yourself or you will lose yourself. Don't believe me. Look at your own life and results. How can you move forward with yourself if you don't affirm yourself? (Duh.)

Three style elements of affirmations

Affirmations energize us to take the next step in personal growth. There is an art to making affirmations truly life changing. Try writing one down, at least in your mind, and remember it a dozen times today. See if it empowers you.

Do you want even more power? Here are three things to supercharge your affirmations that I use at least weekly:

- Repeat the affirmation ten times in the morning. Repetition makes a deeper impression on the emotional mind. Mine has been, "I am an author. I am excited to write today."
- Say the affirmation with emotion. Feel it.
- Connect the affirmation to your life narrative, the story about your life that you tell yourself all the time. "This is part of my life mission. It feels good."

Five qualities of awesome affirmations

Affirmations boost your confidence in a number of ways.

First you are confident of what you know and you are focusing on knowing your own thoughts. You can control them. You are not placing your confidence in what other people think or do.

Second, to be confident, you have to feel confident. The emotional mind can be flakey, but you are driving the truth of your affirmations into your emotions by repeating the affirmations. You can even repeat it a hundred times until your emotions feel it.

Third, this is a morning exercise. You might have to repeat this morning exercise for many mornings. Gradually the affirmations will raise your emotions like air inflating a bike tire. Starting the day with a feeling of confidence will allow you to get on a roll in life. You say your affirmations in the mornings because the mind is more impressionable then and it may have forgotten the positive (and negative) things that happened the previous day.

Fourth, this is a biological exercise. You are reshaping your brain pathways. After the affirmation, you eat breakfast. The nerves have the building materials to build new connections. Caffeine can give an energy boost. Then you jog or walk outside. Sunlight activates the whole brain by boosting glutamate activity in the memory center, according to Zhu and colleagues at research centers in China.[53] Exercise triggers a release of nerve growth factor which is the hormone that tells nerves to grow new connections. Your brain is growing connections to remember your affirmations in the brain's memory center, the hippocampus, and the brain's positivity centers, the amygdala and the rostral anterior cingulate cortex (RACC). You are truly driving the transformation of your brain and yourself.

Fifth, you act on your affirmation. This isn't wishful thinking. You act on your affirmation the day you say it. Now you have driven the affirmation into your life and it is a living part of you. No wonder it can transform how you see yourself and help you let go of the past. No wonder after 20 years of trying to write this book, I have completed my goal. I finally understood how to combine positivity life skills to accomplish my writing vision.

Visualizations turbocharge us

Remember those trillions of connections you have? Put them to work with visualizations, a form of affirmations that uses images.

Visualize step-by-step what you need to do for a project. Imagine what you will see, touch and hear during the whole process. Make your visualizations both realistic and vivid.

For this book, I told myself this: "I'm writing my book today. I'll feel the computer keys with my fingers and see the words appear on the screen. It will feel good to be creative!" That is how the words you are reading got on the page. Let yourself feel excited that your visualization is creating the reality you hope for, because it is.

More boldness: Positivity increases self-confidence

Setbacks add to our self-confidence because we learn from set-backs and can then give ourselves credit for that accomplishment. When you act on what you have learned, you are making progress when things go well and when you have setbacks. This combination makes you unstoppable. And it really works that way. You may have to adjust your life goals to make them more realistic so you can always be experiencing your life moving forward toward your dreams.

Often in life we are more capable than we give ourselves credit for because we haven't been taking our accomplishments personally. When you overcome a challenging time, pat yourself on the back. Give yourself credit. It feels good deep down in your soul like few things are in life. So do it. How else are you going to believe in yourself if you don't give yourself credit for overcoming adversities? Life doesn't hand out medals of honor. Life hands out opportunities to test yourself and prove yourself, and those times have a name.

Adversities.

Welcome them. No matter what, you can learn from them. Make it your goal to learn from an adversity today. Hopefully you will have a setback and you will rise above and learn something from it and now you have made progress on your goal.

Which reminds me of a story.

More meaning in your life: Meaning comes from the story of our life that we tell ouselves

We are always telling ourselves a story about what is going on in our lives, moment by moment. With a positive attitude, this story has a direction, a focus. The meaning of our life is something we feel in response to the story of our life. We feel special because a friend said they loved the gift we gave them. The gift made them feel special too.

Meaning is something we weave into our daily experience as we tell ourselves what just happened and why it matters. "I love my friends." "I loved that gift." "My friends love me." "I look forward to the next time we hang out, it will be so cool." "A good life is made of good friends."

Feeling meaning also means making sense of when there are losses in life. "A friend lost interest in me and left me." Is that a tragedy? No. Is it okay? Yes, people move from friend to friend all the time. "I can make new friends. It's part of people being free and changing." Should I perseverate on it or just let it go? Just accept it and move on. Consider picking friends who are more stable. You learn from a setback and use that to guide your next experience. You are learning from your experiences and it feels good to be growing.

Here, a person's self-talk is focused on being reasonable. "People change. It's okay." And it's focused on adapting. "I can make new friends." But also learning from the change. Such as to avoid making a deep friendship with someone who changes friendships every few weeks. Then there is the focus on goals. Learn from setbacks rather than be damaged by them.

The theme here is the actions that connect all people and things together. There is the common thread woven into all the events as they proceed in a certain direction. The plot explains why things happened the way they did and what they meant. In this story, the plot is positivity. Things happened and you learned from them. Use what you learned to make progress in your life by focusing on goals and taking initiative.

Making Memories: Making memories adds more meaning to our lives

Imagine meeting someone in your town who said he had a meaningful life. And then you asked what memories you have. "None," he said. It would seem unbelievable. You need memories to have a meaningful life. The more the merrier. Making more memories leads to a more meaningful life, but the journey might be uncomfortable at times. Which brings me to a story.

Positivity adds to your meaning by making memories: From low grades and a rejection to working in a medical office

This story illustrates how setbacks can be used to help you:
- Adapt to new situations
- Sharpen your career focus
- Get more energy
- Use pet therapy

Low grades hit Diane hard during her freshman year of college. She had a dream of going to nurse practitioner school, but got bad grades that could destroy that dream. She took the failures personally, but also talked about them with people she trusted. She felt tempted to give up on herself but instead saw a counsellor, listened to self-help podcasts and began taking medication. Four years later, she successfully raised her GPA and finished a biomedical sciences degree.

Diane applied to a nurse practitioner program and was rejected. But her new attitude helped her to learn from everything she encountered. So she got a job as a receptionist in a medical office because it would give her experience in the medical field. She found there were many medical careers to choose from: physician, nurse practitioner, physician assistant and more. She hopes to get more training from the clinic and become a medical assistant in the next months, and get even more experience in the next year. She plans to reapply to medical schools that, based on her research, would be more likely to admit someone with her interest in pediatrics and children's mental health.

Rather than dwell on her failure, Diane focused all of her frustration and anger in a constructive manner, learning why people got rejected who applied to medical school in the year she applied. She found that there were 25% more applications that year than in previous years, so 25% more applications were rejected. The competition was fierce. She decided to get fierce right back and increase her value to both medical and nursing schools. She moved to be close to her parents for emotional support and stayed in touch with friends. She got a dog so loneliness didn't eat away at her motivation to work as hard as she could for her future. She felt good about the progress she was making.

She kept talking with friends and broadened her search for other ways to become a nurse practitioner. She found an easier route! It was to first become a nurse, then go to nurse practitioner school. It was much easier to become a nurse first, so that is her new "Plan A" for her life.

Better life organization skills: Disorganized in college and now is succeeding as an elementary school teacher

This story illustrates the power of positivity to help:
- Focus
- Drive
- Connection to others

Bill was an A and B student in high school, but his grades were dropping to C's in his freshman year of college. His notes were a mess, his dorm room was a mess, his life was a mess. He lacked goals and focus. He felt tempted to give up on college, his future and himself. But his parents encouraged him. Instead of ignoring them, he listened. They noticed how hard he was working and all the potential he had. He accepted the encouragement and talked to a friend. Eventually he mastered a whole series of time management skills. He learned the self-discipline to pick up after himself and take pride in his appearance. Then he could focus and use all the skills he had learned but was having difficulty applying in college.

Bill's next major setback was graduating and getting tossed out into the adult world. Once again his organization was excellent and he sought advice from everyone he knew. He sent dozens of resumes all over the state for teaching jobs. His next setback was that in his new job, he now had to juggle 10 or 15 things at one time, managing 20 kids and 40 parents, the school rules and learning the workplace culture in a new environment. Bill used his planner and to-do lists with a professional sense of self-discipline. He worked from a proactive point of view. He anticipated challenges so he would be ready for them. It worked. Bill did well in his first year in a challenging new job.

One other thing was a secret strategy for confidence: if he ever "got stuck" or had a question, he wrote it down on an app on his phone. This way he was ready to ask his boss questions in a timely fashion. He found the answers to his questions were very helpful. He acted on them. The result of his positivity? Success.

Pro tip: stop taking setbacks personally

Boost your positivity in a minute this way:
- Identify one very small **setback** (that takes 5 seconds)
- Take it as **temporary** (visualize it as temporary for 15 seconds)
- Learn **one** thing from it (that takes 20 seconds)
- **Prompt** yourself to give yourself credit for that accomplishment (Aha! That takes 20 seconds)
- Total time: 60 seconds.

The four quick steps are summarized by the acronym STOP because it stops you from continuing to take the setback personally. In just one minute you change an element of negativity into an element of positivity. You can give your attitude a boost. Boom!

Pro tip: Tap into the power of habits

Habits boost your attitude effortlessly because your brain believes it has to do these tasks and they are not difficult. That is the nature of a routine. You just do it with little prompting from yourself because it is something you have done day-after-day. The trick: you can choose your own routine by repeating something about 10 days in a row. Then your brain will feel like it has to do it. The brain learns by repetition. Use that to your advantage.

Three examples of powerful habits

- Brian was struggling to find time for doing the dishes and finishing homework. He made a routine so he would do the dishes every night while dancing to his favorite music. He listened with his headphones and the time flew by—and he improved his dancing.
- Christy was frustrated she couldn't manage to do her daily workout and keep up with reading a book on meditation. Her mind kept going out of the present moment leading to repeated worrying. She found she could listen to an audiobook she checked out of the local library for free while going out for a jog or bike ride. Fabulous! She was delighted to be able to finish her book and build muscles.
- Felicia was angry her motivation to workout was dropping. She made a routine of going to a group dance workout—picking up on the motivation of group members—every Monday, Wednesday and Friday. After attending for 10 days, Felicia felt motivated to go back, learn more, and build friendships.

Habits are daily or weekly activities you automatically do because you've done them many times before. They are like friends. You wouldn't abandon them. It's fun to be with them. Many people learn to harness the power of routines in social clubs, at summer camps, or at weekend or week-long workshops. At such events, you repeat routines until you master them. The skills you learn may be arts and crafts, professional skills like computer coding, or dancing like salsa and bachata. The payoff: more fun and success!

Because you practiced a routine with a group of excited people, you associate good feelings when you do the routine later. You feel the group's hugs, smiles, warmth and encouragement even when you are doing it on your own.

Pro tip: use your old habits

Habits are huge. They are wonderful ways of doing things automatically every day. With little prompting, we do them. Results then snowball. Because we got to bed on time, we can get up early enough to do our energizing routines: coffee, a walk, meditation and the RAMP method. Because we keep our daily planner open on our desk, we see what we need to do and stop daydreaming. You can't see the results from old habits until you look back months later. If you are feeling stuck in pessimism, ask a simple question. "What are some old habits of mine I can do today?"

Pro tip: Pick up simple habits from what you learn

Habits are awesome. You don't have to go through all the work of thinking what to do when a situation comes up if you have developed a habit for dealing with it. One example might be: you wake up in the morning and automatically eat breakfast and brush your teeth.

Another habit, drawing from the "Look before you leap" story, is when I am looking to accomplish something, I ask, "What's one thing that could go wrong?" I learned it in the turtle story, again while working on farms and in my medical training. This one question has helped me for 20 years. It can make you better at what you do. Answer the question and then develop a plan to be ready for it. You are drawing from your experiences to be better prepared. Do that **all day long** for anything you are planning to do. You are now making a heads-up attitude a part of your daily routine! It's an awesome habit.

Here are some examples of it in action:

- I was working in a traditional media job and saw declining demand for newspapers due to increasing competition from other media. I determined it was time to change careers. Furthermore, I noticed my job had been a bad fit for my personality.
- I was driving down a highway after a rain. I slowed down after seeing water sitting on the highway which could make my car slide. Suddenly, my car went into a four wheel drift, hydroplaning on the standing water. Because I had already slowed down, I quickly got the car under control. The heads up habit saved me from an accident!
- I was writing in this book and thought what's one thing that could go wrong. My computer could malfunction. I made a plan to deal with that. I made up my mind to back up my document every 5 or 10 minutes when I was writing it. Weeks went by. Suddenly one day the computer had a malfunction and froze up! I would have lost all my writing I did if I hadn't backed it up!

Better friendships: tell your friends you love them

Sometimes, the most embarrassing setbacks can happen amongst friends. Not long ago, I flew to Montana to see some friends for our annual spring fishing trip. David, George and Peter are three of my best friends and we hadn't seen each other for a year. That was a setback. But I was going to bounce back from it.

When you meet friends, it's important to share your feelings, be transparent and be real. As I got off the plane at the airport in Missoula, I realized I'd be three days away from my best friend, my chocolate Labrador dog Sammy. So it was with some mixed emotions that I walked out of the airport and saw my other best friends in the world driving up with their fishing boat in tow.

I waved hello; they rolled down their windows and waved back. They piled out of their truck like it was a D-Day landing. They held out their arms to hug me and I held up my hand stopping them. Then I dropped to one knee and pulled out my phone. I spun away from them and took a great selfie: me in the front, them in the background. I took a long moment to appreciate it. It was really a great picture. ONE OF MY BEST.

Then I stood up and David, the second most clever one in the bunch said, "Oh Dr. Positive, aren't you happy to see us?" He was still holding out his arms for a hug. It looked so feminine.

I looked each of my buddies in the eye. "Yes, I'm happy to see you each one of you. I love you guys, you know that. But you need to know that there's someone that I love even more." I paused. They looked puzzled. "And that person would be," I said, lifting up my left eyebrow and pointing at my chest, "moo ahhh (me)."

They had a good laugh and we piled into their SUV. Our adventure was on.

Be ready for the zinger: "You'll be lucky if all you catch is a runny nose."

David had to show me two large tackle boxes full of plastic soft lures that looked like minnows and worms and creepy things from the age of dinosaurs. "Look at all these great lures I have," he said, "we are going to catch a lot today!" Of course, I saw the subtle attention-grabbing maneuver he was pulling on all of us. "Looks really nice, David," I replied, "You'll be lucky if all that you catch is a runny nose."

A moment of silence followed. I waited. We stared at each other, waiting for someone to say something.

Suddenly out of nowhere I was struck by a thought that it would be four days before I'd see my best friend Sammy. I was overcome with sadness. My face showed it.

"Dr. Positivity!" said Peter, "You look so sad." "I miss my dog Sammy," I replied in a moment of awkward vulnerability.

"Ohhh," said Peter, the boat captain. "I think you need someone to tuck you in at night."

We had a good laugh about that comment. David gunned the engine and we barreled out of the airport.

When fishing, as in life, it's always good to keep your buddies off balance because once you're on the water, don't kid yourself, it's a dog-eat-dog competition. With that last wisecrack, Peter clearly was the top dog.

As we got on the highway and headed for the Blackfoot River, we caught up with one another.

"It's great to see you guys," said David. "I've looked forward to this for the past year."

"Me too," said Peter, smiling.

"You must be afraid of the whole world."

I felt suddenly strange. No longer was I the center of attention. David was the center of attention. I was left out. Lonely and alone. Maybe I'd spent too much time on Instragram, Facebook and Youtube. Sometimes it is hard to tell where the feelings come from when you have an existential dark moment of soul.

"I don't know if I really looked forward to this trip," I replied. "I've been pretty emotional lately." I avoided eye contact and looked hard out the window at the barren sagebrush whirring past. Pause. "I, I almost didn't fly out here," I added.

I had seized the initiative. Again I was the center of attention. It felt so good.

"What do you mean?" asked David, a little shocked.

"I guess I've been really emotional lately," I replied. I paused for effect. You could have heard a pin drop. "It's kind of hard for me to let my hair down and have fun with people who can out fish me. I...I...I'm just afraid of anyone who can catch more fish than me."

"Ohhh, Dr. Positive," said David, sounding sympathetic. "In that case, you must be afraid of the WHOLE WORLD!"

It took a few moments for the comment to register in my mind. Then we all laughed.

Once again the center of attention swung away from me. But, coming to my senses, I regarded it as a temporary setback, learned the spotlight can't always be on me, and snapped out of my self-indulgent "poor me" victim thinking.

"The toaster incident."

Unfortunately, this "coming to my senses" didn't last long. We caught a few fish that evening and then bailed into our cabin. The next morning I was slow to rise. I blamed it on jet lag. David announced chores for everyone so we could get on the water and fish as soon as possible. He cooked up the eggs, George whipped up sausage and hash browns, and my task due to my dilapidated mental state, was to make toast.

Everything moved in slow motion for me. I put slices of bread from the freezer into the toaster and pushed down the lever. Nothing happened. I tried again. The lever went down, then popped up. Clearly the toaster was broken. But people need their bread so I sensibly plopped the pieces of bread onto a plate and put it on the table. My job was done. I felt positive about this. I'd done my best and that was good enough. It is always good enough.

Hot steaming plates of sausage and hash browns and scrambled eggs slid onto the table. We sat down. David reached for the bread, took a bite, then howled like he'd stepped on a nail.

Once again, David was the center of attention.

"Who made the toast?" he asked. "I did," I replied. "It's frozen," he replied.

"You don't have to be so negative," I replied. "It's thawing." "Why was it so hard to run the toaster?" he asked. "It's broken," I said, reaching for some sausage. "I pushed the lever down twice and nothing," I replied. "An idiot could see the darn toaster is broken." I looked around for sympathetic facial expressions from my fishing buddies. All I saw was blank faces looking back at me. At this point, I understood I was on my own.

"Is that so?" asked David. "Let's inspect the scene of the incident." He walked over to the toaster. Inspected it. Then grabbed the limp end of the electric cord that was laying lifeless on the counter—not plugged in. He exclaimed, "What is this?" He held it up like he was at the scene of a crime and found found a murder weapon. I avoided eye contact with my fishing buddies. Then in a flash, he plugged it in. He pushed the lever down. A red warm glow emanated from the dark recesses of the toaster.

I'm not stupid. Instantly I saw I'd been "outgunned" in this battle of wits—and once again David was the center of attention. But not for long.

I turned my back to my buddies. I paused. They were quiet. "Guys, I've been thinking about something," I began. I could feel their attention focused on me. "I've been really emotional lately. And I just want to say something."

I paused. My back was facing them. I paused again and said the first thing that came to mind:

"I really love you guys."

"Nothing doing!" said David. He didn't take my bait. "The topic is the toaster! It's not broke! It just wasn't plugged in!"

I recoiled like a snake that was stepped on. I made dramatic gestures with my hands. My eyebrows went up like windshield wipers. I opened my mouth to ask for sympathy but no words came out of my mouth.

"Time to make your toast and stop ducking your responsibilities!" said David. Well that just hurt more than all the other insults.

Once again my efforts were a disaster.

But then I came to my senses.

This was just a setback. Setbacks are temporary. I got busy making toast and soon we were out on the water, fishing. The "toaster incident" was all forgotten. That's the advantage of making mistakes when you are out fishing. Soon they are all forgotten. Fishing is a lot like life.

Pro tip: work with how your mind works

Another approach for dealing with setbacks, is to work with the nature of your mind to wander. That is something you can see for yourself when meditating. Just accept it. Why fight the way things are? But it is also the nature of our emotional mind to respond to what we repeatedly think. So work with that. Your emotional mind will respond to whatever you think about the most.

When your mind wanders, keep refocusing your attitude and get excited about the positive attitude when you have it. Ignore or get bored with the pessimistic attitude when it wanders back into your thinking.

This is what I had done at summer camp. I got excited about what I could learn each day. When my thinking wandered to failure, I ignored it. I walked over and talked to a positive-thinking friend, who was working on a project. I "caught the vibe" as he talked about what he was excited about doing. Then I did like he did, thinking repeatedly about a project and how it would feel so good to get it done. Pretty soon I was motivated because I was visualizing it.

Pro tip: use relationship skills

A common source of setbacks is relationship issues. When romance fails or a friendship falters, it is natural to take it personally. The problem is it doesn't help when you do that. "You" isn't the problem. The problem is something else. Relationship skills. These skills include:

Attractiveness skills. Confident posture. Great eye contact. Flirting skills. Avoiding neediness. Displaying class. Leadership. Confidence. Decisiveness. Showing amazing character. Avoiding rabbit holes. Detecting danger signs. Letting go of a bad fit. Embracing ones that pass your test. Sense of humor. Loving the game of finding love. Music for the vibe. Dancing skills. Showing high value. Finding those who get it and letting go of those who don't.

Deepening emotional connection skills. Knowing your partner's story. Sharing yourself with increasing vulnerability. Deep eye contact. Great sincerity. Openness about what is deeply personal. Spirituality. Earning trust. Gauging another's response. Increasing vulnerability. Moving up the ladder of deeper friendship and love. Discovering shared passions. Sharing life missions. Intimacy skills. Planning ahead to create a great experience. Making memories. Holding hands. Long embraces. Going for a kiss.

Adding "heat" to your relationship. Vulnerability with deep honesty, deep openness and deep truth you believe. Thinking through how to be successful. Surprises. I SHALL skills. Initiative Hopefulness for making dreams come true. Accomplishments that build "us" up. Sacrifices that deepen your love. Learning to build up love.

Electrifying your love. Know the ways we love. **Love patterns:** avoiding, embracing, daring, ridgidness, judging, accepting, adoring, loving to love, listening to improve, listening to love, listening to understand. **Love killers:** harshness, scrutiny, listing errors, resentment, judgmental thinking, facetiousness, sarcasm, bitterness, pessimism, not open to feedback. **Love bloomers:** loving feedback, gauging the other person, riding the roller coaster of romance, patience, mercy, understanding, initiative, thoughtfulness, leaps of faith, tender words, deeply thoughtful actions, set aside times, wing men and wing women, emotionally loaded touch, sensuality that's deeply meaningful, gifts that tell stories, intention loaded with passion, guiding us to avoid the love killers, willing to be guided. **Love templates:** movies, songs, stories, books, podcasts, videos, poetry, spirituality.

Pro tip: use FOMO, don't fight it

In my career, I saw other people earning awards and I didn't want to get left behind. But I was getting left behind. I wasn't winning any awards. We are social creatures. It feels good to belong to a group. But then if the group moves on and does things you are not a part of, you have a "fear of missing out" or FOMO. This is one of the strongest motivating emotions. We will do almost anything to avoid FOMO.

So work with how the mind works and use that to motivate yourself! Get in with a good group of people you look up to, and dive into projects with them! If you are feeling more pessimistic about what you are doing, in or outside of that project, talk or text with one of the group members who is more positive and ask what their motivation is like. Then ask yourself "do I want to miss out on their good attitude?" Boom! Your motivation will increase at least a little because you don't want to feel like you are missing out.

FOMO is something you can use on yourself or someone else can use it on you (like on social media), wasting your time or manipulating you to do something. When you use FOMO to motivate yourself, you will be less likely to be manipulated by others trying to use FOMO on you.

Pro tip: Use the 3 step model of the mind

Another kind of setback is when the mind gets "messed up with emotions" and it is hard to think things through and get things done. It can be very perplexing! Wouldn't it be good if you knew the basic steps your mind takes in order to make progress every day? Then you could see what step you "skipped" that lead to mental confusion. The answer then is just prompting yourself to do that step you skipped and presto! You are on track again.

The three steps the mind takes are: thoughts, emotions and actions. First a person... thinks about a positive attitude. Like perhaps you are now reading this book. Your thinking triggers an emotional reaction to your attitude. You might feel happy about the good things in store for you with positivity. Then you act on those thoughts and feelings. You choose to do something or nothing but one way or another you do something. Your actions trigger more thoughts and the cycle repeats itself: from actions to thoughts to emotions. That is naturally how the mind works.[54]

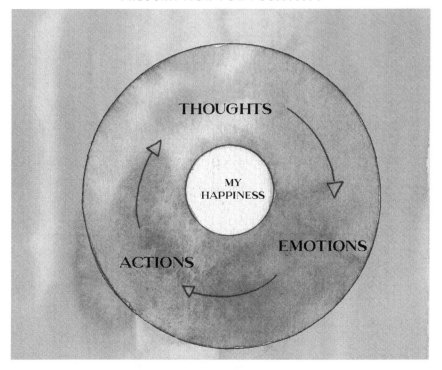

(**FIGURE 1.8.6** The circle model of the mind. By Esther Phingmoo).

The "One step forward, one step backward" problem: how pessimism erases positivity in your life

It continues to amaze me how often this model of the mind works—and works quickly. I use it all the time. Here is an application of it to deal with a setback. When people get started getting their act together, what I often see is the "one step forward, one step back" problem. This is why they're stuck with depression, anxiety or other issues. Notice I am again following the I SHALL acronym to activate the thinking skills for positivity. A person can show initiative and do a good thing for themselves. They can take their accomplishment personally and feel more hopeful in their positive attitude. One step forward. Then they get a setback and take it personally and forget everything else except how awful they feel because they are—unknown to them—acting pessimistic. One step back. This is how pessimism erases the progress of positivity.

This erasure happens silently, in the blink of an eye. That is why I call pessimism the silent killer. It kills people's hopefulness, their joy and their loving feelings. It's like hypertension for the heart. It's easy to ignore and then one day you have a heart attack.

Positivity is the cure for pessimism. Positivity works. Not only for keeping your attitude useful for your life goals in general, but also for making specific progress on specific issues important to you. Here are three more examples, one for weight loss, one for dating and one for relationships. In each story there will be a positive person and a pessimist facing the same problem. They use the I SHALL principles differently—because of their attitude. Pessimism leads them to "skip a step" and not use the power of their mind.

In the first hypothetical story, two women are friends and helping each other lose weight. Both had been walking just 15 minutes or 2,000 steps per day. Both are frustrated when they learn both of them gained 1/2 pound the week after walking 5,000 steps or half an hour per day. Mayra is a positive thinker and focuses the energy of her frustration and gives herself credit for at least walking 5,000 steps per day. That burned up some calories!

Then she acted on what she learned (that she can increase her walking) and walks 10,000 steps or one hour per day and loses 1/2 pound in the next week. She keeps up her energy for walking by drinking lots of tea. She's frustrated by her cravings for sugar. She uses sweet herbal tea to deal with her sweet tooth. It has zero calories. Mayra loves the progress she's making with her initiative. She isn't surprised by her feelings and she doesn't complain. She decides she likes the change to a healthier her! One step forward followed by one more step forward toward her goals. But in the past her pessimism lead her to wallow in self pity and skip the "action step" of upping her excercise daily. She just kept thinking and feeling bad about her weight and skipped the action step of doing something about it. And she didn't even know she was skipping it. The model of the mind is powerful this way, to help people see the step they are skipping. Game changer!

But her pessimist friend Wanda thinks, feels and acts negatively. She quits taking initiative because she takes the setback personally, gives up hope and ignores her own previous accomplishments. As a result, she feels she can't do anything right. Instead of blaming her pessimistic attitude for that feeling and then correcting her attitude, she distracts herself from the whole attitude issue by blaming herself. She skipped the action step in the model of the mind. Pessimism pushed her to that. She felt problems were bigger than her: that is pessimism rearing its ugly head. Can you see how her thoughts and feelings were pessimistic? She didn't take action because she embraced the limiting belief (that is false) that she needed to feel motivated in order to excercise. This is another trick of pessimism to keep us pessimistic and avoiding doing the things we can do to make progress (although yes, some pain and effort is involved).

Her attitude got her in trouble. Frustrated, Wanda can't think of anything to change, making her feel even more hopeless. She doesn't learn weight is just the end result of calories in versus calories out. She isn't even looking at the calorie issue. Wanda wallows in pessimism and self-doubt. She doesn't take any steps to reduce her caloric intake. She comforts herself with iced tea sweetened with sugar. One step forward learning 5,000 steps is helpful (it obviously burned up calories) but not enough and then, with the model of the mind firmly in the talons of pessimism, she triggers an "avalanche" of pessimistic thoughts, emotions and actions:

- another step back (acting against your goals in self-sabotage)
- one step back (taking setbacks personally)
- after another (giving up hope)
- after another (ignoring accomplishments)
- after another (self-blame)
- and another (latching on to what you can't control right away, which is your weight)
- and another (giving up on learning)

Can you see now how attitude is such a game changer? Avalanches of pessimistic thought and emotions are so damaging—and to some extent avoidable. Attitude is a game changer!

FIGURE 1.8.7
Pessimism has a side effect: weight gain. By Toso Borkovic.

Pessimism causes "Yoyo Dieting"

Pessimism is the secret reason why many people are stuck in "yo-yo dieting," a problem where people succeed at weight loss and then gain the weight back again. One step forward and then pessimism pushes them one step back, by getting them to "skip a step."

Here is a second example of how pessimism can undo the progress of positivity.

José focused on adapting to a problem and making a little progress. That's great! He was giving up on the hopeless attitude of perfectionism! Good job! And then, instead of letting go of what he couldn't control, José started fixating on – it. It might have been what someone said or how unfair the world is. It doesn't matter. José was taking a step back and wondering why he felt so stuck and hopeless when he was doing some things that seem to work and then his life didn't change.

The diagnosis? The one step forward, one step back problem. Of course the world is unfair. It doesn't revolve around you and magically work with you. The Paredo Principle and other observations shed more light on this reality. Instead of just making this observation and moving on, Jose made it the central focus of his life instead of his goals and passions in life. Bad choice!

What's the solution to this problem? One step forward and another step forward. Keep using the principles of positivity. Don't negate them by practicing the principles of pessimism. Refuse self sabotage. Assert your intention to succeed. This is the theory of positivity. The following stories will demonstrate the life changing impact of positivity—using simple routines and meditation!

Examples of using nature for positivity

It can be exhausting dealing with setbacks. One way to reduce them is to adapt routines that "proactively" solve problems before they have a chance to blow up in your face. It was hard for Elaine to even get out of bed two years ago. Now she has moments where she is caught up in the joy of life and she is grateful. She got her life back by getting in sync with herself. Nearly every day she uses the RAMP method. Elaine discovered this habit helps her have a good day. There are a dozen things she does every day with her routines, which act like medicine for her soul. She and her husband know that if she leaves one thing out, her mood will suffer the rest of the day, providing a reminder she needs to stay in sync with herself. When she lives this way, she gets inspiration and the most beautiful oil paintings of nature flow from her print brush onto a canvas in her art studio.

Here are Elaine's items in the RAMP approach. It's not a formula but a customized method that she has worked out based on her experience of what fills her soul, what inspires her spirit. It's like a template for a painting.

R stands for reading. Elaine limits her time on social media. She deliberately reads what lifts her spirit up. Words are like medicine for the soul, but the wrong words can be toxic. When she starts to feel her emotions sour, she quits the social media she's consuming. R can also include writing. If she doesn't journal for a few days, Elaine's energy drops and her insight is more limited. She journals just for two to five minutes a day. She also reflects on what she's been writing and finds that empowering, especially when she can share that with her friends.

A stands for activity. If Elaine is inactive, avoiding those actions that inspire her soul, her energy drops that day. The actions include exercising half an hour a day with her stationary bike, walking or hiking and sometimes lifting weights at the health club. Not exercising for a day is not an option.

M stands for meditation. Every day Elaine meditates in some way. She might do a walking or sitting meditation. Five to 10 minutes in meditation gives her an experience of the present moment that she references for the rest of the day. She is keenly aware that her pessimism is rarely in the present moment. Nonetheless, the pessimistic thinking often continues until she interrupts it with a three-step meditation for a few minutes or even 30 seconds. The three step meditation is explained elsewhere in this book.

P stands for practicing "preview and post view" of your day. Elaine's great nemesis in this regard has been perfectionism.

She looks forward at the start of her day and expects perfection. At the end of the day as she looks back, she beats herself up if she didn't achieve perfection. She can think for hours about how she's a bad person and justify the thought by looking at all the mistakes that any of us make, but she takes those mistakes personally. But not if she has the perspective that she is just practicing a mindful way to live. Elaine doesn't have to get it "perfect." The point of life is to try doing your best, and look for progress but not perfection.

In addition, Elaine is keenly aware of her own body's biology. She noticed her mood would be "off" a little after eating sugar or processed food. So she cut them out for the most part. That means she has to spend a little more time every week grocery shopping and planning meals, "but it's for me and it's worth it," she says. She loves cooking in her Italian tradition using foods that inspire her.

These are the routines built into Elaine's day to charge her soul. The result can be seen in the vibrant colors of her paintings of alpine meadows, mountain peaks and majestic grazing elk.

This story shows use of the RAMP method, the medical science model of the brain, and art therapy. Elaine also used nature for emotional support.

Example: her positivity let her have a family

"The media was making me mentally ill," said Rebecca, "and wasting my time!" Two years ago she was overcome with panic attacks after pessimism overwhelmed her. She saw her problems as never-ending. The world was falling apart and so was her marriage and mental health. Due to her pessimistic attitude, when any problem happened with her kids, if her husband was late from work or if she made a mistake in her online business, Rebecca dwelled on those setbacks for hours.

Rebecca didn't know that pessimism was adding to her stress.

Now all the elements of the RAMP method are working quite well to help Rebecca juggle her family life and career.

Rebecca starts her day collecting her thoughts by reading the Bible and meditating on a passage of scripture. She writes a few sentences in her diary, which is in her phone. She visualizes what the day will bring, imagining the course of the morning hours, her husband getting off to work on time, waking with her three kids and seeing them off to school. But she also prepares for what things might go awry.

Rebecca puts her happiness first now. "Mess is a sign of success!" she says. "But in the past, I had the perfect house and made perfect meals and everything was on time, I was crippled with anxiety and panic attacks."

Rebecca prides herself on taking care of herself first and keeping her priorities straight. She organizes her day with to-do lists and a daily planner. For some things, she communicates with her husband using a shared electronic calendar, texts, and voice memos by text.

To build this perspective that she matters, her family matters and people matter more than things, Rebecca has used a variety of resources. She used self-help books, websites, podcasts and a mother's support group at her church, but those only went so far. There were deeper secrets in her soul that she only found out when she spoke with her pastor, where she learned she hadn't forgiven herself for mistakes she made years ago. She was pushing herself so hard because she didn't value herself. After hard work and deep self-reflection, she was able to forgive herself and felt a burden lift off her shoulders.

Even amongst all of these habits, the panic attacks still persisted. She went to a doctor. The doctor informed her that often times the brain becomes wired to respond to situations in a certain way, including having panic attacks. The brain might fight responding to healthy actions, including spiritual activities like prayer. Anxiety may have become the new biological normal in Rebecca's mind. But Rebecca fought back. After several months with medication and orderly routines for her day, finally peace of mind became the new normal.

She was informed that her brain could grow new connections and respond to her healthy habits, because the brain grows new nerve connections every day. In the past, she developed pathways that reinforced fearful ways of reacting to things, but now she was developing neural pathways to remember she is a good mom, a good wife, a good person, a person with integrity and a person with a mission in life to help her family thrive.

This story illustrates use of the I SHALL principles of positivity, the RAMP method, time management strategies and the medical science model of the brain. Over the next several years she tapered off the medication—by working with her team. She used her support network and kept herself accountable to herself and her life mission. She periodically met with her pastor, therapist and best friends and that dedication to those relationships kept her mentally sharp and on track with her positivity. It is easy to "lose your way" by living life with the "lone ranger" approach. While it seemed like she was taking time "out of her life" to use her support system, she found she had more time to do fun things because she wasn't constantly putting out "fires" of problems in her personal and family life. Upshot of all this: support systems save you time.

Examples of positive relationship skills: H.O.T. tickets for love

Jerry and Elaine have a little one on the way. Their baby is no accident—their love has blossomed these past five years as both have put their love and happiness first.

But first Jerry and Elaine had to provide positivity's tickets for love.

Jerry had to have good relationship skills to prove to Elaine he was a quality man who would adore her and be passionate—not a flake.

Elaine knew a pessimist often started dishing out anger, fear, insecurity and impulsivity—she'd seen it so many times. Sometimes she found dates to be just plain boring, or unambitious. She had ambitions; she wanted equality in a relationship and deep emotional closeness. Plus she wanted to travel and have a middle-class lifestyle. Nothing crazy. But she wasn't going to lower the bar and live in a marriage that was boring, loveless or devoid of passion. She'd seen that with some of her older relatives.

For Elaine, gone were the times when it was enough if a man worked hard and stayed faithful. "I work hard too," admits Elaine. "Faithfulness is great. It's a must have." But it's not the end of the road for Elaine. "I want a home and someone to come home to," she admits. "A dog is faithful and takes care of loneliness. I wanted more. I want someone who understands my soul. A dog can't do that."

Elaine is a woman who radiates happiness. She takes care of her physical and emotional health. With men, she knew she had options. Like many women wanting equality and emotional closeness, at first it was hard to get Jerry to understand that.

"When she said she didn't want me to just be a great friend— she already had one of those— it really got me thinking," Jerry confessed. "I loved her and wanted to figure out what to do next. Nobody taught me emotional closeness." He sought out male friends, looked online and read self-help books, but nothing really gave the guidance he was seeking.

Finally he asked Elaine what she meant by emotional closeness. She said it was feeling close to the other person. Jerry said he felt close to her. It wasn't enough. "Why can't you explain what you want from me?" he asked Elaine.

"That pushed my buttons," she said. "He should know. Then we talked and I found he didn't know because no one taught him. Not school, parents, pastors, friends or even previous girlfriends. Poor guy!"

But Jerry found a way. Elaine agrees.

These are the H.O.T. skills for relationships that Jerry learned. H.O.T. stands for:

H   Honest about your feelings
O   Open about fears
T   Truthful about the relationship.

"How can I feel close to him," asks Elaine, "if I don't know what the heck he is feeling about me, him, or us?" Gradually, with the help of a pastoral counselor, Jerry learned to use "I statements," which are statements that begin with I instead of you.

Turn up the heat: dare to be honest

"They had to be honest from the heart," he notes, "then she could know what I was really feeling. And the feelings had to relate to what I was honestly thinking and doing. I couldn't just say pie in the sky stuff."

Jerry's "I statements" were a way of practicing the initiative of positivity. He had a goal of feeling closer to Elaine so he leaped at the chance to learn this powerful skill. "I wanted to say 'I love you' right away but when we were first getting to know each other I had to start with friendship." Examples of this include:

"I like you; you're a cool friend." "I like hanging out like this; you're nice." "You're a fun friend." "I feel good about getting to know you; you're a lot of fun." "I'd like to hang out some more sometime; you're a gas." He expressed what was going on inside, what he thought, what he felt, about himself, about her and about his intentions for the future.

"I liked him too," said Elaine. "But he was such a black box inside! What a relief to see the cool man inside. Nice."

But Elaine didn't like the idea of guiding the relationship. "I already have a dog and a goldfish to take care of," she said. "I didn't want another burden. I'm busy with school and work."

Turn up the heat: dare to lead with openness

So, Jerry took the lead. "I was freaked out at first," he admitted. "I was afraid she would dump me like yesterday's lunch." He learned the skills of following the threads of a conversation and reading her body language.

"I would ask her how her day was and follow up on the threads. If she said her dog got in a fight with the neighbor dog and it was embarrassing—I'd ask about the dog, the neighbor, the neighbor's dog, and how she felt about all three and how everything turned out. Mostly I focused on her expressions. If she looked angry, I'd say that, but if I got the vibe she didn't want to talk about something, I'd say that too and say I respected her wishes. You know, I'd look at her eyes and body language to see where she was coming from."

"He got good at that," Elaine notes with a laugh, "but he was rusty at the start. Still it was cute that he was trying. Then, when he got spot on reading my facial expressions it was like, wow, this guy is getting me. So charming."

"I crashed and burned a lot," Jerry confessed. "But I was like, hey I got to learn this, this is fun, it will blow the doors wide open to get to know her." Elaine agreed. This let her get to know him the more he opened up—at her comfort level. "I backed off if she looked uncomfortable," he said. "It was nice I didn't have to give him the laser beam stare in my eyes," Elaine joked. "I could tell he was trying to take charge of guiding our relationship as it developed."

Likewise, Elaine needed to be honest about her feelings— for him, herself, and "us." Jerry said knowing the issue was key. "I was earning her trust at one phase and moving on to the next. It was helpful to know the progression of romance too." Elaine nodded her head.

Dare to talk about the relationship and do what's good for it

"Here is how we moved forward," she noted. "The progression went like this: strangers...knew of each other... acquaintances...sort of friends...friends...kind of good friends...good friends...really good friends...great friends... best friends...besties...we're really close...we're seeing each other...we're dating...we're serious...we're really serious... engaged...and married!"

"I was terrified at first," said Jerry. "I mean I'm kind of a control freak. I wanted to control the future, her and the whole process. Finally I learned it's just a step-by-step thing. The skills I'm learning will help me meet lots of other girls if need be. So it's not like I'm hopeless if she dumps me. I've got lots of options; she's got lots of options. We are passionate, warm, exciting people. That's what I like about her. So affectionate and playful, she's fun to get to know."

"He finally caught on to the approach," said Elaine. "It's fun at this place in our relationship, and it would be fun to grow to the next phase. And if it isn't fun, oh well. Life isn't always rainbows and unicorns. We will work together. We'll keep it light and fun and make everything work out."

Honesty about feelings is hard at the start, Jerry noted. "Later it got exciting," Jerry said. "So all this work at understanding my inner narrative really paid off. When I found how much she loved me all along it was a big turn on. I'm so glad I dumped my neediness."

Dare to be open about your fears

Openness about fear then rocked Elaine's boat. Jerry built up trust enough so when they agreed they were good friends, Jerry dropped a bomb. "I told her I was afraid of losing her," he said, laughing and shaking his head. "I said good," Elaine noted, "because you don't have me, I'm not your possession."

But Elaine was impressed with Jerry's courage. "His assertiveness was so sweet and endearing," she said. Talking about fears was great, they agree, because it marked a new phase in their relationship: greater depth of openness. "Hey, we all have fears," Elaine remarked. "But at the start of getting to know someone, we don't want to hear about it. It is too much too soon, you know?"

"I was gauging her response," Jerry remarked. "I watched her eyes, face and body language. I was testing the waters."

Elaine laughed. "I saw him reading me and he had no idea I was reading his intentions at the same time. So cute! When I felt a little put on the spot, I asked if we could talk about it later. I was testing to see if he was a control freak or could we work together on something," Elaine said.

Jerry worked with her. They agreed to talk about it later in the week. "The sexual tension drove me crazy!" Jerry admitted. "But I saw women like to go slow in a relationship if they are women of integrity. You know this isn't a joke, this relationship stuff." Jerry saw if he didn't assert himself, nothing happened. That was a put off at the start until he saw he just needed to be sensitive to her and make little offerings for a great level of openness and when she was ready, when he earned it and she felt it, she would agree to talk about deeper emotional things.

"I was afraid of losing him too," Elaine said. "And of flunking out of college, my dog dying, my friends ghosting me, growing old without any love in my life... It was a long list!" As the weeks rolled by, he learned the list and they drew closer.

"What I was afraid of—talking about fears—was my best friend," Jerry said. "But I knew I didn't have to be afraid for us, for our relationship. I mean we were building a better relationship but at the same time testing each other and what we could handle. Neither of us wanted to be in a relationship where you can't talk about your fears. That would be weird as heck."

Dare to earn her trust

By then they were holding hands and kissing. "He earned my trust," Elaine said. "I felt closer to him every week. It was, it is, so exciting. I told myself, 'Oh my gosh, it's happening!'"

Then came the time for truth. The truth of thinking through how they would make the relationship work.

Elaine didn't want to feel like the training wheels in the relationship. "I've got a brain and was finishing a college degree. I wanted to use both and have a family." Jerry led their discussions. Elaine gladly participated. She was glad he was being "The Man" in the relationship, starting talks about their dreams.

The first was about equality. Elaine wanted equal time working and earning money. He agreed. If they had kids, they would each take about equal time off work—even if it meant a drop in income, no vacation and one of them working two jobs.

"To see that daycare cost $12,000 per year for just three days a week was a jaw dropper," Jerry said. "I was glad I'd been improving my employability with classes and at work."

"No joke," said Elaine, soberly. "You kicked butt, my man."

Each of them had personal possessions they had purchased before getting into a relationship. They listed those and each kept them as their own. But everything after that time was shared. They then talked about an emotionally explosive issue: money. They would have separate checking accounts for vacations and recreation, school, and kids' college fund. These were all shared, meaning they planned to share in putting their income in these accounts. Later they added a retirement account. The only exception was each would have a "fun fund" for entertainment that they could spend without checking in with the other person.

Dare to put your family first—with your money

"It was hard to feel my personal freedom vanish," Jerry laughed. But the money planning was also a test in how much they loved each other. Elaine's parents had been giving her $600 per month so she could board a horse at a local barn. "When my parents said they were going to stop after college because I was growing up, I burst into tears. I didn't want to let go of my horse. That was my baby!"

"I let go of my hobby of racing motorbikes too," admitted Jerry. "It was a test of how grown up we are. I realized my attachment was really just self-absorbed materialism. Come on. We want to raise a family. If we are both acting like single people, this thing isn't going to work."

It was very hard for Elaine. Her horse was a living thing compared to Jerry's dirt bike. The horse was like a member of the family. For a time they broke up. Then her horse got sick and Elaine had to work 150 hours of extra time in a second job, just to pay off the veterinarian bill—$3,000. Her parents had long ago told her they couldn't afford the vet bills so she agreed to pay them. She made $20 per hour. This meant she had to work an extra 150 hours. But the bill was on a credit card. That meant an extra 200 hours of work over the next 3 months. She needed to work 40 hours per week to pay her rent and food bills. So she worked two jobs, 60 hours per week, for 3 months. "I was at the point of a nervous breakdown," she admitted. If her horse got sick again and she couldn't afford the vet bills, the horse would die. "I finally had to be honest with myself that the horse is not a person. It's a hobby."

After three months of hardly seeing Elaine, Jerry concluded she didn't have the maturity for a relationship, much less a family. She once even blamed him for not loving her because he wouldn't pay for her veterinary bills. "That was crossing a line," he said. "Blaming me for not taking responsibility for her choices. Wow! Too much insanity for me! I could easily see then that a stressful situation brought out what she really thought and she really felt."

After enduring 3 months of self-induced punishment, Elaine finally started asking the obvious questions. Who was financially responsible for caring for her horse? How much finances did she have? Was she over her head financially in having a horse?

She wondered how all the others in her barn could afford their horses and a family. She asked around and found out an answer that made her sick.

"Most women had married into money or inherited money. They didn't earn it, the money for the horses," she said. A few women did earn the money for horse boarding; they were working professionals. But almost none had children: they didn't have time for children AND a horse. To afford horse boarding plus childcare meant these women had to spend $1,800 per month to have care for one child and one horse. That was to the same as a home mortgage. Elaine did a little asking around and found she would have to earn $30,000 before taxes to have $20,000 after taxes for the luxury of a horse and a child.

Dare to let self-absorbed dreams die!

"I was being so selfish," Elaine admitted. "I had to rethink this whole 'me, me, me' stuff. It was all about me having my dream and if I couldn't have my dream he couldn't have his dream. My selfishness was hammering the nail on the coffin of my dream of ever having a family. I was acting like a spoiled, entitled brat."

At that point, Elaine saw that her school never taught her the life skills of how to share dreams in a relationship. Her parents tried to tell her but she hadn't listened. "It felt like I was being lectured to," she admits. "Now I see they were giving me a yellow brick road to having a happy married life." She saw the utter emptiness of her self absorbed hobby that refused to compromise. She saw how all these years she had used people— her parents, friends—for her hobby. Once when her parents threatened to take "her" horse away because she didn't do her chores around the house, she threatened to commit suicide. Other times she ran away from home or abused marijuana—all to deal with the stress of potentially "losing" "her" horse. She saw her arrogant, selfish sense of entitlement. Because she had a horse in the past, she should have one forever, and her parents should pay for it. The arrogance of all this drama now sickened her. She'd seen other people act that way, spoiled and entitled, and she had contempt for their behavior. She didn't know then she was doing the same thing. She made up her mind to grow up and apologize to Jerry. She hoped he would take her back. She saw many reasons why he wouldn't. But she apologized. He saw the honesty and openness in her attitude, and how truthful she was now about what she was entitled to—nothing. He took her back but she had to gradually earn his trust. In time she did and they openly talked about each others' "issues" so the "issues wouldn't come between us," Jerry said. He'd grown more insightful through all of this as well.

She finally talked to her parents about what is involved in sharing a dream with someone you love. She decided to modify her dreams. She would ride a family friend's horse for free to keep getting her "horse fix." Of course, that stopped once she got pregnant.

One year ago, Elaine and Jerry got married and started thinking, planning, for a family. "She's better than I am at thinking all the things through," Jerry said. "We both had to give up a lot but we figured out we had a lot of selfish dreams, and it was easier giving up on those so we could have some 'family dreams.'"

"All through school they teach you to focus on yourself to be successful," Elaine remarked. "They need to talk about life skills for relationships too. They just taught us about how to avoid sexual assault. That taught me to be afraid of relationships and talks about sharing dreams."

Elaine notes that now, at 25, she's afraid for some of her friends. "They are getting older and asking 'Where are the good guys? Are they all taken? Pretty soon it will be too late for them to start a family. "And that's ok too, but they really want to have kids while they can," Elaine added.

Elaine is so thankful she stayed positive through this whole relationship journey. Jerry is grateful for her attitude too. "She could find all my faults, and I have quite a few, but she is grateful for the man in her life and she knows I'd climb any mountain for her."

"I know you would, Honey," Elaine said. "But we are focused on what's good for us and this little one."

Daring to focus on us...really pays off!

Staying positive has made their marriage so much stronger, both agree. They focus on what is good for them. And now that means for three of them. If they are anxious about talking about something—it means they probably should. They trust one another to call the other one out on some misbehavior. It might be callousness, selfishness or being overly sensitive. But they appreciate one another's growth at the same time and the work that it took.

Building a relationship takes patience. Everything takes time. Life is all about sacrifice. Elaine now remarks that giving up on her horse was the best thing she ever did. "That $600 a month allows us to have childcare so we can go out on a date night once a week or see our friends—and have someone clean the house once a month because I'm so exhausted after work." Also, they have some money to put in a retirement fund. They invest in a mutual fund that reinvests the money earned, called compounding interest. With a little luck, in 30 years they'll have a quarter of a million dollars in it—all from the money she used to spend on her hobby. "If I kept the horse, I would have to work until I die," said Elaine with a laugh. "Some things are so smart to let go of."

Life is all about compromise. Jerry passed up a promotion at work because it meant he would have to travel—and he had promised to help out with childcare. That meant they had to stay in their already cramped townhome. Elaine gave up some horse shows and Jerry gave up some fishing trips. But together they are devoted to something much bigger than a house, much more exciting than a 3lb trout or a horse show ribbon. The object of their affection is a baby girl.

"To think I agonized over that first time when I told Elaine I loved her!" exclaimed Jerry. "It was pure torture! But so worth it."

"And you're worth it," said Elaine, hugging her love.

JOURNAL YOUR LEARNING HERE:

FIGURE 1.9.0
Hopefulness happens when you climb the ladder through pessimism's temptations and get into the light of understanding. Then life is easier. You can sip lemonade with the Sun. By Toso Borkovic.

9

How "Hopefulness" lights up your life!

How hope sets the stage for progress and love

Hopefulness is defined as the feeling of having hope, believing that something you want will happen.[55]

FIGURE 1.9.1
Hopefulness: What Sammy and I saw at lunch.
By Esther Phingmoo.

There is a certain joy in life. It comes from appreciating simple pleasures with a grateful attitude. Then we feel hopeful because the future feels promising. Being playful helps. Not taking yourself seriously is a bonus. Enjoying your freedom and your friends adds to the experience. The Greek philosopher Epicurus said hopefulness and joy come from living the good life. The good life doesn't come from money, status or power. People who have those things worry about losing them. The good life, Epicurus said, comes from our experience with good friends and good food.

My best friend is my dog Sammy. Yesterday I decided to see if old Epicurus was right. I had lunch with Sammy at a restaurant in the city center square. The sun beat down. It was 92°F in the shade. Sammy enjoyed some water in a bowl while tied to a leash and I enjoyed a burger. Then Sammy had fun playing in some fountains with children. It was a great afternoon. I set out to write part of my book as well, and in that regard the afternoon was a disaster. I got nothing written. But today I have something to write about.

Epicurus was right. Good food and good friends make for the good life. I hope to have another lunch like that with Sammy. We made some great memories—for ourselves and others we met.

A hopeful life is a meaningful life. We feel a sense of meaning when we set goals with our own initiative. Then we take action and hope we get a good result. If we accomplish something, it feels good. If we fail, well we can learn from that setback. In either case, we have a meaningful result.

Your progress in this regard is meaningful. You are a human being and everyone is meaningful in and of themselves. You don't have to do anything to prove or justify your worth. Humanity is so rare in the universe. Humanity is so complicated and fragile and yet powerful. It is amazing to look at all the ways people have made their lives better—for themselves and for society. Your progress is just as valuable as someone else's progress. We've made all this progress in the world because individuals like you decided to do something positive and constructive with their lives. You are part of this global progress. I encourage you to take some time to feel it.

The physician and philosopher Viktor Frankl said it is part of our humanity that we reach out to find meaning in our life. We all do it. He saw fellow prisoners do this in Nazi concentration camps when they fed breadcrumbs to sparrows visiting them at their windows. They looked forward to the birds visiting them again. They had hope. Nature was a symbol of hope. Nature was a symbol of God. Prisoners who gave up on hope often passed away, he said. Reaching out for hope and meaning for you is like having a pulse. It is part of being alive. Hope makes you stronger and it is a unique part of your humanity just like your fingerprint. If you let yourself feel the worth of that progress, you are going to feel more meaningful.

The world interferes with this, Frankl said. People try to reduce the meaning of your humanity to something else. Money, status, power, politics and religion can be distractions from the meaning you make for yourself. Society may seem to say you are valuable only if you have money, status or power. Society may imply there is a correct religion, political party, nationality, sexual orientation or race.

To all this Frankl protested. Our humanity is wonderful and worthwhile in and of itself. The field of positive psychology sprung up in part from his inspiring book, "Man's Search for Meaning," which was found to be one of the ten most influential books in the United States.

Frankl said you can create a hopeful and meaningful life by experiencing your unique:
- self-determined free will
- self-determined attitude
- self-determined meaning
- self-determined experience[56]

I call this the FAME approach to self-determination. Authoritarian governments don't want you to do this so THEY can determine your will, attitude, meaning and experience. But then you are not living a life authentic to yourself and your hopes and dreams. You are being a fake. Don't do this!

Is negativity dragging you down? You're not alone. We are all feeling more stressed out, according to a recent Gallup poll. Gallup pollsters working on the "Negative Experience Index" in 115 countries asked people about their experiences the previous day. They found increasing numbers of people say they experienced worry (40%), stress (40%), pain (29%), sadness (27%) and anger (24%). From 2006 to 2020, the Negative Experience Index has been rising.[57]

One thing that can add to your negative experience is pessimism. Hey, we all have to deal with it. If you don't control your pessimism, it will control you. Which leads to the next question. How pessimistic have you been lately? Rate yourself to find out. Go to the Appendix and find the unhealthy pessimism

FIGURE 1.9.2
Stress is attacking the world and its hopefulness.
By Esther Phingmoo.

rating scale and fill it out. Then do it again when you finish this chapter to see if your hopefulness has got a boost by a drop in unhealthy pessimism.

Life skill: tell the story you hope for...stories illustrate our attitudes

Whether we want to or not, we are always telling ourselves stories of what is going on in our life. The stories tell us a lot about what we believe about ourselves and our world. The stories can also be confusing. One moment we can say we are ok, then the next moment we are not. Stories can let us discover things we never knew, never experienced before. Stories can empower us to do things we never imagined possible. Stories also reveal our attitude whether positive or pessimistic.

FIGURE 1.9.3
Get outside the jar of your attitude to read the label of your attitude. By Esther Phingmoo.

Stories are the labels on the jar of our attitude. Stories tell you what kind of attitude you have. The label tells you what's inside but you can't read the label from inside the jar. You have to get outside the jar of your attitude to read the label of your attitude. This book helps you do that so you can have a sharp awareness of your attitude which can shift from one moment to the next. Game changer!

An easy way to cultivate this self awareness of your attitude is to simply ask yourself, "What's my attitude now?" Secondly you can mentally go down the list of qualities of optimism in the ISHALL acronym and ask, "Am I doing this?" This usually takes just a few moments and the answer is obvious. And if you see you are not being optimistic, it is easy to see what to do to be more hopeful. Change your attitude.

In today's social media connected world, the next problem can be other people's attitude. They might be pessimistic. They might ignore your initiative or say it's not enough. Your accomplishments and learning are not enough. You are inferior UNLESS you: Join their politics, join their religion, avoid the politics and religion they see as "bad, avoid groups they see as "bad" and a threat to them.

This is nothing new. People have been playing these "influencer" games since they painted hieroglyphics on the tombs in Egypt. To all these restraints on your freedom to live your best life, Dr. Viktor Frankl said don't participate in this. When you just do what others tell you to do, you give up on your chance to live an authentic life—and live a meaningful, genuine life. Don't give up on your freedom! The good life is a struggle. Even if you are struggling freely to live a meaningful life, it is still a struggle. That's not bad, it's just the way things are when the world doesn't revolve around you. But the world can make that struggle much more difficult if you get caught up in the world's "blame game" of false guilt. It is really quite common. Self-determination is always a fight. Ask Ukraine.

One country can blame another for awful wrongs (that fail a fact check when evaluated in historical documents). Or one race can blame their ills on another race. Or one religion can blame their problems on another religion. It is such an old and tired game, but still quite popular if you look at mainstream and social media. If you get caught up in the blame game, there are consequences: you will start to feel guilt. It is false guilt but it feels just as real as real guilt. Let's look at this in more detail.

Life skill: reject false guilt for more friendships

Guilt comes from "feelings of deserving blame, especially for imagined offenses or from a sense of inadequacy."[58]

Many people "guilt-trip" themselves for awful things they think they did. They are trying to live up to what they imagine are expectations from parents or others. But that is undeserved. Once you are an adult, you don't have to meet anyone's expectations except your own.

Also, people feel guilty because they don't feel they're doing enough, whether it's making grades, earning money or gaining popularity. Once again, having to do external things to meet internal needs is a rabbit-hole that never ends. Don't cross the line and participate in conditional self-acceptance. We are all inadequate in all kinds of ways in other people's eyes and it doesn't matter.

There is true guilt when you have violated a law or moral principle. But 99% of the guilt I see is false guilt. They imagined they did something bad or fell short, and it is all a colossal misunderstanding.

So, what to do about true guilt? Admit to it, apologize and deal with it like an adult. Pay your penalty to society and then you can live with a clean conscience. Forgive yourself. When you start heaping more guilt on yourself, forgive yourself again. I have worked with men in jail and many have that guilt written on their face because they haven't dealt with it. Admit your offenses and pay your penalty, but then give yourself credit. It is an accomplishment to pay for your offenses and make yourself right again in the eyes of society.

For false guilt, regard it as a temporary setback. You were fooled by your mind. Learn from it and move on. Don't wallow in guilt that is just imaginary. That will interfere with your fierce self-determination!

Life skill: dump false shame for more love

The point of these issues I'm reviewing is protect your hope. You can do that in the privacy of your own mind. On a worldwide scale, countries are trying to erode other countries' hope. They are trying to dominate you by getting you to doubt yourself, your country, your faith, your culture, your beliefs. This isn't a game. It is part of the information war fought between countries. If you can get a country to doubt itself, it is then much easier to bomb them into oblivion. There are consequences when you doubt. When you doubt yourself, you negate yourself.

Why are countries fighting so fiercely in this information war? Why is this war even going on in college campuses? Why did some professors of mine question my religious and political beliefs? I think that is because the 21st Century is shaping up to be about self determination. Can individuals determine their life? Can sovereign nations determine their future? That is the big question. And big countries are trying hard to change your mind on those issues by getting you to doubt. Some professors and textbooks are continuing the battle on college campuses too, because they are fighting for the same thing that anti-democratic countries are fighting for: your mind.

Some important notes about shame:

- Shame can get you to doubt you have a right to pursue your future. Doubt you have a right to pursue your future. Doubt your children have a right to pursue their dreams.
- Shame is a much bigger issue than guilt in most people's lives.
- Shame is a painful feeling that you've done something wrong, improper or substandard. Shame can also come when you've done none of that, but you imagine doing it. There is real shame and imaginary shame.
- Shame comes from violating a model for behavior in society, whereas guilt comes from violating morals, and the two can overlap.
- Shame can ruin your life! A feeling of shame can prevent you from asking for help on homework and might result in a lower grade. You might lack self-confidence in that area and drop out of a class or major,

or even drop out of college entirely. If you really did something stupid, own up to it. Don't take yourself too seriously, apologize, learn from it and move on. It can actually be a source of tremendous energy and motivation. I dropped out of a class in the Greek language, felt awful about it and then devoted myself more strongly to a degree in communications.

Common examples of toxic shame today are people who feel they have shame because they are:

- Americans, white, getting good grades, getting a failing grade, living in poverty, can't afford nice clothes, don't have nice social media pictures, are single, divorced, older than others, younger than others, have a child with disabilities.
- The list goes on and on when it comes to false shame. I know all these examples can happen because I've experienced them. If you are too—you know what I mean when I say false shame isn't worth it. Don't be gullible and buy the toxic "shame game" that other people are trying to play on you.
- Take credit for your accomplishments, but not for other people's real or imagined mistakes. Toxic! Not worth it! Like false guilt, false shame is just another side of the ugly face of pessimism, because it gets you to doubt yourself.

How I use accountability to create more hope for my patients

When you treat your customer well, it feels good to the customer. The customer feels like they are in the driver's seat. If they don't like the service they receive, they can tell the business owner or go somewhere else.

As a physician with a private practice, I have to be aware of all the different working parts of what it takes to make a patient visit work for the patient. As I go through all these points, you can see how things work when the doctor is directly accountable to the patient, and there aren't any middlemen interfering. I am going over how I use accountability to do a good job because when I give myself credit for being accountable to my patients, it helps "deflect" feelings of false shame or guilt. Disgruntled patients may claim all sorts of things that a doctor did. But if a doctor (or other health care providfer) can sort through how they've been responsible to the best of their conscience and ability, it can soothe their soul in the stormiest of emotional seas. And that's important for health care providers to do. As elsewhere noted in this book one survey found about 20% of health care providers in the last several years simply quit healthcare entirely because of stress. So this is an important issue, obviously, and I would argue having a solid system of personal accountability in place can help insulate a healthcare provider from some stress. (This is also a demonstration of how capitalism with a conscience works, but that is another issue.)

Let's look at my daily routine as a doctor as an example of personal accountability to my patients:

First, I see the patient on time. My time and their time are both valuable so I start on time. I may remind the patient how much time we have by saying, "Great to see you. I see we have 15 minutes for this visit. How are things going?"

I start with an open question and there's some idle chitchat and catching up that is done for a minute or two, during which time I glance at the previous notes where I've written down the history of what happened at the last visit.

To keep the patient (or customer) happy, I have to think about 5 things at one time. The customer just thinks about one thing at a time: what is on their mind.

What am I so busy thinking about to provide good service? Here are the layers of thinking I am processing—all at the same time—as I'm listening to what the patient is saying:

1. What was the situation last time? What were the medical issues? What were the biological and psychological and social issues and the treatment plans for each? What were the medication or counseling changes and the predicted results?

2. What were the actual results and why?

3. What was the doctor going to do last time? What was the patient going to do?

4. What is the attitude of the patient towards their goals? What is interfering with the patient's freedom to live their life for their goals and hopes and dreams?

5. What can the doctor do to remove hurdles preventing this person from thriving? Organize the hurdles by category: biological, psychological and social. Have a plan for each by the end of the session.

On my electronic medical records, there is a box labeled "Notes." Here I list the person's goals, and there might be anywhere from two to ten. I stay focused on their priorities in the context of what priorities they shared in the past, in the context of how I see things and what the medical issues are, and in the setting of what this person is trying to accomplish this week, this month and this year. "Hurdles" to a person's progress are only listed if in fact the hurdle causes anxiety or depression for the patient. Hurdles are not included if they are simply "personal improvement issues."

Here I appreciate the person's uniqueness and precious individuality. How much do they want to work? How much do they want the doctor to be involved? What are their values? What kind of support system do they have? Regarding medication: do they want none, the least needed or whatever it takes to control the symptoms? Do they want to get off it as soon as possible or stay on it as long as necessary? How much work do they want to do on their lifestyle to allow a decrease in their medication? How often do they want to see me? How fast do they want results? How long do they want the results to last?

This is called personalized medicine. The doctor is basically a guide in positivity, helping the patient achieve their goal which is reducing their suffering from some illness such as depression or anxiety. As you can see, the doctor can see "some things" in the person's life much better than the person themself can see. For this reason, people with a guide make much more progress than people without a guide. I am here trying to follow the wisdom of Dr. Frankl as earlier reviewed.

The person's values are held in the highest regard. People don't visit their doctor to make the doctor happy. The doctors is there to help the patient overcome illnesses and thrive. The doctor isn't there to force his values on the patient. The doctor is a guide. This also might be a model for other people in their business.

Life skill: she kept hoping when 3 nations failed her

Hopefulness can be a fragile flower, especially if you don't ask for help, are pessimistic, or are rigid in how you do things. In this regard, the world has seen Ukraine keep it's hope alive—because they have asked for help, stayed optimistic and also it has had a healthy dose of healthy pessimism. Instagram posts from Kyiv, Ukraine mayor and world heavyweight boxing champion Vitali Klitschko are full of messages acknowledging that freedom is never free. Freedom is always a struggle. Freedom is always a fight. Self determination is always a fight. That is the message in Dr. Frankl's book as well.

To make matters worse, entire countries can either actively interfere with your self determination (as Russia is doing to Ukraine), or countries can just not support you. Then you have to take matters into your own hands. Angie's story illustrates this perfectly.

Hopefulness is a struggle—a good struggle but it is always a struggle. Angie liked helping people and that's why she got into a career in insurance, investigating hail damage and other problems. But she could never get ahead financially with the rising costs of food, gas and rent. The promised promotions never came. She felt like giving up. She felt trapped by feelings of guilt that she had somehow failed in life, but she rejected those feelings as false. She felt a sense of shame sweep over her as she thought about asking for help from friends and how she would look to them. But she rejected that too as false. Good friends will always think well of you when you are trying to make your life better.

Angie reached out to her support team. This included her brother, sister, several close friends and her therapist. She quit being a Lone Ranger. Angie talked with her therapist, friends and siblings to explore dozens of different career options, writing down a list of her strengths and weaknesses and likes and dislikes. She asked for feedback. All this led to an interest in a career that matched up with her strengths and the goal of becoming financially self-sufficient.

But she had another problem: she lived in a country with poverty because it was run by a dictator. Venezuela. She had another problem: she had no money. She found help with a kind and gracious country: Saudi Arabia. There she worked for several years and saved up enough money to get a master's degree in business, something she felt she needed if she was going to be a big success in real estate and business.

She wanted to go back to Venezuela but the grinding poverty and rampant crime left her afraid to return. Still her rich Latino culture with it's wonderful salsa and bachata music lifted her spirits. She found she could travel to Spain and a university there would accept her in an MBA program. Once she got the degree, she had another problem: finding a good paying job. For that, she looked everywhere but the best opportunities were in the United States. The very country that, as a child, she was told was evil. She moved to the United States anyway. Then she found another problem: Americans can't dance as well as people do in Venezuela. This she found a way to overlook. And through Latin dancing she made friends that eventually helped her find a good job and the Latin culture she loved so much.

To keep her hope alive, she lived in four countries. Each country helped her with one issue, then failed to help for another issue. So she moved to keep her hope alive. Not everyone has this energy or drive. But many do in the Latin culture! Don't be afraid to move to another town, another state, another country, to keep your hope alive of pursuing your dreams.

What happened once Angie settled in Florida?

Angie focused on a career in real estate and developed a plan to get her real estate license within six months. She worked part time jobs and survived on savings (thank you Saudi Arabia!) while she studied for the licensing exam. Everything was focused on getting that license. Later, a family friend said that Angie could work in her real estate company for a few years until she goes out on her own. Now Angie has a game plan she can really be enthusiastic about! To succeed, she needs to make every minute count, and she can. She has great daily routines that allow her to get up early and dive into her studies, checking items off her to do lists.

Angie loves her freedom. She is free to succeed and free to fail every day. But she knows she can learn from both and does so. This is so much better than that pessimistic feeling of being trapped forever in a dead-end job. For her, it is such a great comfort to know that she's not doing all this alone. She has the emotional support of her siblings and her dear family friend is helping her pursue her dreams. For Angie, she jealously guards her hope. For her it is everything. For some people struggling in addictions, however, hope is nowhere to be found.

Life skill: use hopefulness to overcome addiction

It is too simplistic to say a person should be positive about everything. A case in point is addiction. Tens of thousands of people in the US die every year from addictions to narcotics, nicotine, carbohydrates and alcohol. Studies show some addicts have an **unhealthy optimism** that they can use addictive substances and somehow escape the harmful consequences. (Wrong!) And once they become addicted, they have an **unhealthy pessimism** that they can't overcome their addiction. (Wrong again! People overcome addictions all the time).

As you can see, the wrong attitude can really mess up your life. For that reason, it is important to say whether your positivity or pessimism is healthy. Otherwise you are being too simplistic.

Here is a situation. What if someone offers you a cigarette? It contains nicotine which is highly addictive. You could start smoking it and get addicted. One study found cigarette smokers lacked a healthy pessimism about the consequences of smoking. Non-smokers, however, thought smoking would likely shorten their life—that is why they didn't smoke (healthy pessimism).

But smokers thought smoking somehow wouldn't shorten their life though they understood it would impact other smokers' lives. Wrong! This is unhealthy optimism. (In fact, contrary to smokers' unhealthy positivity, once a smoker is diagnosed with lung cancer, a large percentage of them will be dead in 10 years from that cancer.)

For more on this topic, see "Smokers' unrealistic optimism about their risk," in the British Medical Journal, "Tobacco Control." Authors ND Weinstein, SE Marcus and RP Moser. https://tobaccocontrol.bmj.com/content/14/1/55.short

This controversial study seems to suggest that exposure to an addictive substance warps an individual's attitude on a biological level. In fact, many brain imaging studies have found substances of addiction (processed food, heroin, alcohol, cocaine) biologically change the structure and function of brain areas, specifically in part the area called the "amygdala." As you might recall from earlier in this book, the amygdala along with the rostral anterior cingulate cortex are two areas active in thinking in a positive manner. So in that sense, it is not surprising that if the amygdala is affected in addictions, then attitude will also be affected. Addiction biology is the horse pulling the cart of the psychology of addiction. Somethiing to keep in mind if you are feeling tempted to smoke a cigarette.

Smokers clearly needed to have more healthy pessimism about the impact of smoking on their health. And they needed to get rid of their unhealthy optimism. It is irrational. The upshot: nicotine addicts are examples of how the wrong attitude can and does have fatal consequences. The lack of healthy pessimism and healthy optimism among nicotine addicts kills thousands of people every year in the US.

Unhealthy pessimism is the opposite of positivity and can get rid of your positivity. It's important to know what it is and what it can do to you, for obvious reasons. It is called unhealthy because it works against your optimism or positivity. Take the quiz below and put a number on the power of this dangerous attitude.

Unhealthy pessimism self-report rating scale

Rate the following on a 1-5 scale: 1 is strongly disagree, 2 is disagree, 3 is neutral, 4 is agree, 5 is strongly agree. These questions assume you are focused on healthy activities in a negative manner.

1. I am **not** taking initiative today. _____
2. I **don't** take setbacks as temporary. _____
3. I am staying **hopeless**. _____
4. I am **not** taking my accomplishments personally. _____
5. I am **latching onto** what I can't control. _____
6. I **don't** take life as for learning. _____
7. If I can't control everything, I feel disappointed. _____
Total unhealthy pessimism score: _____

On the other hand, you can be overly optimistic and then have problems because you didn't anticipate what could go wrong. This is unhealthy optimism. Take the following quiz to see how often you are doing that.

Unhealthy optimism quiz

Rate the following on a 1-5 scale: 1 is strongly disagree, 2 is disagree, 3 is neutral, 4 is agree, 5 is strongly agree. These questions assume you are focused on healthy activities but without regard for the consequences of your actions.

1. I am taking initiative today but **not thinking** about the consequences. _____
2. I ignore how long some setbacks can last. _____
3. I am ignoring what could **hurt** my hopefulness. _____
4. I am ignoring who helped me achieve my accomplishments. _____
5. I am letting go of what I **can control** because I'm so idealistic. _____
6. I don't feel like I need to learn much because things are so good in my life. _____
7. I feel I can control all outcomes in my life. _____
Total unhealthy optimism score: _____

Total of these two unhealthy attitudes: _____

(see the "Tools" section at the end of the book) to get your total positive attitude score and write it here: _____

JOURNAL YOUR LEARNING HERE:

FIGURE 1.10.0
Burden. Accomplishments can occur when you get rid of the boulder on your back: a self-destructive attitude. Unhealthy pessimism. By Toso Borkovic.

10

How "Accomplishments" occur when you "Let Go"

Life skill: hopefulness saved him from heroin addiction

Friends had given Eliza up for dead. He had lost jobs, cars, apartments and girlfriends all because he couldn't stop using heroin. He felt hopeless. He almost lost his life in a heroin overdose. But his family didn't lose hope in him and instead sent him to a doctor where he was prescribed buprenorphine. Soon, all his cravings for heroin were gone. The gorilla was off his back. But Eliza still felt worthless to the world. If that kept up, he would quit buprenorphine and then his addiction would be back again. Instead, he saw a job counsellor and learned skills while working at a convenience store. He felt more useful, but not meaningful. It was a start. In quiet desperation, he saw a therapist for help. He wondered how he could feel some meaning in his life. Therapy didn't seem to help but poetry did.

Eliza began to habitually read poetry. In poetry he found his soul echoed. "Society is crazy," he said, "I'm just a different kind of crazy, but a healthy crazy because I love my family and all that. I can't remember some things. Street drugs did a number on my hard drive or something. But I'm ok if I can get to work in the morning?" He ends the last sentence with a question mark because to him to pronounce himself "ok" is to take away from the mystery of life and the mystical experience of his own humanity.

Elizah's doesn't believe in society or technology. He hates cell phones, money and fake attitudes. He believes in being a good friend and boyfriend. Most of all he believes in being real. "What else matters if you don't have that?" he asks. "What good is fake?"

That kind of getting-real-about-life attitude has been Elizah's saving grace. It lets him be part of a slowly evolving poem that is his life. That attitude lets him be vulnerable and feel the love his family has for him, as risky as that feels sometimes.

"What's a metaphor for what your family's love feels like to you?" I ask.

Elizah's thinks a few seconds. "Biscuits and gravy when you're hungry? Maybe?" he replies, fidgeting in his chair.

Eizeah's positivity fits well into any of the definitions in this book. He's obviously focused on goals of being real while simultaneously seeing life as a precious and soul-fulfilling dance. This is the hopefulness of a healthy positive attitude—in action.

What you get when you let go...

Today, I regularly see people getting hung up on three things. These things cause so much stress. People are hung up on trying to control:

➤THE FUTURE. If I can do this one thing right, it will guarantee I'll have a great future and won't fail. Perfect grades. High GPA. Super job. Perfect salary. Holy grail of people. What happens: people get stuck in perfectionism. Someone will get a great job but become a workaholic. Society wants us to live ideally, go to extremes. This is a rabbit hole. This is sacrificing your happiness on the altar of material success. Not ever worth it. This is a rabbit hole. Hang onto it and you'll go down that hole and you may never find a way out.

➤ OTHER PEOPLE. Others: hopeless. incorrigible. People pleasing. Like Facebook posts. What if she doesn't like my fb or ig post, people post perfect pictures to get the most likes. I'm popular if other popular people like me. People pleasing. Pathetic. Be yourself. Society of pathetic people pleasers.

➤THE WORLD. There can't be a COVID virus. Can't be happening. Well it is. We tend to lapse into thinking in catastrophic ways. We're going to die because we are all wearing masks. Gloom and doom. Let go of feeling a need to fall into the narrative the media is putting out there. The media is forever crying the end is near. Let go of this in your own inner narrative. Since the dawn of time, humaniity has weathered a never ending succession of epidemics and pandemics. It is a challenge, not a world-destroying catastrophe. Sorry!

All these add to pessimism. Hopelessness. Future is hopeless. But it isn't. People are ok. The world is full of conflict at turmoil, yes. It is full of injustice and human rights violations. I'll give you that. But I won't buy the argument that the world is hopeless. As I've noted earlier, progress is being made in every country. There are a few exceptions, such as Ukraine. But the world is full of hope. There is even hope for Ukraine. They have fought for their self determination since they were first founded in 882 AD. Since then they've repeatedly fought and won back their country. They let go of material comforts. They recently endured an estimated 20,000 bombs per day for months at a time. They've let go of many things—peace, property, even loved ones—but they refuse to let go of their right as a country to self determination. Ukraine is full of hope. Just ask the Ukrainians.

We can opt out of letting go and retreat like a snail into its shell. Letting go is hard to do. It is hard to let go of your pride. It's hard to take a chance to succeed—or fail. But it sets you up for success by developing your boldness. It is hard to let go of pets, such as when they pass away. But that makes you more soulful. It is hard to let go of friends, such as when they move or change. It is hard to fail in a relationship and get a wounded heart. That too makes you more soulful. More lovable. More wise. These hardships can make you a better parent. Experiencing hard times gives you the tools to prepare your kids for hard times. People can't relate to you if nothing bad has ever happened to you, if you never had to let go of someone you became attached to. You become shallow and emotionally frail.

In an unexpected way, letting go allows you to gain something you'd never have if all you did was hang on and get attached to everyone and everything around you—and never dared to do something different for fear of failure. That is pride. In that way, life is like a dance, where letting go allows you or your partner to do a move—and now you can dance in rhythm with the music.

If you are too proud to take a chance, that pride comes with a fall. A fall from growing and thriving. A fall from life. A fall from being creative and daring. A fall from being able to have a family and bring new life into this world.

Letting go of your pride—that you are too good to take chances—is good for:

- Love
- Affection
- Resilience

Jim kicked addiction and anxiety by letting go

Nowadays, Jim installs sheet rock by day and moves mountains by night for his family. What kickstarted all this progress? He let go of having to control the future. Jim will do anything for his family. Ten years ago, however, he would drink to run from his problems because he couldn't control everything and know every future outcome. He was a control freak. He lost his job and his girlfriend threatened to leave him. Jim knew that he could lose everything that mattered in his life from this problem, but he just couldn't stop drinking. He reached out and found powerful help from his family and friends. He felt like he wasn't the thing causing the problem in his life. But rather, it was his boss, his job, his past and the hundred ways people had looked down on him for 25 years. He wanted to escape his past but he couldn't control it. He wanted to control his future. He was allowing his need for control to define him. He was stuck. He was hopeless. And he knew this was his problem to solve.

Jim saw a counselor. "The past doesn't define you unless you let it," the counselor said. Stress comes from the words you use to think your thoughts, not from situations. Your feelings come from your thoughts. Change your thoughts to change your feelings. Your attitude defines you for better or worse. Pick a take charge positive attitude.

Jim accepted this advice. He let go of his limiting "I'm a victim" beliefs and got sober. He focused on his personal and work goals and followed through on them. He kept his promises. He valued his time with to-do lists and a planner. He fought the temptations to drink with the force of his will. He didn't give himself the option to fail. He stayed devoted to his job and was promoted. His great character impressed his girlfriend who later married him. The two of them now have two happy young children. He couldn't be happier, he says. "I'm married to a woman I love and my kids are happy. What more can you ask for?"

To review, Jim let go of:

- The desire to control the past
- The need to control the future

- The need to control people
- The need to control every emotion

Once he let go, he had lots of time to be the devoted, loving, salt of the earth guy he wanted to be. Letting go of control issues can be difficult. But letting go of limiting beliefs can seem scarey. Like a person feels when they step out of a plane for a parachute experience, when you let go of limiting beliefs it can feel like you're in a free fall and you don't know where you are going to land. But those feelings are deceptive. It's good to let go of limiting beliefs. It's how we all grow.

She let go of bad thinking habits to boost her grades!

This fictionalized story is about how a person can let go of limiting beliefs, like "I'm a bad student," "I can't get organized," and "I can't get a social life." Life was hopeless for Ariana two years ago. She was a B-average student in high school but then in college her grades took a nosedive to C's and D's. She was shocked. She felt humiliated. She told no one. So her grades kept falling. Ariana obsessed about all her failures and felt like one herself. She gave up on herself and it showed. She talked to a pastor, who encouraged her to read the Bible and remember that she is a wonderful person. God loves her. She has value in God's eyes and deserves the opportunity to tap into her potential, a potential God gave her. She prayed with the pastor and that got the ball rolling in her life.

The media talked about endless problems in politics and the environment. Ariana saw she was getting more depressed the more time she spent on social media, so she quit it. She got more depressed listening to traditional media so she stopped that too. Her friends feared for her safety when she talked about how hopeless she felt. They said see a counselor.

The counselor helped Ariana rediscover her many strengths. She was kind, caring, intelligent and disciplined, but depression ran in her family. She was depressed with all the biological signs of depression: low energy, low motivation and insomnia. Her mood was empty. The therapist said all these symptoms came from being judgmental towards herself when her real problem was lacking certain life skills.

Ariana agreed that her mind was being judgmental. The counselor showed her that not knowing how to get out of judgmental thinking got her in trouble. She was stuck in a cycle of self-doubt and self-hatred. She learned how to meditate and experienced self-acceptance for the first time in her life. She accepted herself totally in those 30 second moments of meditation. It felt wonderful. The pastor said this is similar to the acceptance God has for her. Still her life lacked meaning and she went back and visited the family's pastor and discovered how to apply her faith in God. She felt a lot more meaning in her life after doing some spiritual exercises. She volunteered to work with young children in the church's Sunday school. It felt so rewarding to be putting her faith in action.

But Ariana was still disorganized. No one had showed her how to use to-do lists and manage her time wisely to achieve her goals. And her depression was dragging on. She saw a doctor who taught her organization skills and gave her a medication to help her mood and focus. Once she learned those skills, her life was much more orderly. Exercise and healthy eating boosted her energy. The medication helped her depression get better. Then her emotions responded more to all the good things she was doing for herself. The medication boosted serotonin activity in her brain which was low because of a medical condition—it wasn't her fault.

Her grades were still low but instead of dwelling on the questions she missed on tests, she learned from them and improved her study skills, which were the root of many of her problems. She picked up new study skills and routines. She practiced principles of optimism every day with daily routines. She started studying for tests after each lecture. Her grades picked up each month, dramatically. "Everyone was talking about how hard the material was, but I just took it as a big challenge. I started studying for the test a lot sooner than anybody else," she said. "I guess it paid off."

She had a doctorate level of study skills and techniques for time and task management. Three doctors had taught her: a doctor of divinity, a doctor of psychology and a doctor of medicine. She was eager to apply what she learned. It's no surprise her grades skyrocketed over the next several semesters.

Discussion about letting go of limiting beliefs

This is a great story to illustrate you can let go of limiting beliefs and embrace empowering beliefs. First let go, then you can embrace. Empowering beliefs are cancelled out by limiting beliefs. First you need to get clear about what are the limiting beliefs in your life.

Limiting beliefs make you feel dragged down, anxious, insecure. That is the tip off they are at work in you. That is pessimism in action. They are often underlying beliefs, in other words you are not aware you are thinking those thoughts at that time. But you often had those thoughts in the previous hours and days so the emotional consequences are now coming back to bite you. There are thoughts that are weird; they are not conscious use of words like you have when say you read something. There are thoughts that are impressions like a paint brush sweeping colors on a canvas. I call them thought impressions. So there are thoughts you are aware of having with distinct words, like "I'm bad," and there are impressions with images and patterns of emotions put together, like a section of a movie. For these movie-like impressions, you can reverse engineer them and guess what the movie's screen play was like. This is how you sort out limiting beliefs.

Let me explain. If you feel sad, in some way you have a belief you've lost things or fallen short of some expectation. If you are angry, you may have beliefs you've been cheated or lied to or betrayed. If you are anxious, you might have thought you are not safe from threat of failure or shame or guilt. In most cases, there is a limiting belief behind the sadness or anger or anxiety.

Limiting beliefs are "can't beliefs."

You can't learn certain things. You can't achieve. You can't make the first move, get through the setback, feel hopeful, feel good about accomplishments, let go and learn. You can see I'm using the I SHALL acronym of positivity here, because I'm trying to organize your awareness that limiting beliefs can limit the power of your positive attitude.

In the above example with Ariana, she had limiting beliefs— lots of them, like a net tying her down. You can't fight what you can't see. Over time, Ariana saw those limiting beliefs and one-by-one rejected them and got free from them. Not by acting alone. She first talked to her pastor and then a counselor and doctor, so over time she had three people advising her with real wisdom. Her limiting beliefs were mostly "thought impressions." The limiting beliefs that were ruining her life included:

- I'm a bad student
- I can't survive getting bad grades
- If I get bad grades, I've ruined my future
- I can't learn from my mistakes on tests
- I can't get better grades from learning from mistakes
- I'm hopeless
- I can't break big problems down to smaller ones
- I can't solve smaller problems easily
- I can't change what I do
- I can't change what I think
- I can't stop looking at social media
- All my emotional problems are psychological—not chemical
- I can't ask for help from a counselor
- I can't ask for help from a doctor
- I can't take medication
- I can't learn new thinking strategies
- I can't get better organized
- I can't learn a sophisticated time management system
- I can't talk to my pastor
- I can't learn to have a better relationship with God
- I can't accept God's love for me
- I can't ask for God's grace and mercy
- I can't let go of judging myself even though God has
- I can't feel good about myself if I make mistakes
- I can't love myself

When you stop to look at all her limiting beliefs, then it is easier to see why she felt hopeless.

Acting on empowering beliefs—changed her life

The results of letting go of her limiting beliefs were amazing but only because Ariana embraced empowering beliefs and acted on them every day. The empowering beliefs didn't do anything for her feelings until she acted on them. Ariana's empowering beliefs rained down on her every day like rain falling in a desert, allowing flowers to bloom. She wrote out her empowering beliefs and read them every day in a long list. It was quick and easy. See the list that follows:

- I'm a great student
- If I get bad grades, I will learn from them
- Bad grades are an opportunity to learn better study skills
- I can learn from my mistakes on tests
- I can get better grades from learning from mistakes
- I'm hopeful
- I can break big problems down to smaller ones
- I can solve smaller problems easily
- I can change what I do
- I can change what I think
- I can stop looking at social media
- I can have biological problems
- I can solve biological problems in my body
- It's responsible to take care of biological problems, not ignore them
- All my emotional problems are not just psychological—they can be biological, spiritual or social
- I can ask for help from a counselor
- I can ask for help from a doctor
- I can take medication
- I can learn new thinking strategies
- I can get better organized
- I can learn a sophisticated time management system
- I can talk to my pastor
- I can learn to have a better relationship with God
- I can accept God's love for me
- I can ask for God's grace and mercy

- I can let go of judging myself like God has done
- I can feel good about myself if I make mistakes and learn from them
- I can love myself
- I can love life and its opportunities
- I can make more opportunities for myself

Consequences of acting on empowering beliefs: It's like winning the lottery

These empowering beliefs were often implied beliefs as Ariana wrote down items in her to-do lists to act on her goals. "Talk to pastor" and "prepare for Bible study" were in her personal to-do list. For school, she wrote "ask tutor for help," "be ready to ask professor questions right after lecture today" and "skim material before lecture on chapter 7 in physics." There were other items. "Ask tutor how I can study differently." "Ask friends what they want to do for a party this weekend." "Be grateful today God loves me."

These empowering beliefs have real consequences. They make you more attractive. Ariana found more people wanted to plan a party with her because she had such a positive vibe. Empowering beliefs make you more effective. Ariana found her grades got better each month though she wasn't studying for longer periods of time.

Empowering beliefs also help you manage your emotions. Ariana got upset less often. Because of better self-control, empowering beliefs allow you to manage people more effectively. Other women wanted to work with her to plan parties. Some even became a "wing girl" and set her up with guys for a date. She returned the favor! (Great idea here.)

Her new skill set made her also able to become a manager wherever she worked. You can check out the fact on your local job listing web site, as I have on Indeed.com. But managers make more money. You have to pay people another 5 dollars an hour to manage 5 or 10 people. And To manage 10-20 people you often have to pay another 10 dollars an hour—or the good managers just won't apply for the job.

Now do the math for empowering beliefs. There are 2,000 hours in a working year. Take that times 5 dollars per hour, and these empowering beliefs that allow you to learn people management skills and handle the stress well, allow you to make another $10,000 per year. Take that times working another 40 years if you are 25 and you can see that these beliefs will allow you to make another $400,000 in your life—at a minimum. Most likely it will be double that—$800,000.

Living guided by empowering beliefs is like winning the lottery. Positivity increases your value.

Of course it's not all about money—but money doesn't hurt. What you are winning is a rewarding life. You are overcoming great hurdles. You are tapping into potentials you didn't even know you had. You are helping other people in ways they highly value. Not only that, but finding the right empowering beliefs helps you live a meaningful life. You are living your beliefs. Not that anyone can do that perfectly. Life is full of sacrifice and compromise. But now you have something to sacrifice for.

She let go of negativity and stands to gain $8 million

Jessie is focused. Every day she keeps her to-do lists and weekly planner open on the desk beside her. She is disciplined. Every day she is just focused on keeping up with her classes. And now she is poised to reap the rewards society has for her.

"I just have to pass my nursing boards in September," Jessie confesses. But she is staying positive. "I can do it; I just have to stay with my routines."

For four years, Jessie's to-do lists, planner and daily routines haven't failed her. She passed class after class. But before getting her "ducks in a row," she was getting C's and worse on tests in her freshman year in college. She felt awful and pessimistic. She didn't know what was wrong. Too full of fear and shame to ask for help, she braced herself for the inevitable: she was going to flunk out of college. Then she talked to a friend who went through the same thing. She learned there was hope. Women support women and she received that support—and put her new knowledge in action. She talked to professionals and learned to be positive.

Now there is a quiet confidence in how Jessie talks, how she smiles, how she thinks before responding to questions. Positivity is part of her personality. She's weeded out all that cancer of pessimism and self-doubt. Life is so rewarding now. She loves these challenges. She has a love-hate relationship with tests but admits with a stoic smile that tests are a great way to "show what you know" and "get credit" for what you've learned.

Jessie is a Hispanic woman but neither demographic has been a factor in her school or in her work. Equal rights are working in America and in her hospitals.

Although Jessie hasn't finished school, she made herself into such a high value person she already has a job. She is studying in Nebraska and a hospital there has hired her to work in a rehabilitation unit for $30 per hour because her grades and the quality of her internship work were outstanding. Jessie likes the intensity of starting IV medications and precisely controlling their output—and how that heals people, who might be battling anything from cancer to infections to heart attacks.

Jessie let go of her disorganized and self-absorbed thinking that filled her freshman year in college. She is a living example of making social justice happen in her life. She did it. When asked where she would be without optimism and organized time management, she has a one word answer she delivers with a wry smile:

"Nowhere."

Jessie's positivity will help her heal hundreds of people in the course of her 8-year career as a nurse. At $60,000 per year for 8 years, she will earn $480,000. After that, she hopes to spend the last 30 years of her nursing career working as a nurse anesthetist at $250,000 per year, totaling $7.5 million. For all her hard work as a woman and as a minority, America will reward her handsomely with nearly $8 million. Without college, Jessie might make $30,000 per year for 40 years or make $1.2 million. Taking risks and working hard with a positive attitude is paying off. She also knows that earning more will allow her to donate more to charity and spread her fortune to help others. Money isn't everything, but it sure helps to achieve one's goals in life. She doesn't tell her friends what she is making. That might trigger resentment or other negative emotions in others. She keeps her success to herself.

Money also isn't why Jessie got into nursing. And as a woman of color, living in a cancel culture that loves to put people down for succeeding, she doesn't feel she has to defend or apologize for her successes in school, work or life. She doesn't feel bad about doing good. She has worked hard and increased her value. That much is clear in her mind. She stands to make more by being able to do more—without working longer hours.

There are no handouts here. Jessie will earn every penny through hard work, just like everyone else. She will make sure she is paid a competitive wage. She is an example of how competition works to bring out the best in people. Among other things, Jessie also looks forward to volunteering to help people overseas with nonprofit organizations like Doctors Without Borders and Engineers Without Borders. These professional organizations are using modern technology to make the world a better place, including the poorest places in the world. Western Civilization works.

Western Civilization is full of success stories like this, of individuals improving themselves, their communities and the world in general. They are excellent examples of how positivity works—big time. Money isn't everything. But it will allow Jessie to afford a home, health insurance and a family one day. She also is going to volunteer overseas one day and share her nursing skills with an underserved community. Her money will pay for that. She gets it. Isn't Jessie the kind of nurse you would want caring for you if you had a heart attack and were lying in a bed in an intensive care unit fighting for your life?

Not everyone gets to be born in a wealthy country interested in personal success. How can positivity help people born in poverty and victimized by abuse?

Positivity helped her overcome abuse in Oceania

Theresa lived on a Pacific island where tourists came to experience a Paradise. But as a native islander, she was a victim of sexual abuse there and felt like she was in a prison. She felt she had to tell people around her whatever they wanted to hear so they would say nice things to her and she could just try to forget about the abuse — by not being herself.

"The world inside me is so beautiful and every day I'm thankful I discovered that," Theresa now says. She had a pivotal moment in her life when she could take action and quit living a lie. She chose to be true to herself and discover the wonderful person inside her.

"I know I was abused. I know my parents neglected me. It can happen in any country. I love the country I came from but I felt I just couldn't be myself around people. I had to pretend I was ok so no one would ask about what had happened to me, because it was too painful to talk about."

Then she came to America. "Your people were facing their problems and asking for help to overcome them," she said. "That helped me feel comfortable to do the same."

"I am seeing a counselor to get rid of the bad thoughts about myself. I am now married and my husband totally supports me but I'm afraid of sex. So I started seeing a sex therapist. Then I learned I have a chemical imbalance called attention deficit and I'm getting medicine for that." Because she can focus better, she saw things she never saw before. Biological change lead to psychological change.

Theresa saw she had great potential to have a wonderful marriage, to have a successful career in nursing and to have a positive view of herself. But she saw she was getting in her own way by not asking for help. False shame was imprisoning her.

The pivotal moment came when Theresa realized she had so much opportunity to grow and all it took was reaching out her hand, asking for help and being willing to just see what happens.

Positivity has helped Theresa in this journey. She sees life as an adventure and truly hers is. She doesn't know what's going to happen tomorrow and she is okay with that uncertainty. She is taking charge of each day one day at a time.

"I've had so many accomplishments it's easy to forget how much I've improved. My sex life is so much better. I look at myself more positively. I even love myself now. I see the beautiful person that was inside all along but was covered up by a people-pleaser."

Theresa educated herself by reading about being a people-pleaser and realized that was how she was running from her true self. She was focused on pleasing others instead of understanding what she needed to be happy and how to get those needs met.

"I'm so excited to be taking back the power in my life now by focusing on what I need to be happy. In the past I was so focused on what other people needed and then I lost myself just trying to take care of others."

Theresa looks back at the whirlwind of self-improvement she's been striving for over the last 12 months and is amazed. To pull it all together, she has routines in her life. She has set times for going to sleep and getting up and for her meals. There are also set times for work and for studying in the evening.

"Goals are so empowering to me now. Before they were not such a big deal. Now they are ways for me to write a new chapter in my life and it is so exciting!"

There have been setbacks. Many things didn't work out as Theresa planned. Everything she accomplished took more time and energy than she anticipated. But the progress she's making now is thrilling.

"I used to feel stuck like nobody cared about me. Not now!" she says.

Theresa organizes her day with a day timer and to-do lists to help plan how the week will go. She takes the time to visualize what things might come up to slow her progress and how she will deal with them. She is like a train barreling down the tracks, unstoppable.

Full of ambition, Theresa is now strategizing how to realize her dreams. She realized she can pull down a small but improved income working as a nurse with a two-year nursing degree, and with that money she can go to school and get her four-year nursing degree.

Theresa has had to make many adjustments to all this change. She wanted to change how she automatically feels when things go differently than she planned. She's used to feeling guilty or shameful. Thinking things through, Theresa realized a lot of those emotions were a carryover from her past abuse. By journaling, she organizes all her thoughts around one topic. "I focus on improving myself," she says. When she journals, Theresa is able to connect the dots and see how she is improving herself. "That helps me keep my feet on the ground." She feels firmly in charge of her life, with a clear understanding of where she is now, where she wants to be in the future and how she is going to get there. It's all on paper in her journal. It is a diary of her dreams and how she is making them come true. For her, positivity is the yellow brick road for making dreams come true.

Theresa's dreams were to be able to afford health insurance, get married and create a wonderful family life., Now she has a good salary and a loving husband. They hope to have kids one day, once she makes more money. In five years, she should have her four-year nursing degree and that will help them afford a family. They will be able to afford to buy a house in two years.

To juggle her finances, Theresa created a budget. With self-discipline, she and her husband say no to overspending, keeping a keen eye on their future goals of raising children.

"I loved the book Prescription For Positivity," Theresa said. "It helped me see that I need to be true to myself and not be a people pleaser. Other people's opinions don't matter; they don't know you or understand you. You are the only one who really understands what you need. Your words can hurt you if they're full of negativity, so you have to be honest and truthful to yourself and not beat yourself up."

Theresa has encountered other people who are full of negativity. She is a minority in this country and she has had to face racism and sexism. "There is a little of that," she says. "But these are mostly mean people doing what they do, being mean. I can ignore them, avoid them and then because I'm not wasting my time caring about other people and their opinions, which don't matter, I can make progress in my life. Is racism happening? Yes, but it's not stopping me. Is sexism happening to me? Yes, but it's not stopping me. Look at how far I've come in just the last two years! I'm so grateful." She has a positive attitude in part because she's surrounded herself with positive people. But what can people do who are surrounded with harrassing people and can't get away?

Letting go of an issue kept her out of jail!

There are those who say attitude doesn't matter. Attitude is just silly, petty thinking. Don't tell that to Brenda. "A positive attitude kept me from attacking my brother and going to jail. For real!" she said.

Brenda lives in Kansas in a rural area that has high levels of drug abuse. Her brother went to jail for selling crystal methamphetamine, commonly known as meth. Then he came home on probation and went right back to snorting crystal meth even though he risked going back to jail.

"He yelled at me and my parents when we confronted him," Brenda said. "He was using the stuff in our house so he wouldn't get caught. But then we could all go to jail. It pays to be a pessimist when it comes to dealing with addiction behavior. I was an addict once myself, so I know."

When Brenda's brother got high and had screaming matches with her parents, Brenda reached her limit. "My little brother and sister saw all this going on and I know that is how addiction can start," she confesses. "They see bad behavior and start imitating it when they get in their teens. Monkey see, monkey do. He was poisoning the lives of my own innocent brother and sister. That was too much!"

Brenda admits she lost it. She got pessimistic even about herself and she crossed the line and wanted to control her brother although she knew that wasn't possible. "My own post-traumatic stress issues kicked in under all that stress," she noted. "I knew my safety plan was to walk away from triggers like yelling, but I didn't."

The anger escalated so much Brenda lost all common sense. Her emotions no longer responded to her positive, rational self-talk like they usually do. "I planned to beat him up and I had no remorse about the idea," she said. "Out of control anger can do that to you. You figure you can't stop yourself from doing something bad. It's a victim mentality. You don't care if you go to jail because you aren't in control." She even contemplated committing the unthinkable: murder.

She explained this has been a pattern in her family. A person is a victim of violence from a family member, and then later they do violent things to other family members and act like it's not their fault. This is called a chain of violence, where violence becomes part of the culture of a family and continues from one generation to the next. This pattern is very common. Parole officers hear these stories all the time.

Brenda had a choice. Would she break the chain of violence or continue it?

"My negativity was getting me nowhere," she admitted. "It was getting me more angry. So I chose to shift to being positive. I chose to focus on my goals. That was simple. I asked my counsellor for help. I asked my doctor for help. I asked my mom for help. I took action."

Brenda had a safety plan for what to do when overwhelmed and she kept it in a drawer in her bedroom. She got it out and read it. There she made a promise to herself to not act in violence. If she couldn't control herself, she had a safety plan to call her doctor. She called. Over the phone they changed her medication. In an in person visit she got more help. Counseling and a new meditation technique. The meditation gave her something no medication ever did for her: the ability to control her thoughts.

Brenda felt better. She felt positive. She focused on her goals. She used art therapy and painted about her anger. She sketched scenes in nature there in Kansas, imagining what Vincent van Gogh might paint or sketch. It was spring and she drew leafless tree branches that reached up lifelessly to the waiting sky. That felt like a metaphor for her beaten spirit, reaching out to others for help. She knew God reaches back through other people when you reach out for help. She accepted the comforting words from her mother and counsellor. She read in the Bible and accepted comforting words there. She felt a calming presence after doing these things.

Positivity helped her when one person was out of control and verbally violent. But can positivity work when there is rampant physical violence against your family? Can it help even after you've been kidnapped?

Letting go helped Katie's family leave a violent country

FIGURE 1.10.1
Avoid bad advisors and bad situations. Some will set you up for endless conflicts and blame you for it. Stay away!
By Toso Borkovic.

Life was scary when Katie was a child. Children she knew were being abducted by drug lords and held for ransom in Columbia. Her parents left for Canada and later came to America for the freedom and opportunities promised. Then she came down with a medical condition. She talked to her friends about it but they got so stressed out hearing about it that they said they didn't want to talk to her anymore. She eventually was hospitalized. Then the hospital said they couldn't find any doctor who took her insurance for outpatient follow up. So Katie didn't get any treatment after she left the hospital. There was a county mental health center where she could get low cost medical care. But in the waiting area were people who were scarey to look at. They had tattoos and dirty ruined clothes and bad body odor that made her gag. Sitting in the waiting area, her anxiety got worse than ever—she thought she was going to end up like the people she was sitting next to. Her condition worsened. She went back to her home country to get started on a medication. When she came back to America, the co-pays and deductibles with her insurance were so high that she couldn't afford basic medical care.

Katie found a therapist who helped her find a way to make her insurance work and continued her medication and doctor visits. The therapist found another clinic that wasn't frightening for her. A family practice clinic for the underserved.

Katie's advice is to find a mentor, some person you can really believe in and who can advise you on the best things to do in your situation. This might be a therapist or a close friend. The medical system in America is so broken for poor people that it often takes a "guide" to help you find care you can afford. Katie finished her college degree and, in part from all she learned in her difficult times, she now has a rewarding job helping people find advisors that can help them solve problems in their organization. Because she made herself more valuable to others, she became a high value employee. Employers pay her a higher salary with benefits to keep her, and one of the benefits was health insurance. She earned it.

Of course none of these things would have happened if she and her family had listened to bad advisors and did what they said—stay in bad situations.

Some of you might be thinking, rightly, "What if you can't find a guide? What if the bureaucracy you face is hopelessly complicated? What if nobody you know knows what to do? Good questions.

FIGURE 1.11.0
Learning optimism lets you come alive like never before.
By Toso Borkovic.

11
The focus on "Learning": your genie in a bottle

Positivity incubators make it easy to be positive!

By now you might be wondering, "How does a person learn all these different life skills? It seems overwhelming!" Of course, tragically, some people will never get the help they need for their medical care. Some will be stuck in mental health nightmares and not know about the thinking traps they are creating for themselves. That's one reason I wrote this book. This book might fail some people. Some people might fail to let this book, or any other help, work. Unfortunately, in life there are no guarantees. Inequalities surround us all. Extremes of poverty will keep some people trapped their whole life. That's why I support democracy. It supports individual achievement. It rewards it.

Where can a person start if they feel overwhelmed by adversities? I suggest keep it simple. Just try to make a little progress every day. That was the advice The Good Professor gave me when I was 15. That advice still rings true. Just focus on learning a little every day. Soon your little bits of learning will come together as a mountain of learning.

If you have focused on learning things that help others solve big problems in their life, you have improved your value in the world. If your community or country doesn't value your skills, then move to somewhere that does value your skills—in real dollars and cents. I've met many people from Africa, South America, Latin America, Eastern Europe and Asia who did just that. So this idea of make yourself valuable, then go where you are valued, isn't pie in the sky. It is really working for thousands of people. It is yet another example of positivity in action around the world. Hurray for that!

Developing a positive attitude can vastly improve your life. Where does training in a positive attitude tend to occur naturally? Summer camps, workshops on self-improvement, church camps, computer coding bootcamps and sports camps of all kinds! People attend these events because they want to get better at some activity or gain knowledge. They discover they feel caught up in the energy of the group wanting to learn the same thing. This camaraderie makes it easier to leap forward in personal change. The vibe is infectious! At these events you will find many of the principles of positivity in action:

- **Initiative**—to attend the event
- A **setback**—your lack of knowledge on the topic
- A **hope**—to learn more from teachers and the group
- **Accomplishments**—happen more easily and are celebrated with the group's support
- **Let go**—of your failures because learning is exciting
- Just focus on **learning** what you can; that's what everyone else is doing

I first learned to be positive at summer camp. A potential problem? People often let their positive attitude fade as the months pass after such an event. I first attended summer camp at age 11, caught the "vibe" of positivity and let it fade. I didn't have a male role model. I quit sports and quit Scouts. Four long years would pass before I'd give positivity another chance at summer camp. And I've already told you how that went. It was fabulous! Organized events like this, that last for days or weeks, can become "hinge moments" where a young person can learn a positive attitude and many life skills to support it.

If you've been to an inspiring event, don't let the vibe fade. On it's own it will fade. It is up to you to keep that flame of optimism burning brightly. The answer: look forward to your next event!

You too can seek out camps and workshops for your hobbies and faith, to boost your positivity and meet people who share your values. Another way to keep the vibe alive is to share what you have learned with your friends.

An Example from My Life

What if you are working hard, learning alot, and still are struggling to pay your bills? Wouldn't it be nice if there was a quick test to see if you are learning to be higher value to others—or staying where you are at? There is a simple test like that. It's your to do lists. They are like a "blood test" of your attitude. If you have no to do lists, then pessimism has taken over for sure. If you have to do lists, that is good. Now let's take a closer, more clever look at them.

When I looked back at my to-do lists when I was a news reporter, I found I was working hard but didn't have much to show for it. I asked myself, "How could that be?" Eventually I learned that my skills just were not valued in the marketplace. My skills were low value. People just didn't want to pay much to read an article in a newspaper. It wasn't solving any big problems in their life: like health problems or financial or relationship problems

I needed to go back to school to learn skills to make myself more valuable to employers—and the general public. That epiphany eventually led me to a career search and eventually going to school to be a doctor.

To-do lists can be powerful tools. They are like a "blood test" of your life, allowing you deeper insight into what you are doing, what is valuable and what is worthless. I had believed I could afford to support a family as a writer. I was wrong and my to-do lists helped me be more realistic about my future. My to do lists were valuable like a good friend is valuable: they are willing to tell you things you don't want to hear!

Epiphany: I Was Believing An Empty Promise!

I got this idea from my liberal arts education, I believed. I, of course, take responsibility for what I believe. I was a fool.

No one ever said, "You are going to live in poverty with this education." I learned that later. My good instructors taught me as promised. I learned my writing skills as a result. You are reading the results. As I looked closer at my past, I couldn't find anyone who even talked about what kind of income I would earn. Honestly, it was me who told myself I could make a good living and raise a family on the income of a common news reporter. I just made that story up in my head. When I came to that conclusion, of course, it was quite demoralizing and embarrassing. I wanted to blame someone else for my poverty but no one else had made my thoughts or took my choices. If I wanted to look for someone to blame I needed to look no further than the closest mirror. No in the end, no professor let me down. They taught me skills and knowledge as promised in each course outline. What I did with those skills was my business.

Looking at just what I was doing with my life was easy. I just needed to look at my to do lists and ask, "How is this improving my value? In practical terms in the real world?"

Looking at my to-do lists, it became clear to me if I stayed working as a news writer, I would never be able to afford a house or a family. The path I was on was a mistake.

Epiphany 2: I Still Have Time to Change!

Looking further at my to-do lists, it was also clear to me I had matured in the years after graduating from college. I was much more organized and focused. I could work long hours and think faster. I had the time and energy to change my career and rescue my life. What an amazing realization! After realizing this, I undertook a career search using techniques reviewed earlier in this book series.

➤**NERD ALERT:** successful people are good at doing things that really matter for their goals and not, I repeat not, letting themselves get tripped up by time wasters. Look at your old to-do lists when you finish each one. Ask yourself, "Did this really help me get where I want to go?" "Did this waste my time?" "Was there a quicker way to get this done?" "Could I have left this out?"

I love that last question.

By simply avoiding toxic people, unhelpful projects and social media surfing that wastes your time, you will automatically be accomplishing 10-30 percent more tasks in any given week. You will also have more time to chill and have fun with your friends. By reallocating your time, you boosted your sophistication. It doesn't take any time out of your day. You can do this kind of reflecting when you are doing the dishes every evening.

Positive people, who seem to effortlessly get a lot done and help others too, give off a great vibe, especially when they are not bragging to attract attention to themselves.

See how a positive attitude with positive techniques are a wicked combination? They are like Space X booster rockets.

Just load them with fuel and reuse them. You are also practicing social justice in real time: you are lifting yourself out of poverty.

Positivity is about creating a happier experience for yourself and making the world a better place while you are at it. It is about having fun taking personal responsibility to make your life better. You can save a bunch of money while you're at it, too.

Handling stress and having fun

Over thinking used to be Gary's middle name. Now it's positivity. He's applied all the tips and techniques in this book and it has made, "such a difference in my world," he said. He would overthink with an attitude of being detail oriented and conscientious. But privately, he confessed, his underlying attitude was that of a people pleaser. "I was worried I would upset my wife or my boss," he confessed. Notice him taking responsibility for other people's unhappiness in how he worded that sentence.

The pivotal point came when Gary decided to make his happiness only depend on himself. He firmly and decisively let go of being a people pleaser—and his wife loved that. "I spoke my mind openly and honestly," he relates. "She loved a man taking leadership in the family. She had her hands full with our three kids."

Because Gary spoke up and said what he wanted in their relationship—more date nights, more romance, more intimacy—he got it. He and his spouse were both working and had grown apart. Because he had feared rejection, he had hesitated to talk about their relationship. They had become more like roommates than two people in love. "If you can't talk about something, it's hard to fix it," he noted. He used positivity's "think things through" approach to work out a basis for feeling good about himself based on his opinion. He realized that he knew himself best, so he should base his self-esteem on his opinion and he chose to view himself as a champion. Winning at home, winning at work.

At work, Gary saw many problems nobody wanted to talk about. He negotiated a new position for himself that would make the company more money by cutting overhead—he was getting better at thinking things through in a deep and confident manner. This position took initiative and he showed it. He negotiated a pay raise. If he was doing more, he should get paid more. Gary justified his desired pay on spreadsheets and his supervisors agreed. They could see he solved setbacks and made the company more valuable to their clients. His company provides tech support for the recreation industry. His hopefulness made him more likable to his coworkers and more lovable to his wife.

"I used to look at the facts first and just get sucked in justifying hopelessness or pessimism," Gary admits. "Now, after applying these principles for a while, I see you can justify whatever attitude you want. The first question I now ask myself as I start my day is 'what kind of attitude do you want today?' And 'what would the positive version of myself do today?' 'What would the negative version of myself do?'" His wife was getting tired of having to cheer him up. Not now. He's the strong, happy and encouraging man she married. Family life is fun and adventurous.

Part of Gary's change involves giving himself credit for his accomplishments. He sought out more leadership roles at work. He works to create more fun and rewarding parenting moments at home. At work, he is the "boots on the ground," going out and visiting customers in mountain towns all over Colorado. Each trip is an accomplishment. He gives himself credit. He also asks his coworkers to take their accomplishments personally, which has boosted company morale. Tourist business was down during the COVID-19 quarantine. "I told everybody it is a setback, and every setback is temporary, so focus on your accomplishments in detail," he said. "And I want to hear personally, face to face, about your accomplishments. I know they will be great." His employees appreciated having a boss who supported them. And true to his prediction, after the quarantine, tourism business in Colorado boomed—and so did his business.

The key to making a positive attitude part of Gary's life is a lively internal dialogue. "That's where your attitude comes alive," he notes. "I start my day with that RAMP method. I read something positive. Then I visualize my day. Often it's at breakfast with my wife and kids. I flip from optimistic to realistic depending on the situation, but I'm always optimistic about my family." He used to start his day looking at the chores he needed do. It was depressing. Now he is focused on growing each day, learning something new and facing new challenges. His positive routines help that happen. Before breakfast he takes a brief walk, mentally rehearsing his day at home and at work, visualizing how to apply a positive attitude in situations that can come up suddenly.

"I ask myself, would I want to be positive or pessimistic in these situations. Maybe it's my son having a tantrum or something like that. I think it is really true you can't be both optimistic and pessimistic at the same time.'" He pauses and thinks a moment. "I used to drag people down with all my people pleasing. I felt that was how I had to be. Now, with visualizing my day, I am aware of all the choices I have. I live more freely rather than trying to fulfill one obligation after another. I can talk to my son, for instance, and tell him three positives for every negative. I remember to share my heart with him so he knows I am talking to him out of love and not anger. This is an example of how positivity has made me a better father."

Gary sees the power of letting go with a positive attitude. "Overthinking is such a trap in pessimism, such a trap. This is the chain of events in my mind:

I'm overly conscientious…worry that I can't control like what a customer thinks of me…I think this is a good thing…it becomes more and more difficult to separate what is my business and what is someone else's business…they gradually get to looking the same…reality perception gets more and more skewed… pessimism leads me to think problems are bigger than me…my emotions react more and more strongly…I believe my emotions more and more strongly…I feel weaker and act weaker…joy leaves my life…I start making up problems that don't even exist." "That's the pitfall of pessimism!" he says with a laugh. "But positivity isn't a pitfall. My life is now expanding. I am doing more at work. My marriage has more intimacy and love. We feel closer than ever. I used to be afraid of us growing apart. Not now. I know where we are at. And our kids are taking on new things every month, it seems. I wondered if life was just full of pitfalls. I used to think nobody really lives a fulfilling life. Not now. A positive attitude is like being on an open highway."

Your happiness is up to you. You've learned many ways to make it happen. Knowing certain thinking strategies are available can make such a difference. Knowledge is power. But not if you lack awareness. If you can't remember what to do —within seconds— at the time... some stress happens, you will likely go back to old ways of thinking and acting. We are creatures of habit. And one of the worst habits to kick is the people pleasing habit. In the next story, one man faced the fact that his people pleasing had to stop or he was going to lose the love of his life. But when he tried to give up on people pleasing, he found himself facing the fight of his life—with his own mind.

Learning to focus on yourself

Hiroto was a people pleaser but now he's a "me pleaser." He starts his day focused on what he needs to be happy, with a take charge attitude. He is assertive, firm, fair and consistent. Privately, Hiroto is putting love first. He has been engaged for 3 years. With all his people pleasing at work, little time was left for his fiancée.

Hiroto finally said, "enough is enough."

But how do you not people please? Hiroto found first he had to develop a positive attitude. That was the game changer. He focused on his goal in life: to put love first. He wanted to be a great man for his fiancée.

That meant setting limits. "That's what I made up my mind to do for us," Hiroto said, referring to himself and his fiancée. "In my last job, whatever someone asked, I'd say okay first, then figure out how to make that happen. Once I started doing that, they asked for more. It became a dynamic. I saw I had to leave. I was just a hamster on a wheel and it was hurting my relationship."

Hiroto used assertiveness skills to jumpstart the job-hunting process. He used positive self-image skills to be more appealing in job interviews. He looked in a mirror while he recited answers to common job interview questions. He used job hunting tactics reviewed in this book to find an employer that would likely respect him when he said no to working overtime or taking on too much.

Then Hiroto crushed the job interview and got the job! He knew he still had to practice good limit-setting. It was all about knowing how much is too much. Hiroto felt like caving into being a people pleaser again but he resisted.

"I had a talk with my boss," Hiroto explained. "I told him that when I say no to things, it's not out of disrespect but just me taking responsibility. I don't want to overdo it. It's not good for the company to have stressed out employees taking on more than they can handle and not setting limits. My boss said he got it."

Hiroto breathed. "This has been so liberating," he said with a big smile. "My fiancée likes it too. We have more quality time together. Our relationship has a chance to grow into something wonderful."

New nerves grow every day to assist your successful attitude

Hiroto learned the story of his relationship wasn't done yet—he had a chance to guide it. Likewise, the story of your brain isn't done yet, either.

The story of your brain.

Every day your brain grows more nerves. Millions of new nerves grow every day in the memory center alone, according to some scientists in this controversial area of research.[59] Your neurons anyway make millions of connections every day, so you can adapt to your experience or not, so you can adopt a successful attitude or not. In this interesting article, Croatian researchers Judas and Kostovic review just how many nerves grow, what kind they are, and where they are located. It shows dynamic growth of new nerve to nerve connections doesn't suddenly stop at birth—it just keeps on going![60]

In the nerve center for our sense of smell, named the olfactory bulb, and the memory center, named the hippocampus, new nerves grow in response to demands placed on them. As they are used, there is a release of nerve growth factors and other hormones, many released by thinking and moving. One of the five forms of nerve growth factor is primarily released during exercise strenuous enough for a heart rate of 100 beats per minute.

You were literally born to think and move vigorously.

Some of these newly born nerves are thriving now in your brain

The nerves themselves can move. Some new nerves have been shown to migrate along threads of connective tissue short distances to other locations in the brain.

Our brain is truly a dynamic, ever-changing wonder. Your brain is a gift from God. Your brain yesterday is not the same as it is today. It is humbling to consider the brain's awesome dimensions.

Having such a powerful tool comes with rights and responsibilities. You have a right to use your brain but you have the responsibility to take care of it. That is where keeping track of your attitude comes in. Your brain can do many things but one thing it cannot do is steer itself. That is your job.

If there is one thing clear in viewing the awesome architecture of your brain, it is this: it is loaded with potential.

Tom took a new perspective and found a meaningful work life

After high school, Tom worked in a warehouse, got married and had two children, but somehow felt like life was passing him by. He started journaling and saw he wasn't giving himself credit for all his accomplishments. He fell into the trap of pessimism and didn't realize it. He wasn't one to talk with his friends much about his feelings, but journaling and an attitude check really helped him get a perspective that he had been making all kinds of progress in life. He needed to quit comparing himself with other people and give himself credit for all the progress he had made.

There was a creative part of Tom that needed to come out. He loved painting and decided to take classes in modern art and painting on weekends. He made friends with local tattoo artists and came up with an idea to do large paintings of peoples' tattoos. He now felt like he was making the kind of progress that he wanted in life. He has a day job to pay the bills and weekend work to explore his creative side. Finally Tom truly felt that life was an adventure. As great as this sounds, it is easy to take this gift for granted and let your brain fail you. That's what happened to Tom. Tom had an advantage. He came from a loving family. What if you grow up without loving parents? That was Richard's problem.

Richard learned to accept guidance and love

Richard was a little pessimistic, but it was hard to blame him. His mom had often been drunk or high when he came home from school. His dad was always at work. There was nobody who really cared for him. Richard felt cut off from the world, as did his sister, and he grew cynical. He felt the world was cold and uncaring, and he was bitter about his chances for being able to do anything interesting or useful with his life.

"How was your day today in school?" his Grandma would ask when she picked him up from school. She encouraged him to come up with one thing that he learned every day. But being a budding pessimist, Richard would often say nothing. His Grandma wouldn't give up being positive. She could see how he was internalizing what was going on with his parents, taking it personally and feeling like his life didn't matter.

His Grandma loved him! If Richard learned something in math and then he said it was useless, his Grandma would point out that he had learned how to solve a problem. She would say, "You learned to use certain rules to solve a problem, and that

FIGURE 1.11.1
What advisor are you goiing to listen to? The wise ones or the deceivers? By Toshow Borkovic

is a lesson for life! Life is about solving problems and making progress on your goals."

If Richard didn't respond, she would say, "When you pay your bills, you have to make sure you don't overdraw your account. You have to use math to manage your finances. What you learned today will help you when you're older." He didn't care and she wouldn't stop caring.

Now that Richard is in college, he has drifted away from the habit of appreciating one thing he's learned every day. But he's making an effort to get back into it. He still talks with his Grandma. She still asks him what he is learning and encourages him to be grateful. With her positive encouraging attitude, Richard will succeed more in life. His relationship with his Grandma helps him stay connected with his true passions in life and focus on how to make himself more useful, both for achieving his own goals and to the world in general.

For a time, Richard had pushed his Grandmother away and did not take to heart her encouragement and wisdom. He played the Lone Ranger role. But then, he started to ask questions like, "Who really cares about me? Who cares enough to ask how my day went? Who cares about my future, my hopes and my dreams?" It was always his Grandma. Realizing that helped him be open to feedback from others who care about about him.

Richard's Grandma was a lighthouse in a storm. He is grateful for her. Richard had someone who loved him. His problem was he didn't love himself. In time he started working on that. He is learning that learning often takes a relationship experience— where both people make a committment to each other from the heart. For personal growth to happen, he had to let go of caring about all those "friends" who didn't care about him. He had to start caring for the one person who truly cared about him: his Grandmother. But Vivian's problem was different—she loved herself but her automatically reacting emotions were ruining her life.

Vivian is learning to take charge of her life—no more catastrophizing

"It feels so good to be in charge of my life again," says Vivian. Gone are the days of automatically reacting to situations negatively." Daily routines reinforce her deep sense of self-acceptance. She meditates every morning. "It's like having breakfast for my emotions," she relates. Then she gives herself credit for her self-discipline and self-awareness. "I completely accept myself," she says. Her daily routines are planned out with to do-lists and a planner.

If something doesn't go according to plan, instead of catastrophizing, Vivian reaches out to her husband for feedback and support, "not because there's something wrong, like I can't do everything by myself, but because there is something right; we're married and supporting one another." There are still echoes from the past, temptations to obsess in self-defeating ways. Vivian notices times when she is slipping. She looks at her to-do lists and schedule for the day.

Then she says, "I don't have time for that." It's true. She used to feel caught up in automatic emotions with names like fear and hatred and doubt. Now she sees she can take charge of those emotions. She can be a force for good for herself—and it is all in the words you use to think your thoughts. A subtle truth that, two thousand years ago, helped one man become an emperor and the most powerful man in the world in his day. How do we know that about Marcus Aurelius? We have his private diary where he confessed his thoughts to himself.

"Words color my soul," he wrote. A profound truth he would use throughout his life so he could, truly, live his best life. He had his faults. We all do. But today, historians regard Marcus as one of the five great emperors of Rome. He focused on what was good for the common citizen. He regarded everyone as having a spark of the divine and he saw himself, the most powerful man in the world, as a citizen of the world. He backed up these beliefs with actions. When the Empire ran short on finances, he sold some of his family's dishes to raise funds. How many world leaders can say they did that? Words can lift you up or beat you down, inspire you to overcome adversities or ruin your hopefulness for the future.

It's all in the words. Words are so powerful!

You hold that power. You choose the words to use to think your thoughts. You chose how to respond to setbacks and accomplishments

If you blame others for your suffering, you will yourself into a victim. You will have given someone else power over you. Say goodbye to your emotional freedom and hello to pessimism.

If you accept the good as well as the bad, and learn from them, something else happens. You become in control of your emotional experience.

Reflect on experiences instead of reacting and you stay in control.

Take setbacks as temporary and emotionally detach from them. See if you can learn from them and study them like a high school student studies her textbook. Something amazing will happen. You will get free from your setbacks emotionally. They will have no hold on you. Instead of defining your life, your setbacks will become tools for learning something to help you follow your dreams. Instead of spending energy of anger, you will do something practical.

That will be a real accomplishment, to detach from a setback and let it energize you. You will demonstrate your free will! You will switch gears and take a setback with detachment and acknowledge your accomplishments. You will feel good about that progress. You will take time to appreciate your effort. It will feel good deep down in your soul.

You can learn from setbacks and accomplishments with the support of friends and family. But only you can think your thoughts and feel your feelings. No one else can do that for you. Do so with an eye fixed on your hopes and dreams, like Odysseus focused on sailing through one storm after another because he wanted one thing and one thing only.

To get home.

Likewise, you can't think other people's thoughts. That's their business. Others might be cold or uncaring toward you. Oh well. We might have hoped for better. It's disappointing when others act out of jealousy, resentment, anger and the like. What others do is their business. All you can do is your best and hope others learn to live with kindness. If they don't, that's up to them. It would be irresponsible to go around judging people and telling them how to live their lives.

Say, "Now I'm learning from my experience. Now I'm in charge of what I think about my experience. Now I'm in charge of my happiness. I'm learning from everything, when things go well or when things go bad. I learn from things no matter what happens. I'm in the center of control in my life experience. My hands are on the steering wheel of the car of my life."

The second you begin blaming others for your unhappiness, your happiness depends on them. If they like what you do, you're happy. If they don't, you're unhappy. Goodbye freedom!

We all do that from time to time every day. That's ok. We can learn from making that mistake. We are so good at learning. It is so liberating!

What are you going to do with what you learn? If you see it as marvelous, special and amazing, you'll see yourself the same way. Because you are. Your mind is unique, like no one else's mind in history. You think with the power of four million (4,000,000) times more connections than the number of stars in the Milky Way Galaxy!

Treasure what you learn. Remember it, protect it, use it and pass on your wisdom. Hopefully, others will share their wisdom with you. Then you both will have more wisdom and the freedom that comes with it to live your dreams.

It's all in the words we use to think our thoughts.

What will happen for the rest of today? You are ready for it. What will you experience tomorrow? Well, whatever it is, you will learn from it and move on. Did a bad thing happen? Learn what you can and move on. Did a good thing occur? Learn from that and take time to revel in those special experiences that make such good memories in our lives. We feel meaning in our lives when we achieve goals, experience dreams coming true or make special memories. There is a bonus for those who live this way. You can live with INCREASING levels of boldness. You can learn the art of inner strength and rock solid self confidence. Because no matter what happens, you can learn from it. That makes you unstoppable. Unless of course you forget to use this attitude. And, alas, sometimes the Good Professor did just that.

Professor John Curtis taught me to learn from everything. Be satisfied with a little progress every day. Shrug off setbacks as temporary. Don't take setbacks personally.

But sometimes he forgot all of that! And then again, sometimes don't we forget those lessons as well?

Things usually wouldn't go well when he took a setback personally. Like the time he got angry at a Canadian Border Patrol agent. We were going to a a festival celebrating the ways of First Nation people in Manitoba, Canada, celebrating indigenous peoples of Canada and mountain men. The Border Patrol Agent did his duty and searched through our camping gear. I wasn't afraid. What could go wrong? We were going camping. Then the agent reached into John's pack and pulled out a black round ball.

"Whose is this?" the agent asked, visibly upset. John smiled and raised his hand. "We are going camping at a mountain man rendezvous in Spruce Woods Provincial Park. This is just a mountain man item to trade. It's a lead ball."

The Border Patrol agent raised his eyebrows. "This, I'll have you know," said the agent, "is a deadly weapon." Now, John was careful and conscientious as the day is long and to be accused of smuggling a deadly weapon pushed him over the edge. He raised his voice and argued with the agent. He threw his arms in the air. He got red in the face.

I saw where this was going. So did the agent.

"If you don't calm down right now," the agent told John, "I'll call the Royal Canadian Mounted Police. Do you know what they will do, sir?"

I felt the heat waves come up off the black pavement.

"No," replied John.

"They will come to take you away," said the agent. "And impound your vehicle. And impound your boat. They don't come to discuss things. Is that clear, sir? Now I want you to back off."

It was about 500 miles back home to Minneapolis. It would be a long journey for me—without a vehicle. So I repeatedly said "excuse me" and forcefully pushed myself in between the two men. I felt my shoulder bump the agent. A wave of fear shot down my spine. I grabbed John by the shoulders and pushed him into the cab of our pickup truck, with the 6 foot 4 inch tall border patrol agent following close behind.

"You wait here while I investigate this," the agent told both of us.

We both nodded.

"I'll be right back," he said.

About two sweaty hours later he returned. "You can go now," he announced. "But not with this." He held the ball in his hand. We expressed our apologies again and again.

There wasn't even a hint of a smile on the Border Patrol's face.

That was a major setback. There are different degrees of setbacks. Minor ones have no consequences. Major ones can have lots of consequences. John learned to not argue with Border Patrol agents and not to bring lead balls across the border. And after that he didn't. We had learned our lessons. Later, it became a fun story we'd tell around a campfire, making fun of our foolish decisions. We learned to carefully inspect all camping gear for anything that might be taken as illegal, such as a fillet knife that we might take on a fishing trip.

Canada remained one of our favorite adventure destinations and the Canadian people our favorite people to meet. What a great country. We didn't let one bad experience keep us from enjoying a place we loved.

Despite such setbacks, John didn't dwell on them or take them personally, or at least not for long. He charged forward and took life as an adventure. Learn your lessons and move on to the next adventure.

Nature electrifies your initiative: The lightning storm story

I lacked a sense of purpose when I worked my second year at summer camp. I taught archery. I showed boys how to tie knots and lash logs together. I hiked 20 miles and canoed ten more and even slept out all night under the stars alone. But none of this seemed special to me. I slept in one morning and they threw me in the lake. I didn't do that again. I thought to myself, "What did all this have to do with the real world?"

One night, rain slammed onto my tent like gravel dumped out of a truck. Lightning flashed. The tent lit up like I was inside a Japanese lantern. Thunder boomed and the clock radio rattled on the metal shelf next to my bed. Metal shelf! That made my tent a lightning rod. I felt nervous. My ears rang from that last crack of thunder.

Sometime later in the night, I saw my wooden tent post shake and heard a faint voice say, "Help!" I peeked out and a little camper stood there shivering in the beam of my flashlight. "Our tents almost all blew down," he said, "and lightning hit a tree. We're in our leader's tent and could you help us?" He was shivering.

I thought a second. This is what camp staff does. "Sure," I said and threw on a poncho. We walked down the dirt road half a mile through the aspen woods. Lightning flashed and thunder cracked. We stepped over half a dozen trees that had fallen over the road. I just followed the dim light of my flashlight. We slogged up a muddy trail to the campsite on a hill and found his crew, 10 kids and a leader squeezed like sardines into a tent flopping in the breeze. The campers got out of the tent and pointed flashlights in the clearing about 100 feet from their tent. White chunks of an aspen tree the size of bowling balls were scattered all around after a lightning bolt exploded the tree about twenty feet off the ground.

Trouble is here to test you

"Come on, I'll help you," I said. It was exciting. I knew what to do to save people and I hoped I wouldn't die. All of us squished our shoes down the muddy trail for 20 minutes. Back at my tent, I grabbed a candle. We trudged farther down the road to a cabin I knew of on the far side of camp. The campers piled in, shivering, wet and afraid.

"Grab me some dead twigs and branches outside," I said. In a moment, I had an armful of wet wood. I piled them into a teepee in the fireplace and lit a candle under them. In ten minutes, the twigs were dry under the candle flame. A wisp of smoke snuck out from the teepee. Ten minutes later blazing twigs caught branches on fire that dried out logs and caught them on fire too. This felt like a metaphor for life. Soon we had a blazing fire to warm our hands and hot water in cups to warm the rest of our cold, shivering bodies.

The cabin warmed up and the campers piled onto bunk beds. A few hours later, it was daybreak. The camp director saw smoke coming out of a chimney and came to investigate. He stepped in the cabin and saw the whole affair. "Why didn't you come get me?" he asked. "I didn't need you," I said. "I learned all this stuff so I knew what to do." He just shook his head and talked to the campers. I acted like it was no big deal.

Use trouble to work on your leadership

The point of this story is leadership. You need to be the leader in your life. Positive people need to be ready to lead. Leadership is knowing what to do and being the first one to do it. I was eager to help out. Sometimes life is a race and there is no second place, only losers. When I found those campers, they were huddled into a wet tent held up by a tall wooden pole on top of a hill in the middle of a lightning storm. Don't kid yourself. That tent was a lightning rod and those kids knew it.

Turbocharge your positivity with the medical model

Sometimes the only thing people hang onto for safety is the most dangerous thing around but they don't know what else to do. They need a leader. Ask anyone addicted to drugs or alcohol and they will tell you. We need more results-oriented leaders to help this world so full of pessimism.

Helping people in trouble gives you a sense of purpose, but you must know what you're doing. Helping yourself when you're in trouble also is an opportunity to solve problems and feel a hard-earned sense of purpose. Problems are great opportunities to hammer out a sense of purpose in life. Look to working on them. The new normal for understanding how the brain works is the biopsychosocial or medical model. It uses the results of billions of dollars of research into brain science to understand what influences our thoughts, emotions and actions.[61] The most influential medical model for understanding how the brain works in this "self improvement" effort is the chemical model. Another model says how the brain works is based on thought and feeling, the psychological model. Another says the brain is what you do with other people, the social/spiritual model. They are all right. The model that puts them all together and what is taught to medical students is the biopsychosocial model.[62]

In this model, all these factors are just different qualities of the same thing: the whole brain. Each quality affects the other two qualities. And authority figures such as doctors should put themself at the same level as anyone else—because we all share the same kind of brain. Yet there is a certain hierarchy here. A healthy biology in our body supports a thriving psychology. Biological problems can therefore put a big halt to a person making progress in their psychological and social life. Biological problems, such as headaches, are often best treated with biological treatments as the main intervention: a pain medicine plus water.

Sometimes medical issues stop people from making progress in their life. Here are fifteen quick examples of people overcoming such biological hurdles to start making enormous progress again in their life—often within hours or days.

1. Attention deficit disorder.

Within hours of taking the right amount of Adderall for his attention deficit disorder, Will found he could focus for hours, learn professional time management strategies and do well on tests. Later, he got the college degree and the job he wanted. Promotions allowed him to afford to travel.

2. Anxiety.

Within weeks of taking the right amount of a selective serotonin reuptake inhibitor (SSRI), Beatrice felt her nervous tension melt away. It had plagued her for years. Now her brain calmed and responded to positive thinking strategies that, over the next several years, replaced her medication. Meanwhile, she completed a network engineering certificate and got a higher paying tech job. This allowed her to afford a house and a family.

3. Depression.

A week into taking an antidepressant, Fran felt her depression begin to lift. Her emotions responded to positive affirmations and social experiences as the weeks went by. Several months later, she had the best mood she'd had in years. This motivated her to socialize more and that led to her finding a good boyfriend.

4. Obsessions.

Jorge felt his self-doubting obsessions weaken a month after starting a medication. This felt so great! He crowded out the obsessions with audio books and threw himself into self-improvement projects. He was thriving as a single dad. His new won self-confidence led to getting a promotion, a new girlfriend, and a condo that became a home for his son.

5. Anger issues.

Ida had a hair-trigger anger. She found herself to be rigid, perfectionistic, and demanding. Everything seemed like a big deal and someone else's fault. Four weeks into an SSRI, she felt her original personality come back. She once again felt relaxed and understanding. Optimistic thinking strategies helped her find joy in life again.

6. Insomnia.

Stress from tests led to insomnia which just added to struggles studying for tests. It was a vicious cycle for Leo. Then a sleep medicine helped him get good sleep regularly. He felt refreshed and his memory was much improved.

7. Sleep apnea.

Margaret gained weight and began to wake in the middle of the night. Poor sleep, fatigue and procrastination followed. With a CPAP machine, she lost weight and felt refreshed from a good night's sleep. She exercised more and her zest for life came back.

8. Chronic fatigue.

Nate felt like his feet were in deep mud all day. Work and house chores took all the energy he had. Within days of starting a new medicine his energy and motivation got a big boost. He felt his energy was 40% better. Now he had the motivation to pursue his hobbies and go out on dates.

9. Chronic pain.

For Celia, low back pain sapped the life out of her. It led to insomnia, fatigue and depression. All of this improved 50% when she started a new medicine, gabapentin. She attended concerts with friends and felt like she was living again.

10. Panic.

Leaving the house or meeting new people terrified Dawn. Any moment her heart could beat like a drum in her throat and she felt like she might die. All this stopped in 15 minutes once she took her medicine. Then her emotional mind responded to affirmations and desensitizing strategies. Her social confidence grew.

11. Post traumatic stress disorder (PTSD).

Nightmares and triggers of his trauma left Tim walking on eggshells when he tried to do anything public, like go to the grocery store. Three different medications brought his fears under control. Then his emotional mind responded to counseling. A year later his PTSD was almost gone.

12. Addiction issues.

Brenda's cravings for alcohol alarmed her. She had already dropped out of college due to a DUI but still the urges to binge on alcohol stalked her night and day. The medicine Acamprosate sliced the cravings by 80% and then her positive thinking let her get on with her life. A year later she was back in college.

13. Compulsive overeating.

Roger's hunger for carbohydrates led to back pain and insomnia and diabetes. An anti-obesity medicine dropped the cravings 50%. Then affirmations and self-coaching helped him get on with his life. He lost 60 lbs, his back pain improved and he slept better than he had in years.

14. Nicotine addiction.

Francine couldn't stop smoking. When she heard a comedian say kissing a smoker was like kissing an ashtray, that was the last straw. A medicine blocked her nicotine cravings and positive thinking let her create a life around her passion: ceramics and meeting other artists.

15. Pain killer addiction.

Aaron had a dirty secret. A bike accident had broken his foot. Then pain killers after foot surgery created intense cravings for narcotics. Months later, he was hooked on heroin. An opiate-craving-blocker medicine gave him the control he wanted. Six months later he was off the medicine and had his old life back.

JOURNAL YOUR LEARNING HERE:

Conclusion

Let positivity electrify your life

Let positivity electrify your life like a lightning storm. If you are feeling down and out about yourself, about your future, that is just pessimism up to its old tricks. Don't blame yourself. Pin the tail on the donkey! The problem is pessimism.

A meaningful life is all about your experiences, as Dr. Viktor Frankl taught us. Don't reduce it to something else, such as money. If you do, you will feel less meaningful. Then you will feel less hopeful. A meaningful life doesn't come from letting yourself be controlled by religion or politcal parties or street drugs. That is just a way to let someone else control you. Then you have become a puppet on a string. Then you will feel less hopeful and less meaningful. In the end, a feeling of hope and meaning come from your authentic struggle. The struggle is good. Don't cave into the temptation to let someone or something else control you with the promise that then you will feel a deep and abiding meaning.

Instead, share stories of what is cool and unique about you. Feel your awesomeness. Send out those posts on Facebook, Instagram and Twitter. Respond to others. Engage. React. Let's all celebrate our awesomeness. We are awesome in and of ourselves. We don't need popularity to make us feel good. We don't need big government or big anything to be happy. We just need to accept ourselves. We just need to take ourselves as we are: amazing. Don't go down some rabbit hole of negativity, like needing others' approval to feel good about ourselves.

You are awesome just the way you are. From one day to the next, you don't know what will happen. And you don't have to. But now you are ready for it. You can learn from anything. Taking the good times personally and the bad times as just a bad day. You know life is an adventure. And now you are in the game.

Such is the power of positivity to live your best life. Is this book then all of it? No. It's not even half of it. Since I started writing this book two years ago, so many more things have happened in the world. New challenges abound. So I have two more books in store, loaded with new techniques, new ideas and yes, new illustrations. Back by popular demand, Tozo has a new dazzling array of illustrations that entertain and intrigue. He calls them "signposts" for how an attitude can help you for that most wonderful thing in life—to live your best life—in a persistingly pessimistic world.

About the author

Harris Jensen, MD is a psychiatrist and author who has taught thousands of people the power of a positive attitude for more than 20 years. He draws on his Midwest values and medical training to empower an attitude excited about making progress in one's personal life. He shares these ideas in workshops, public speaking engagements and private consultations.

Find him on Instagram and Facebook @ harris.jensen.md

For more information see www.harrisjensenmd.com.

A list of works in progress by the author:

- Prescription for positivity: Life skills to live your best life
- Prescription for positivity: Action steps for your best life
- Prescription for positivity: Get a grip on your best life
- Prescription for positivity: A workbook for your best life
- Ukraine Is Strong (Written with Mykola Kovalchuk, PHD of Law.))

For more information on his writing and videos, see www.harrisjensenmd.com/books...Prescription for positivity: A video guide for your best life. For request for speaking engagements or to appear on podcasts, send email to: hjmedicalpractice@outlook.com

See articles and videos that illustrate ideas in this book by going to Instagram and Facebook **@harris.jensen.md** for more insights into and examples of--the power of a positive attitude.

JOURNAL YOUR LEARNING HERE:

Acknowledgments

➢**MY THANKS TO:** Rachel Dugger, project administrative assistant, you were awesome in a countless ways to keep me on track; and Steven Fryberger, you encouraged me when this book was just an idea. Chris Federman—you encouraged me when I had a vague idea for the book! Thanks to the many people who encouraged me along the way: Kathleen Reiter, Jim Smith, Meghan Tenge, Kris Martin (my administrative assistant), Caela Manley and Doug Manley, Manny Manolis (my salsa friend), Guy Cresap (my boyhood buddy!), Em Curtis, Pierre Tchenawau (dance instructor), Alejandra GC (dance instructor), Alejandra Fontao (dance instructor), and Ken Lejeune; Esther Phingmoo (find her on Fiverr.com) for your creative illustrations that seem to glow on the page; and Marko Markovic, such an excellent book designer—you inspired me alot! (You can find him on www.5mediadesign.com) Much appreciated are the excellent illustrations by the maestro, Toso Borkovic (on Facebook as ToshowToshow). And where would I be without my teachers? Many thanks to my instructors at the University of North Dakota School of Communications, UND School of Medicine, University of New Mexico residency program, and the University of Minnesota Hospital residency program. Also my thanks to Colorado State University and it's wonderful students!

Thank you to the first readers of my early chapters. Your comments were so helpful.

Thank you to great editors: Valerie Costa and Jennifer Nobles.

Thank you to my writing coaches Christine Smith and Geoffrey Berwind. Thank you to Steve Harrison and the Get Published Now program—so helpful!

JOURNAL YOUR LEARNING HERE:

Appendix

Positivity Tools

Rate yourself to chart your progress!

What was your positivity at the start of this book? Take the quizzes below and find out! If you have used each of the qualities of pessimism to power your positivity, you can add the "constructive pessimism" score to your positivity score to get your total positivity score. If you have stayed aware of unhealthy pessimism and unhealthy positivity—give yourself credit for that too. Rate these unhealthy attitudes and subtract those scores from your "total positivity" score to get your "realistic positivity score." This is a deep dive into your attitude!

➤**FIRST:** Rate your healthy positivity and healthy pessimism

The healthy positivity rating scale

Rate the following on a 1-5 scale: 1 is strongly disagree, 2 is disagree, 3 is neutral, 4 is agree, 5 is strongly agree. These questions assume you are focused on constructive activities.
   1. I am taking initiative today. _____
   2. I am taking setbacks as temporary. _____
   3. I am staying hopeful. _____
   4. I am taking my accomplishments personally. _____
   5. I am letting go of what I can't control. _____
   6. I learn from life. _____
   7. I can't control everything but I can improve some of my outcomes. _____

Total positivity score: _____
Total score before reading the book: _____
Total score after reading the book: _____

Healthy pessimism is a good thing to have. It is commonly known as having "healthy skepticism." It is tracked with the following rating scale.

The healthy skepticism rating scale

Rate the following on a 1-5 scale: 1 is strongly disagree, 2 is disagree, 3 is neutral, 4 is agree, 5 is strongly agree. These questions assume you are focused on **anticipating** what might cause a problem so you can avoid it.

1. I will take **initiative** to avoid things that are not healthy. _____

2. I understand some **setbacks** can have longer-lasting consequences. _____

3. I understand **hopefulness** can be damaged by bad or weak behavior. _____

4. I can see how **accomplishments** can be undone by bad behavior. _____

5. I can envision problems caused by not **letting go** of what I can't control. _____

6. I understand I can create problems by not **learning** from my mistakes. _____

7. I know that if I think I can control everything, I will be disappointed. _____

Total healthy skepticism attitude score: _____

Add your healthy positivity and healthy skepticism scores together: _____

This is your total positive attitude score!

Total score before reading the book: _____

Total score after reading the book: _____

Factor in your unhealthy attitude scores!

However, unhealthy pessimism and unhealthy positivity can take away from this positive attitude. Rate these unhealthy attitudes below:

The unhealthy pessimism self-report rating scale

Rate the following on a 1-5 scale: 1 is strongly disagree, 2 is disagree, 3 is neutral, 4 is agree, 5 is strongly agree. These questions assume you are focused on healthy activities in a negative manner.

    1. I am **not** taking initiative today. _____

    2. I **don't** take setbacks as temporary. _____

    3. I am staying **hopeless**. _____

    4. I am **not** taking my accomplishments personally. _____

    5. I am **latching onto** what I can't control. _____

    6. I **don't** take life as for learning. _____

    7. If I can't control everything, I'm disappointed. _____

Total unhealthy pessimism score: _____

Total score before reading the book: _____

Total score after reading the book: _____

The unhealthy optimism quiz

Rate the following on a 1-5 scale: 1 is strongly disagree, 2 is disagree, 3 is neutral, 4 is agree, 5 is strongly agree. These questions assume you are focused on healthy activities but without regard for the consequences of your actions.

    1. I am taking initiative today but **not thinking** about the consequences. _____

    2. I ignore how long some setbacks can last. _____

    3. I am ignoring what could **hurt** my hopefulness. _____

    4. I am ignoring who helped me achieve my accomplishments. _____

    5. I am letting go of what I **can control** because I'm so idealistic. _____

    6. I don't feel like I need to learn much because things are so good in my life. _____

    7. I can control everything in my life. ____

Total unhealthy optimism score: _____

Total score before reading the book: _____

Total score after reading the book: _____

Total these unhealthy attitudes to get your total unhealthy attitude score: _____
Total score before reading the book: _____
Total score after reading the book: _____

Subtract your unhealthy attitude scores from your healthy attitude scores to get your total realistic attitude score. Total healthy positivity score _____ - Total unhealthy attitude score = Total realistic attitude score _____
Total score before reading the book: _____
Total score after reading the book: _____
Now you've measured your progress. Thanks for taking the time to invest in your most precious asset: your mind!

Positivity Life Satisfaction Scale

Rate the following on a 1-5 scale: 1 is strongly disagree, 2 is disagree, 3 is neutral, 4 is agree, 5 is strongly agree.

1. I feel good about my life. _____
2. I feel good about doing my part in my experience. _____
3. I feel good about my taking initiative. _____
4. I feel good about focusing on my goals. _____
5. I feel good about following through on my to-do lists. _____
6. I feel good about my accomplishments. _____
7. I feel good about what I have learned from my setbacks. _____
8. I feel good about the kind of progress I have been making. _____
9. I feel good about knowing what I need to do to make more progress. _____
10. I feel good about my friendships. _____
11. I feel good about the good times with my friends. _____
12. I feel good about how I have encouraged others. _____
13. I feel good about my attitude. _____
14. I feel good about my romantic relationships. _____
15. I feel good about my school life. _____
16. I feel good about my work life. _____

17. I feel good about my relationship with nature. _____
18. I feel good about my family. _____
19. I feel good about my home and pets. _____
20. I feel good about my relationship with myself. _____
Total score: _____

Positivity definition: Positivity is an attitude of being excited about the progress you can make in your life by rebounding from setbacks and making accomplishments. (See "Preface.")

My Declaration of Independence

I am so happy to be pursuing my happiness.
I won't let anyone stop me.
Setbacks be damned!
I'll set goals and take my accomplishments personally.
I won't take setbacks personally.
I will learn from everything, somehow.
I will live my best life, one day at a time.

The good life is hammered out one tough day at a time.
My life will only be as good as I make it.
Good things don't come easy.
Every good thing takes work.
Work is good.
Love and family are so good.
I refuse to let the world take my love away from me.

I love my friends and family.
I love my freedom and self-reliance.
I will fight any effort to take away my independence and self-reliance.
I love taking personal responsibility for the things I have. This is how I keep my freedom.
My setbacks help me build a better future for myself and my family.

I defy victim thinking. It makes me weak.
I deny anyone who would weaken me.

I defy anyone who would control me.
I reject any effort to label me.
When you label me, you limit me, and I reject that limit.
I refuse anyone who tries to control my thinking.

My Positivity Bill Of Rights

It is my right to choose my attitude.
It is my right to take setbacks as I want to—with detachment.
It is my right to set goals and make progress.
It is my right to make a good life for myself.
It is my right to bring beautiful things into this world.
It is my right to have private contempt for the ugly actions of others.
It is my right to expect more of myself.
It is my right to be content with myself.
It is my right to feel worthy.
It is my right to feel my own self-worth.
It is my right to live the life I imagine.
It is my right to defy anyone who would limit me.

Steps in a relationship

Here are the steps in a relationship and some sample conversations. This is a reference you can use to talk with someone about where you are at and where you want to be:

1. Strangers. "It was fun to get to know you a little. Let's do it again."

2. Acquaintances. "It was fun to catch up with you."

3. Buddies, as in walking buddies, hiking buddies, dance buddies. "You're a fun dance partner."

4. Friends. "I enjoy getting to know you. I feel like we're friends, that's cool."

5. Good friends. "We've known each other for a while. We have had some great talks. I feel like we are good friends. What do you think?"

6. Really good friends. "I really enjoy these times we meet. I feel like we have so much in common. You're so much fun. I feel like we are really good friends."

7. Great friends. "We've had such great times and great talks. I feel like we're great friends."

8. Close friends. "We have had such awesome times. I love our heart-to-heart talks. I feel like we're close friends."

9. Really close friends. "I enjoy spending time with you. I like being able to talk about our friendship."

10. Seeing each other. "I like our time together."

11. Dating. "I like how we can talk about anything."

End Notes:

1   *Oxford English Dictionary*, 2nd ed. (Oxford: Oxford University Press, 2004), s.v. "Pessimism."https://www.oed.com

2   *Oxford English Dictionary*, 2nd ed. (Oxford: Oxford University Press, 2004), s.v. "Positivity."https://www.oed.com

3   Conversano, Ciro, Alessandro Rotondo, Elena Lensi, Olivia Della Vista, Francesca Arpone, and Mario Antonio Reda. "Optimism and Its Impact on Mental and Physical Well-Being." *Clinical Practice & Epidemiology in Mental Health*, no. 1 (2010): 25–29. https://doi.org/10.2174/1745017901006010025.

4   Written by John McKenna, Senior Writer. "Most People around the World Are Overly Pessimistic." World Economic Forum. Accessed May 30, 2021. https://www.weforum.org/agenda/2017/12/you're-probably-too-pessimistic.

5   "The Perils of Perception: Data Archive." Perils of Perception I Data archive, December 13, 2016. https://perils.ipsos.com/archive/index.html.

6   "Perceptions are not reality: what the world gets wrong." Perils of Perception I Data archive, December 13, 2016. https://perils.ipsos.com/archive/index.html.

7   Rosling, Hans, Ola Rosling, and Anna Rosling Rönnlund. *Factfulness: Ten Reasons We're Wrong about the World - and Why Things Are Better than You Think*. New York, NY: Flatiron Books, 2020.

8   https://www.gapminder.org/upgrader/

9   Lukianoff, Greg; Haidt, Jonathan. The Coddling of the American Mind. Penguin Publishing Group. Kindle Edition. 2018.

10 Pluckrose, Helen and Lindsay, James. Cynical Theories. Pitchstone Publishing: Durham, North Caroline. Kindle Edition. 2020.

11 Martin E. P. Seligman; Can happiness be taught?. *Daedalus* 2004; 133 (2): 80–87. doi: https://doi.org/10.1162/001152604323049424

12 A Reflection on Harnessing Learned Optimism, Resilience and Team Growth Behaviour in Order to Support Student Groups
Chadwick, Melinda. Student Success; Brisbane Vol. 10, Iss. 3, (Dec 2019): 104-111. DOI:10.5204/ssj.v10i3.1410

13.. Career Adaptability, Hope, Optimism, and Life Satisfaction in Italian and Swiss Adolescents, Journal of Career Development, /Volume 44, Issue: 1, page(s): 62-76. Sara Santilli, Jenny Marcionetti, Shékina Rochat. https://doi.org/10.1177/0894845316633793.

14. Burris, Jessica L.; Brechting, Emily H.; Salsman, John; Carlson, Charles R. *Journal of American College Health*. Mar/Apr2009, Vol. 57 Issue 5, p536-544. 9p. 3 Charts. DOI: 10.3200/JACH.57.5.536-544.

15. https://www.nobelprize.org/prizes/medicine/1986/press-release/

16. Friedman, Alan. "New 5G Apple IPhone 12 Models Feature the Fastest Chipset on Any Smartphone." Phone Arena. PhoneArena, October 13, 2020. https://www.phonearena.com/news/new-5g-iphone-12-models-sport-the-fastest-cpu-on-any-phone_id127793.

17. Sporns, Olaf, Giulio Tononi, and Rolf Kötter. "The Human Connectome: A Structural Description of the Human Brain." *PLoS Computational Biology* 1, no. 4 (2005). https://doi.org/10.1371/journal.pcbi.0010042.

18. Azevedo, Frederico A.C., Ludmila R.B. Carvalho, Lea T. Grinberg, José Marcelo Farfel, Renata E.L. Ferretti, Renata E.P. Leite, Wilson Jacob Filho, Roberto Lent, and Suzana Herculano-Houzel. "Equal Numbers of Neuronal and Nonneuronal Cells Make the Human Brain an Isometrically Scaled-up Primate Brain." *The Journal of Comparative Neurology* 513, no. 5 (2009): 532–41. https://doi.org/10.1002/cne.21974.

19. RodriguezRamos, Jaime. "Brains vs. Computers." Medium. Becoming Human: Artificial Intelligence Magazine, May 21, 2018. https://becominghuman.ai/brains-vs-computers-f769548010f1.

20. Garber, Megan. "How Many Stars Are There in the Sky?" The Atlantic. Atlantic Media Company, November 21, 2013. https://www.theatlantic.com/technology/archive/2013/11/how-many-stars-are-there-in-the-sky/281641/.

Note: It is fun to calculate the connections in your head that are galactic in porportion! Here is how. When you multiply large numbers you just add the suprescripted numbers. 1 X 10 to the 3rd multiplied by 2 X 10 to the 4th, is 2 X 10 to the 7th. So...

There are 80 billion nerves in the brain. 8 X 10 to the 10th. Each has about ten thousand connections or 1 X 10 to the 4th. Mutiply those and you get 8 X 10 to the 14th total connections in the brain. Mind boggling but true! Then...

The Milky Way has a minimum of 250 million stars, or 2 X 10 to the 8th stars. Now divide 8 X 10 to the 14th by 2 X 10 to the 8th, and you get 4 X 10 to the 6th. That is 4 with 6 zeroes, or 4,000,000 (four million). There are four million times more connections in your brain than there are stars in the Milky Way Galaxy. Do the math yourself if you don't believe me!

21. Nagarajan, Naveen, and Charles F. Stevens. "How Does the Speed of Thought Compare for Brains and Digital Computers?" Current Biology 18, no. 17 (2008). https://doi.org/10.1016/j.cub.2008.06.043.

22. Sharp, Tim. "How Big Is Earth?" Space.com. Space, September 15, 2017. https://www.space.com/17638-how-big-is-earth.html.

23. Sharot, T., Riccardi, A., Raio, C. et al. Neural mechanisms mediating optimism bias. Nature 450, 102–105 (2007). https://doi.org/10.1038/nature06280

24. Herzberg, P. Y., Glaesmer, H., & Hoyer, J. (2006). Separating optimism and pessimism: A robust psychometric analysis of the Revised Life Orientation Test (LOT-R). Psychological Assessment, 18(4), 433–438. https://doi.org/10.1037/1040-3590.18.4.433

25. Sulkers, E., Fleer, J., Brinksma, A., Roodbol, P.F., Kamps, W.A., Tissing, W.J.E. and Sanderman, R. (2013), Dispositional optimism in adolescents with cancer: Differential associations of optimism and pessimism with positive and negative aspects of well-being. Br J Health Psychol, 18: 474-489. https://doi.org/10.1111/j.2044-8287.2012.02096.x

26. Sulkers, E., Fleer, J., Brinksma, A., Roodbol, P.F., Kamps, W.A., Tissing, W.J.E. and Sanderman, R. (2013), Dispositional optimism in adolescents with cancer: Differential associations of optimism and pessimism with positive and negative aspects of well-being. Br J Health Psychol, 18: 474-489. https://doi.org/10.1111/j.2044-8287.2012.02096.x

27. Kubzansky, Laura D. PhD; Sparrow, David DSc; Vokonas, Pantel MD, and; Kawachi, Ichiro MD Is the Glass Half Empty or Half Full? A Prospective Study of Optimism and Coronary Heart Disease in the Normative Aging Study, Psychosomatic Medicine: November 2001 - Volume 63 - Issue 6 - p 910-916

A meta analysis of the topic is at: Rozanski A, Bavishi C, Kubzansky LD, Cohen R. Association of Optimism With Cardiovascular Events and All-Cause Mortality: A Systematic Review and Meta-analysis. JAMA Netw Open. 2019;2(9):e1912200. doi:10.1001/jamanetworkopen.2019.12200

28. Ramírez-Maestre, C., Esteve, R., & López, A. (2012). The Role of Optimism and Pessimism in Chronic Pain Patients Adjustment. The Spanish Journal of Psychology, 15(1), 286-294. doi:10.5209/rev_SJOP.2012.v15.n1.37335

29. Kwok, S.Y.C.L., Gu, M. The Role of Emotional Competence in the Association Between Optimism and Depression Among Chinese Adolescents. Child Ind Res 10, 171–185 (2017). https://doi.org/10.1007/s12187-016-9366-2 6-2. See also the follow reference:

Teaching an optimistic attitude protects against depression symptoms in the following study. Yu, D. L., & Seligman, M. E. P. (2002). Preventing depressive symptoms in Chinese children. Prevention & Treatment, 5(1), Article 9. https://doi.org/10.1037/1522-3736.5.1.59a

30. David B. Feldman, Maximilian Kubota,
    Hope, self-efficacy, optimism, and academic achievement: Distinguishing constructs and levels of specificity in predicting college grade-point average, *Learning and Individual Differences*, Volume 37, 2015, Pages 210-216, ISSN 1041-6080, https://doi.org/10.1016/j.lindif.2014.11.022. (https://www.sciencedirect.com/science/article/pii/S1041608014002349)

31. Ahmed, M. (2012). The Role of Self-esteem and Optimism in Job Satisfaction among Teachers of Private Universities in Bangladesh. *Asian Business Review, 1*(1), 114-120. Retrieved from http://www.ischolar.info/index.php/ABRABC/article/view/54427

32 {$NOTE LABEL}. Luthans, K.W., Lebsack, S.A. and Lebsack, R.R. (2008), "Positivity in healthcare: relation of optimism to performance", *Journal of Health Organization and Management*, Vol. 22 No. 2, pp. 178-188. https://doi.org/10.1108/14777260810876330
    Positivity allows elements of perfectionism with less impact on mood, in the following article. Jessica Black, William M. Reynolds, Examining the relationship of perfectionism, depression, and optimism: Testing for mediation and moderation, Personality and Individual Differences, Volume 54, Issue 3, 2013, Pages 426-431, ISSN 0191-8869, https://doi.org/10.1016/j.paid.2012.10.012. (https://www.sciencedirect.com/science/article/pii/S0191886912004941)

33. Manju Puri, David T. Robinson,   Optimism and economic choice, Journal of Financial Economics, Volume 86, Issue 1, 2007, Pages 71-99, ISSN 0304-405X, https://doi.org/10.1016/j.jfineco.2006.09.003. (https://www.sciencedirect.com/science/article/pii/S0304405X07001122)

34. Neureiter Mirjam, Traut-Mattausch Eva, *Inspecting the Dangers of Feeling like a Fake: An Empirical Investigation of the Impostor Phenomenon in the World of Work*, Frontiers in Psychology, 7, 2016, 1445 pages, https://www.frontiersin.org/article/10.3389/fpsyg.2016.01445, DOI: 10.3389/fpsyg.2016.01445, ISSN: 1664-1078

35. Gabriele Prati & Luca Pietrantoni (2009) Optimism, Social Support, and Coping Strategies As Factors Contributing to Posttraumatic Growth: A Meta-Analysis, Journal of Loss and Trauma, 14:5, 364-388, DOI: 10.1080/15325020902724271
    (I grew out of my post traumatic experience as a teen by adapting an optimistic attitude, accepting social supports and reappraising my past trauma of Mom and Dad's health issues—by accepting them and not seeing my future limited by them).

36. Conversano, C., Rotondo, A., Lensi, E., Della Vista, O., Arpone, F., & Reda, M. A. (2010). Optimism and its impact on mental and physical well-being. *Clinical Practice and Epidemiology in Mental Health*, 6, Article 25-29. https://doi.org/10.2174/1745017901006010025

37. 1. Masiero M, Riva S, Oliveri S, Fioretti C, Pravettoni G. Optimistic bias in young adults for cancer, cardiovascular and respiratory diseases: A pilot study on smokers and drinkers. Journal of Health Psychology. 2018;23(5):645-656. doi:10.1177/1359105316667796

38. Optimism is associated with exceptional longevity in 2 epidemiologic cohorts of men and women Lewina O. Lee, Peter James, Emily S. Zevon, Eric S. Kim, Claudia Trudel-Fitzgerald, Avron Spiro, Francine Grodstein, Laura D. Kubzansky
    Proceedings of the National Academy of Sciences Sep 2019, 116 (37) 18357-18362; DOI: 10.1073/pnas.1900712116

39. Kapikiran, N.A. Positive and Negative Affectivity as Mediator and Moderator of the Relationship between Optimism and Life Satisfaction in Turkish University Students. *Soc Indic Res* **106,** 333–345 (2012). https://doi.org/10.1007/s11205-011-9807-8

40. Gallagher, M.W., Lopez, S.J. and Pressman, S.D. (2013), Optimism Is Universal. J Pers, 81: 429-440. https://doi.org/10.1111/jopy.12026
    Here is a global survey article:
    Baranski, E, Sweeny, K, Gardiner, G, Funder, DC; Members of the International Situations Project. International optimism: Correlates and consequences of dispositional optimism across 61 countries. *Journal of Personality*. 2021; 89: 288–304. https://doi.org/10.1111/jopy.12582

APPENDIX

41. Van Soom, Carolien, and Vincent Donche. "Profiling First-Year Students in STEM Programs Based on Autonomous Motivation and Academic Self-Concept and Relationship with Academic Achievement." *PLoS ONE* 9, no. 11 (2014). https://doi.org/10.1371/journal.pone.0112489.

42. Boehm, Julia K., Ying Chen, David R. Williams, Carol Ryff, and Laura D. Kubzansky. "Unequally Distributed Psychological Assets: Are There Social Disparities in Optimism, Life Satisfaction, and Positive Affect?" *PLOS ONE* 10, no. 2 (2015). https://doi.org/10.1371/journal.pone.0118066.

43. Chen, Yongyong, Jing Su, Zirong Ren, and Yongquan Huo. "Optimism and Mental Health of Minority Students: Moderating Effects of Cultural Adaptability." *Frontiers in Psychology* 10 (2019). https://doi.org/10.3389/fpsyg.2019.02545.

44. Brian Domino and Daniel W. Conway, "Optimism And Pessimism From A Historical Perspective," in Optimism and Pessimism: implications for theory, research, and practice. Edited by Edward C. Chang, 2001. Washington, DC: American Psychological Association, pp. 14-19.

45. Pinker, Steven. *Enlightenment Now: the Case for Reason, Science, Humanism, and Progress.* London: Penguin Books, 2019.

46. Pinker, Steven. *The Better Angels of Our Nature: a History of Violence and Humanity.* London: Penguin Books, 2012.

47. Rosling, Hans, Ola Rosling, and Anna Rosling Rönnlund. *Factfulness: Ten Reasons We're Wrong about the World - and Why Things Are Better than You Think.* New York, NY: Flatiron Books, 2020.

48. https://www.amnh.org/exhibitions/permanent/planet-earth/why-is-the-earth-habitable

49. https://www.amnh.org/exhibitions/permanent/planet-earth

50. Technically he was an associate professor of English at Minot State University, Minot, ND. Also he was a visiting lecturer at the Cody Museum in Cody, Wyoming, for the University of Wyoming.

51. https://www.minotstateu.edu/artsnsci/emeriti.shtml

52. https://www.thomasfamilyfuneralhome.com/obituary/john-curtis

53 Hongying Zhu, Ning Wang, Lei Yao, Qi Chen, Ran Zhang, Junchao Qian, Yiwen Hou, Weiwei Guo, Sijia Fan, Siling Liu, Qiaoyun Zhao, Feng Du, Xin Zuo, Yujun Guo, Yan Xu, Jiali Li, Tian Xue, Kai Zhong, Xiaoyuan Song, Guangming Huang, Wei Xiong. Moderate UV Exposure Enhances Learning and Memory by Promoting a Novel Glutamate Biosynthetic Pathway in the Brain. Cell. Volume 173, Issue 7, 2018, Pages 1716-1727.e17, ISSN 0092-8674, https://doi.org/10.1016/j.cell.2018.04.014. (https://www.sciencedirect.com/science/article/pii/S0092867418305075)

54. I learned of this model at a workshop put on my Donald Meichenbaum, PhD. For more by him see this website: https://melissainstitute.org/scientific-articles/meichenbaum-d/

55. https://www.oxfordlearnersdictionaries.com/us/definition/english/hopefulness

56. https://en.wikipedia.org/wiki/Viktor_Frankl. See also his acclaimed book: "Man's Search For Meaning," Viktor Frankl. 2006. Boston, Massachusetts: Beacon Press. www.beacon.org.

57. https://news.gallup.com/poll/352205/2020-sets-records-negative-emotions.aspx

58 Merriam-Webster.com, online dictionary

59 Elena P. Moreno-Jiménez, Julia Terreros-Roncal, Miguel Flor-García, Alberto Rábano and María Llorens-Martín. Evidence for Adult Hippocampal Neurogenesis in Humans. Journal of Neuroscience 24 March 2021, 41 (12) 2541-2553; DOI: https://doi.org/10.1523/JNEUROSCI.0675-20.2020. This issue of the journal also provides a paper with the opposite perspective:

Shawn F. Sorrells, Mercedes F. Paredes, Zhuangzhi Zhang, Gugene Kang, Oier Pastor-Alonso, Sean Biagiotti, Chloe E. Page, Kadellyn Sandoval, Anthony Knox, Andrew Connolly, Eric J. Huang, Jose Manuel Garcia-Verdugo, Michael C. Oldham, Zhengang Yang and Arturo Alvarez-Buylla. Positive Controls in Adults and Children Support That Very Few, If Any, New Neurons Are Born in the Adult Human Hippocampus. Journal of Neuroscience 24 March 2021, 41 (12) 2554-2565; DOI: https://doi.org/10.1523/JNEUROSCI.0676-20.202

60 Kostovic, I and Judas M. Early development of neuronal circuitry of the human prefrontal cortex. The Cognitive Neurosciences. Researchgate.net. 1: 29-47. The MIT Press, MA, USA. https://www.researchgate.net/profile/Milos-Judas/publication/257946095_Kostovic_I_Judas_M_2009_Early_development_of_neuronal_circuitry_of_the_human_prefrontal_cortex_In_Gazzaniga_MS_Ed_The_Cognitive_Neurosciences_4th_Edition_Cambridge_MA_-_London_The_MIT_Press_pp_29-48/links/56f9a6a308ae7c1fda311b08/Kostovic-I-Judas-M-2009-Early-development-of-neuronal-circuitry-of-the-human-prefrontal-cortex-In-Gazzaniga-MS-Ed-The-Cognitive-Neurosciences-4th-Edition-Cambridge-MA-London-The-MIT-Press-pp-29.pdf

61. Deacon BJ. The biomedical model of mental disorder: a critical analysis of its validity, utility, and effects on psychotherapy research. Clin Psychol Rev. 2013 Nov;33(7):846-61. doi: 10.1016/j.cpr.2012.09.007. Epub 2013 Apr 8. PMID: 23664634.

62. Papadimitriou G. The "Biopsychosocial Model": 40 years of application in Psychiatry. Psychiatriki. 2017 Apr-Jun;28(2):107-110. Greek, Modern, English. doi: 10.22365/jpsych.2017.282.107. PMID: 28686557.

Made in the USA
Las Vegas, NV
14 December 2022

62425584R00223